Natural History of the Mind
(New Views on the Relatedness of Life)

Natural History of the Mind
(New Views on the Relatedness of Life)

William R. Sickles

Assistant Vice President/Art Director: Maria Ester Hawrys
Office Manager: Annette Hellinger
Graphics: Frank Grucci
Acquisitions Editor: Tatiana Shohov
Book Production: Ludmila Kwartiroff, Christine Mathosian, Maria A. Olmsted and Tammy Sauter
Editorial Production: Susan Boriotti
Circulation: Cathy DeGregory and Maryanne Schmidt

Library of Congress Cataloging-in-Publication Data

Sickles, William R.
Natural history of the mind: new views on the relatedness of life / by William R. Sickles
    p.   cm.
Includes bibliographical references and index.
ISBN 1-56072-516-8
1. Mind and body. 2. Philosophy of mind. I. Title.
BL161.S48   1997   97-40891
128'.2—dc21   CIP

Copyright © 1997 by Nova Science Publishers, Inc.
        6080 Jericho Turnpike, Suite 207
        Commack, New York 11725
        Tele. 516-499-3103   Fax 516-499-3146
        E-Mail: Novascience@earthlink.net
        Web Site: http://www.nexusworld.com/nova

Printed in the United States of America

As assistant to George W. Hartmann, then at Columbia, I had the unique opportunity to meet and know members of the original Gestalt group which had emigrated here from Germany. It was a rare experience, for I found their interests and outlook quite similar to my own. I "belonged." This was more than half a century ago, and all are now long since gone. So I welcome the opportunity to make this affirmation:

In Memoriam

*Since your passing, the winds of theory have blown every which way. But they are still only winds, not answers, and the facts remain unchanged. One never understands anything from particulars alone, nor does any living thing consist of "parts." All life and mind are matters of the belongingness, one feature with another -- the **whole**-someness that is always **more** than the sum of any parts. The parts are of our making. It is the "more" for which I search.*

"Whoso itcheth to philosophy must first set to work by putting all things to the doubt." -- Giordano Bruno, *De Minimo,* I, 1. (Charged with heresy and burned at the stake 17 February, 1600.)

Contents

Preface
Acknowledgment

On the Mind/Body Relationship

How it all Began

Contents

Journey into No*"thing"*ness

Minding the Overmind

Contents

Biosphere, Gaia -- and What Else?

Through a Glass Darkly: The Mechanism of Mind

Preface

"Myself when young did eagerly frequent
Doctor and saint, and heard great argument
About it and about: but evermore
Came out by the same door wherein I went."
--- Omar Khayyam [1]

Little has changed in the centuries since Omar. Automobiles have replaced some of the camels. They save time -- whatever that is. But the revolving door is still there. The naive pass in one side, receive a thin coat of polish, and pass out the other. From the fog of my early years I remember Will Rogers saying, "it ain't that we don't know nothing, it's just that what we know ain't so." This stuck with me, a mustard plaster on the raw idealism of my youth. Another well remembered shocker is attributed to Thomas Edison. He is reputed to have said that we know less than one-thousandth of one percent about anything. When I first heard this, it amazed me. It seemed so obviously false. But that was fifty years ago. Today it appears self-evident.

What could Edison and others have possibly meant by such comments? The answer, I would suggest, is straight-forward. All our highly touted "know how" is precisely that. It is know *how* -- engineering information as it were. And what we are engineering is the unknown! It is much as if every act were the performance of a mime. There is no substance to it. For example, we know how to put a living man on the moon. But we can't explain what the word "living" means. As for the word "man," even the Supreme Court can't decide where an individual's life begins.

To call the human an organism is mere name switching, verbal musical chairs. It explains nothing. And to say that he is living matter only compounds the problem. We don't know what matter is. We can play musical chairs with this one too. We can say it is energy. Now, try to explain energy. Consider those presumed opposites: matter and mind.

Certainly no other two concepts seem so far removed from each other. Can we distinguish between them? Not if we trust our authorities! Eminent scientists like Sir James Jeans and Sir Arthur Eddington have assured us that matter is "mind stuff." [2] And just what does this tell us? Shaking the facts out of our body of knowledge is like shaking warm beer. Precious little if anything, is left. It all turns to foam. Kurt Vonnegut coined the term "foma" [3] which he defined as "harmless comforting untruths." It is a convenient term. Most of us pass through life completely fomatized. It is part of the mind's defenses -- aspirin for the ache of ignorance.

For all we know, matter, life and mind just simply *are!* Explanations aren't necessary! It may be that asking about their origins is nonsensical, like asking what lies outside the universe. Must everything have a beginning, end and a purpose? Suppose all such mental cravings merely result from the way the mind works. If so, then there aren't any "true" answers!

When truth is defined as an accurate statement of "that which is," it has to change. All things change, and especially that which is. This is why the founder of Zen (Bodhidharma, ca. 520) proclaimed all doctrines to be equally false -- simply because they were *doctrines* Theories are built. Theories crumble away. And after watching enough of this, the latest "ultimate" truths lose something of their credibility. God may have created this world out of nothing. I don't know. But if He did He must have left plenty of it lying around for us to theorize with!

All of which brings me to this book. I felt it served a need. Present-day orthodoxy may be read anytime anywhere. Libraries are full of it. So this was written to provide some of the alternatives. No claim is made that it contains absolute and final truth graven in stone -- for it is also necessarily theory. But it is theory from a different angle, something designed to provide new and interesting perspectives for those who tire of wandering through the aisles of ready-to-wear ideas.

When scrounging through the ashcans and back alleys of science like Mehitabel the cat, one often comes up with strange findings. For example, the contention that cells are intelligent. They communicate with each other chemically because the brain is essentially a huge gland. Evidence indicates they can learn, and this implies a mind. Genetic memory plus simple decision making compels them to create a social structure -- the infant. Adult humans then extend this socializing process.

The mind not only grows within the brain, but possibly proliferates within the still larger social body called a culture. There are even overtones to sex, pheromones and unfairomones, with love as long range Van der Waals forces. We are said to look at the world through the wrong end of a microscope, and there is reason to think it may not be real.

Back to theories. Despite their flimsy nature, they are necessary to provide lodging for the facts. But there are never enough rooms. Facts get selected to fit the theory. Many get turned away, and nothing gets lost quicker than a loose fact! In a sense, therefore, the present work is a welfare program for data lost, ignored, or summarily rejected by the orthodox establishment. When assembled, they tell a story quite different from the dogma-of-the-day. It is *not* a story intended as criticism, however. It is merely meant as mental recreation, something a cut or so above crossword puzzles. It says look -- here are the questions they didn't ask, and the answers may be a bit startling!

Admittedly, the title sounds exotic. It could just as easily have been called "Perspectives on the Mind-Body Problem" and classified as philosophy of science. But that sounded like chloroform in print. And who wants to be put asleep by a dull book? The present title was selected because the work actually was envisioned as a natural history of the mind, or at least what little is known about it -- its origins and consequences for all life -- possibly even that of plants! Hopefully, it will be found interesting.

For those who are chronic skeptics like myself, copious notes are provided. These won't prove anything. But they may help keep the reader awake, and possibly even slake some of his curiosity.

W. R. Sickles

The primitive area,
Idaho, 1997

Acknowledgment

Concepts often have deep roots. These date back to the early forties with some publications on perceived orderliness. By the time twenty years had rolled by, their implications had grown to a large volume which was carefully reviewed by Karl Pribram, then nearby at Stanford. The present work was selected and edited from this earlier tome. Though very belated, I must express my gratitude for his efforts during those bygone days.

The first draft of the current book really began more than five years ago and slowly culminated from discussion with various individuals in different disciplines. A comprehensive review was recently undertaken locally by John L. Phillips, Jr., an individual with broad scientific interests and an author in his own right. He went through it with a fine tooth comb and came up with a number of important suggestions since incorporated into the text. I am indeed thankful for his assistance. If there are still further shortcomings they have been introduced later by myself.

Last, but certainly not least, I am indebted to my family. My son Kurt gave me a computer, Garth provided the much-needed expertise, and my wife (Joey) checked for errors and clarity of expression.

On the Mind/Body Relationship

Chapter 1

Is there Truly a Ghost in the so-called Machine?

(Strange and little-known facts about the brain suggest that it is independent of the body, and that the mind may be something equally independent of the brain.)

Gusts of early autumn romped through the leaves and nipped playfully at nose and ears. Overhead a distant goose formation honked its way south. They too had felt it. As I entered the old ivy-tangled building called "Life Sciences" I couldn't help reflecting how well the tangle symbolized the subject. To my right the classroom door was open. Empty seats were visible in the front. Taking attendance this first week would be fruitless. Registration would be up and down like a yo yo. After today's opening lecture it probably would go down again. I meant to set a precedent, deal with a topic my hard-nosed colleagues painfully avoided -- the nature of the mind. After all, it was a class in biological theory, and nothing's much more theoretical than the mind. The question was "Is it biological?"

"This is not going to be an easy course," I warned. "As often pointed out, the mind is not simple to understand. If it were, we would be far too simple-minded to understand it anyhow. To compensate for this assumed hopelessness, I'll do my level best to make the subject interesting.

We can begin by ignoring the history. Man's effort to understand the mind goes far beyond any history. It gave rise to his religion and philosophy, then supposedly switched to science. So it seems strange to find the third millennium approaching with the quest still getting nowhere.[1] We can get to the moon but apparently can't get into the mind. As a result, there are those who deny that a search for mind is meaningful. Present-day dogma has it that your body is you, *all* of you. There is nothing else. If anything further is expected then it has to be spiritual -- beyond definition or scientific investigation. It was your body that became modified during evolution, they say. The brain was just another organ of the body, a sort of tag-along. Please note that this is the same brain which houses the mind. So the mind is accorded even less status. It occupies a very low position on the totem pole of being. Description pictures it as nothing more than the 'workings' of the brain. And since no one presumes to know exactly how the brain works, this doesn't tell us anything. Sometimes it is referred to as an energy system, type unknown. But more often brain and mind are simply lumped together, then vaguely referred to as a neural network system. There are still many others who feel it better just to ignore the subject entirely.

Needless to say, the public has never found any of this acceptable. And why should they? There is direct experience of the movement of mind during thinking and dreaming. If we are to make sense of the subject therefore, we must explain what is meant by the term mind. We must at least describe it in enough detail to make it meaningful. Otherwise it becomes just another vacuous word and may as well be labeled 'X.' This will be the purpose of our study. We'll develop a more concise definition as we go along. Those having theories of their own are free to draw any inferences they wish. They may use terms like soul or spirit, or if they prefer, computer algorithms. A name is a name is a name is a name. In the meantime, we shall be looking for something a bit more substantive.

To begin, a radical shift of 180 degrees from orthodoxy is proposed. Mind goes to the *top* of the totem pole. There it may be examined as possibly the germinal aspect of all life. This is not meant to imply anything supernatural. It merely suggests that final analysis could reveal the mind to be integral with nature in general and living matter in particular.

As a starting concept, let us define the mind as simply the mechanism by which the brain acts. We may then begin by discussing the brain. First things first. As will be depicted here, the brain definitely is *not* just another organ of the body. Quite the reverse. The body is judged to be the original and most basic organ of the brain. In every sense of the term, the brain transcends the body. During the last century or so it has enhanced its repertoire of organs by including microscopes and telescopes (eyes), planes and autos (feet), and amazingly complex manufacturing machinery (hands). Its senses have expanded to include energies unknown before. Indeed, even as we speak it is busy extending itself into the environment, and in doing so is increasing its own thinking capacities with computers.

Who is to say that these things contrived and used by the mind, are any less a part of the mind? They are not parts of the brain. But they *are* parts of the mechanism whereby the brain acts! If not, then how do we explain their origins?

By contrast, the structure and functions of the body have changed but little in the last half million years. It still consists of only the rudiments necessary for continued brain survival -- much as it did in proto human times. To put the argument in somewhat fanciful terms, the body is merely the basic cocoon which the brain initially weaves about itself to ensure survival in an otherwise hazardous environment. As noted somewhere by the playwright George Bernard Shaw, it is the mind that makes the body, and not the body the mind. Thus, when surgeons pronounce a person 'brain dead' he is presumed to be dead *in toto*. This makes it permissible (though gruesome) to salvage other workable parts for use elsewhere. The brain is universally recognized to be the seat of the mind. As the nucleus of the central nervous system (hereafter CNS), it handles all communications to and from the body. Accordingly, one would expect it to develop early in the process of foetal growth. And indeed this is the case. To explain, let us glance back at primitive marine life. When living cells first allied with one another to become multicellular beings, the most noticeable change was their specialization. Certain cells took over food-gathering, others reproduction, and so on. When locomotion became possible, this early cellular matrix had to decide which end was front -- what portion was going to do the leading. And ever since that fateful decision the front end, site of the brain, has been in command.

Much as with the beginning of life in general, every human life also starts with specialization. The cellular mass becomes divided into three layers. The outermost of these (ectoderm) is destined to produce the brain and its subsidiaries such as senses and glands. Well before the baby develops, therefore, sources of the brain and its emissaries are set aside, ear-marked for something special.

Though the body develops from the other layers, all growth thereafter proceeds from this critical area in expanding fashion from head to tail and outward on either side. Embryologists speak of it as a 'cephalocaudal gradient.' It strongly suggests that the brain acts as a germinal center from which the rest of the body grows. In the meantime it also grows. But its growth is maintained separately from that of the body. It is much more rapid. Charts of brain growth, plotted against age, bear little resemblance to comparable charts for the body.

Using an electron microscope, Swedish photographer Lennart

Nilsson recently provided spectacular evidence of this seedlike sprouting of the human body. [2] The drawing shown here is a month old human embryo still less than half an inch in length. The predominance of the head mass is clearly discernable at the left. At the right the long curved beginnings of a spinal cord and protective vertebrae are seen emerging from the head portion. There is yet no face, limbs, nor organs other than a small heart to provide blood flow. The early appearance of this latter is necessary to feed new cells and possibly carry chemical control messages from an equally rudimentary brain. The imagination needs no stretching to recognize this as a germinating process. It even bears a rough similarity to what happens when bean or corn kernels send out their first upward curving sprouts.

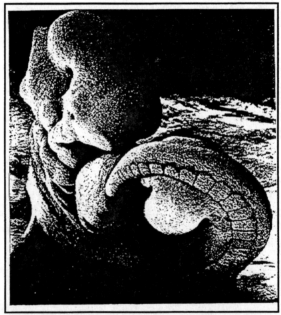

FIGURE 1. Drawing of a one-month-old human embryo (Approx. ½ inches in length). Note the germinating vertebral column and cord at right. After Nilsson, in: *Science '83*, 4, 7, page 45.

With a moment's thinking one is also haunted by innuendoes about heredity. The thought occurs that all heredity is transmitted from parents to child via the child's brain. Testes and ovaries are not even visible in the blueprint at this time. Like everything else, they are features which appear in the course of body growth. There is no way of detecting any developmental 'chain of command.' All we know is the sequence and direction of cellular proliferation. And in this respect it is significant that the brain comes first and gives rise to the cord and senses. The heart follows as first of the organs, and the remainder of the body branches out later.

Early embryonic growth and behavior appear to be left mostly to the cells themselves. They seem to know what they are doing and are enthusiastic about it. For all we know (which isn't much), instructions from headquarters may not be necessary. For instance, heart cells synchronize, then settle into a steady beat long before nerve connections are established. And in the walls of intestines and blood vessels, smooth muscle cells also team together to produce peristaltic motion. The entire picture is one of cellular cooperation. These early cells at least, appear to be working pretty much on their own initiative.

In germinating plants all traces of the original seeds soon disappear with growth. This does not happen with the human brain. From earliest beginnings the brain dominates the organism and becomes man's most distinctive feature. While still a developing embryo it enlarges until it is easily more than half the total mass! At birth the child's head is so large it creates a major problem at delivery. Brain growth slows to a halt soon thereafter, whereas body growth goes on for many years.

Cessation of brain growth is generally thought to mean that we are born with nearly all the brain cells we shall ever possess. There are obvious disadvantages to this. But absence of turnover in the cellular population makes for a stable system. It can now concentrate on its own internal organization without interruption. And the resulting organization is what we know as mind. It is bewildering that such a system should ever have been considered just another organ of the body, i.e., something the body 'needs to keep it running.'

When the baby is born all physiological systems are on, set to go. It has a brain which is essentially complete. But it is empty and in need of information. There are only the barest of foundations indicating a mental structure. These may be such that only a shed can be built, then again, they may allow for a mansion. In other words, the upper limits of intellectual capacity, whatever this may be, are most likely hereditary.

The building process is called learning. And the first step is to become familiar with the body. This begins by feeling one hand with another, then the hand-mouth relation, hand-foot, and so on until the child gains full awareness of his equipment. [3] Inside equipment (soft machinery) is on autopilot. It comes pre-set with old brain regulation and requires very little learning. Acquired control over the muscles, on the other hand, depends upon both learning and maturation. Some muscular patterns having to do with walking, talking, sex, and the like, may be partially instinctive. They do not make their appearance until extensive body development has occurred. It is noteworthy that body usage is *learned!* This, in itself, is evidence for the primacy of the brain. If the brain were only an organ of the body why should it have to learn how to use the body?

Let us return to the foundations of the system. The baby arrives with a rather detailed layout of his body inscribed at the top of his cortex or 'new' brain. However, there is no instruction sheet. Though eyes and ears are coordinated, these are agents of the brain. Body muscles are quite another matter. He can only bat at what he wants to reach. And he has no locomotion of any sort. Interesting evidence for the foundations layout comes from what are known as 'phantom limbs.' If some individual loses a limb later in life, he may continue to experience pain from the area where the limb once had been. These apparitions can be quite realistic and troublesome. And there is even evidence for their existence in cases of congenital absence of limbs.

In a very real sense there is also a basement lying below the cortex. This old brain contains all controls for essential heating, plumbing, and chemical processing. These are operational at birth. Many early psycho-analysts felt that this basement was inhabited by all manner of spooky reptilia which had hitched a ride from the dim evolutionary past. And it is possible that such archetypes, ids, prototypes, and spec-sheets of antiquated models do, indeed, exist. Nobody could prove otherwise. However, they should be viewed with considerable skepticism. Hypnosis has reached down to almost every level of the mind without unearthing any such fossils. Presupposing they existed, one would think that countless generations of genetic mixing would have equilibrated most of them throughout the population. And this should have removed any individual diagnostic value they might have once possessed.

On the other hand, it could be they simply go unrecognized. Consider dogs. They have been domesticated almost as long as humans (some would say with better results.) But dogs still mill about in close circles before lying down, ostensibly to make a bedding of leaves or grass. They also paw haphazardly at the earth before defecating, and render a few symbolic covering kicks after having done so. Thus, it would appear that inherent behavioral archetypes is still an open issue. In this respect I have often wondered about the incidence of morning sickness among humans. Could it be a residual from having once vomited food for the young?

So much for speculation. When living things or their systems are both critical and vulnerable, as is the brain, Nature has always provided safeguards. Were it not so, they would have become extinct. Thus, it may be assumed that the CNS is highly protected. And such is indeed the case. No other part of the organism, not even the vital heart, is so carefully guarded. Since this aspect of the organism is rarely discussed, it might help to mention a few of the protective measures. Some of them are truly astonishing. In fact, the brain and cord are even protected against the body itself! No monarch was ever so isolated.

Let us begin with structural features. Unlike beetles or crabs, we have a skeleton which is internal. The only external portion of the skeleton is the skull. The CNS is the one part of the body wholly encased in bone. Inside this bony shell, it is further wrapped in three separate membranes. Between two of these is the spinal fluid. This provides a hydrostatic system that distributes any stresses caused by movement. You may twist your body or shake your head in any direction without producing any point-pressures on the CNS. Even when you stand on your head, the spinal fluid and blood pressures of the brain will rise only momentarily, then readjust themselves back to normal. [4] Though the brain regulates blood pressure for the body, its own pressure and flow are under private control. Suppose someone gets stabbed (a la Hollywood), and begins to bleed all over the place. The blood pressure of the body will drop in a consistent fashion. Blood pressure in the brain, on the other hand, will remain constant. In such instances, the CNS apparently recognizes that its own blood supply is endangered. So it contracts cerebral blood vessels in order to maintain its own pressure levels. In doing so, of course, it contributes to more rapid loss of blood by the body. This grim scenario is played to the finish when consciousness is lost. The point to be made is this: the brain will always sacrifice the body to save itself. [5]

Any emergency where the chips are down and a choice must be made between brain and body, the body will lose. I'll give another example. Everyone knows that the pregnant mother should increase the calcium content of her food. If she doesn't, the developing infant may remove it from her bloodstream, possibly even her teeth. Far less known is the fact that the brain will behave in the same autocratic manner. For example, starved and emaciated infants reveal the same brain weight as normal infants of comparable age and length despite the ravaged body. Among adults starvation may reduce body weight by half or more. Even the heart, critical though it is, will lose in almost prohibitive proportions. Loss of brain weight, on the other hand, is rarely more than 5 percent. [6] Though the brain regulates body metabolism, its own metabolism is again under private authority. Moreover, it is remarkable for its constancy. Experimental procedures have been used which drastically reduce carbohydrate usage by the body. And except for insulin, these leave the brain unaffected. Procedures for increasing body metabolism have proved equally ineffectual for the brain. It is common knowledge that people with goiter (hyperthyroidism) may have basal metabolic rates 75% or more above normal. But when examined, it is always found that brain metabolism is within the usual limits. [7]

At one time this constancy of brain metabolism seemed quite baffling. There appeared no relation whatever between events in the brain and the brain's measured usage of energy, or metabolic rate. People could do arithmetic, solve puzzles, even undergo extremes such as grand mal seizures, and little or no change would occur in brain measurements. As it turned out, the answer was simple. The brain draws out of an energy storage bin, as it were. This contains ATP and PC (adenosine triphosphate and phosphocreatine) which are readily broken down to create energy. Oxidative processes feed into the bin on the one side. And from the other side, the brain uses from the bin as needed. Thus, it is independent of immediate energy production.

Despite all that has become known in the last decade or two, there are still certain aspects of brain metabolism that remain mysterious. It uses about 13% of the heart's blood supply, and a whopping 20% of all the oxygen. Both are completely out of proportion to the brain's relative weight. One would think that were this amount of oxygen used in oxidative metabolism, the resulting heat would literally cook it. In any case, these are further indications of the radical differences existing between brain and body processes.

Ever since the classic work of W.B. Cannon it has been recognized that the bloodstream is kept amazingly pure. [8] Even so, it is not always pure enough to satisfy the brain. As a consequence the CNS has perfected its own protective screening technique known as the 'blood brain barrier.' Exactly how it operates is still not fully understood. Its effects, however, can be readily demonstrated. Many materials injected into the bloodstream are freely distributed about the body. But they never show up in the brain. Somehow, somewhere, they get screened out. Proteins are especially forbidden entry. This is understandable. Neural tissues are engaged in protein synthesis, and alien proteins would be disruptive. Anaesthetics and narcotics are not so understandable. But they obviously could not achieve their effects were they not able to penetrate the barrier. The food used by the CNS is particularly interesting. As of this writing the brain, cord, and testes would appear to be the only body parts known to subsist almost exclusively on blood sugar. The inclusion of the testes in this unique category immediately leads one to wonder about the ovaries. Can it be that the brain has some sort of inbuilt genetic relationship with the sex glands? Can there be any significance to the thought that the brain is a producer of new ideas, whereas the germplasm is a producer of new people?

Would it not truly shake up orthodox genetic theory to discover that the germplasm is not so isolated as they assumed? Suppose it were isolated from the body (somatoplasm). This would have no particular significance. The CNS is even more isolated from the body. The critical issue for the Mendelian people is whether the germplasm is immune to influences from the CNS. As will soon be seen, the CNS appears to have absolute control over all other parts of the body. So it would be indeed strange if such control did not extend to include the germplasm. Physiologically at least, there is not a shred of evidence that the sex glands are any more independent of the brain than other parts of the body.

This stated independence of the germplasm became dogma solely because it provided a convenient argument against possible CNS influence upon heredity. Nonetheless, there are various observations leading one to suspect such influence at one level or another. For instance, many animals release eggs from their ovaries during or immediately following coitus. This has been shown to be mediated by the pituitary which is integral with the old brain. Further, several research studies strongly suggest that at least some animals can predetermine the sex of their offspring to compensate for changes in social and/or environmental conditions. And finally, as noted above, there are vital physiological features common only to the brain and testes. Changes have even been reported in contralateral portions of the brain with testicle removal, and vice versa. [9]

So much for the physiology. After awhile it begins to drag. Let us turn to behavior for a change. Here there is abundant evidence for the primacy of brain and mind. Note the profound difference between the active 'I touch' and the passive 'I am touched.' This exists even though sensory events are identical. For survival reasons, no creature confuses these. They are among the immediately experienced facts which one simply cannot ignore. Theory is one thing. Direct experience is something else. For example, 'I' will allow surgeons to snip off any parts of 'my' body which might interfere with 'me' surviving as an entity.

One of our more prominent brain surgeons, Wilder Penfield, has performed numerous open-brain operations on patients who were awake and conscious. This is possible because there is no pain in the cortex. Such procedures allow for some interesting observations. If the muscle control area of the cortex is stimulated, and the patient's arm is made to move, he reports, 'I didn't do that. You did it!' Penfield notes that the patient invariably recognizes involuntary behavior brought about by agents outside himself. For Penfield, this meant that the mind had to be something separate and apart from the brain -- else how could the patient distinguish so readily the acts 'he' initiated from those triggered artificially in the same brain? [10]

We are all familiar with dogs and cats. They may not be able to reason abstractly, but each has a mind -- an ego or self. The fact that they preen themselves is evidence enough. Suppose a dog gets one of his paws injured by a passing motorist. He usually makes every effort to escape. And if the injured member interferes with this escape, he can often be observed to growl and snap at it. Though it is still part of him, it has become a liability, something best 'depersonalized.' Behavior of this sort is not peculiar to dogs. It occurs among wild animals which have unfortunately caught a foot in a steel trap. Painful though it must be, it is none-the-less common for them to gnaw off the foot in order to escape.

Humans carry this program to even more spectacular limits. Body parts such as arms, legs or eyes get depersonalized. If they have somehow become associated with extremely distasteful incidents, they may be judged better ignored. Though the limbs are otherwise healthy, their existence and usage are no longer recognized. The offending parts either become stiff or simply nonfunctional. Indeed, the mind will even segregate and ostracize any unacceptable areas of its own memory. This occurs despite the fact that these memory areas are integral with the brain and mind itself. The disorder is known as amnesia. It were as if the mind simply refuses to pay any attention to structures of the body, or even parts of itself, when these are seen to be inconsistent with its own welfare.

Consider the phenomenon of suicide. It is clearly contrary to the first commandment of life, namely, self-survival. Thus it is quite rare among other creatures. Among humans, however, it has always been common. This paradox can be understood only if one recognizes that self-survival depends on what is defined as the 'self.' Other creatures do not possess the elaborate mental structures of humans. And it is the survival of these latter structures which is at stake. They are the true 'me' and the true 'you.' They are never considered mere parts of the body. Rather, they are what we call 'us'. They have a life of their own. They *are* what we are. The body, by contrast, is viewed as little more than a tool or vehicle, perhaps even less. Few people would treat their automobiles as poorly as they treat their bodies. Though painful to repair, and totally irreplaceable, bodies are frequently treated almost as if held in contempt. Witness the dare-deviltry, death defying sports, martyrdoms, duels, and eating fugu.

On the other hand, a threat to the ego (rather than body) reverses the entire picture. Any of the above madcaps might endure extreme hardship, even torture, and still fight to live provided his hopes and ideals were still intact. But if his face were against the wall, and he had to choose between continued living and foregoing some aspect of his mental being, he would choose to escape via death. The phrase 'mental being' is used advisedly. It represents the true 'he.' The remainder is only body. In all instances the mind has final authority. It evaluates the body in its own terms according to the circumstances. And if there is discord it may take some kind of action against the body (conversion hysteria, suicide), or even against portions of itself (amnesia).

Occasionally rebellions flare up within the body. These are known to physicians as autoimmune diseases. Characteristically, one subsystem of the body (the immune system) takes action against some other part of the body. This usually occurs without central control (the mind) being aware of what is happening. The total is so incredibly complex that internal misconduct or error should not be surprising. Self-initiated disorders of this sort sidestep central control. They can and do arise within the body itself. Unless specific internal sensors are alerted, they go undetected until external symptoms become obvious, usually too late for correction by internal means.

The organism may be viewed from many perspectives. I prefer to look upon it as a Chinese puzzle box -- a set of hierarchial systems, one within the other. The mind is innermost, so authority is delegated from mind to CNS, and thence to subsidiary systems of the body. However, the bonds of authority are not rigid. Thus, delegation of supervision sometimes has the same sad consequences observable in government, business, and social groups. Things 'get out of hand.' Despite these disadvantages, permissive discipline of this sort is necessary if lesser centers are to perform local corrections. Moreover, it does not prevent the mind from stepping in and taking over control when necessary.

Somewhat startling is the fact that the mind can simply *kill* the body.

This can occur even though the person is otherwise healthy. Not all suicides involve direct violent action. The authority of the mind is final. And it may choose to turn everything off completely, i.e., put all systems into the 'no go' mode. Action of this sort probably takes place via the autonomic and endocrine systems. These are liaison structures or intermediaries enabling the old brain to regulate the body. Whatever the mechanism, the results are the stuff of romantic novels. People die of 'broken hearts.' Dogs languish to death on the graves of masters. Voodoo artists hex people into the great beyond, etc. There now exists a large quantity of statistical evidence that some terminally ill patients tend to speed up or deter their dying to coincide with dates of importance to them -- anniversaries, birthdays, and the like. It has long been known that widowers tend to die disproportionately soon after the death of the wife. [11]

Within recent years, and especially following publication of Norman Cousins' volume, *Anatomy of an Illness*, [12] the medical profession has done further thinking about this mind/body relationship. The result has been a veritable spate of books high on the list of best-sellers. All are full of case histories and suggestions for getting the patient to help himself. Instead of the negatively oriented mind/body relationship described above, emphasis is placed on the positive side of the relation. In short, they have recognized that what can be turned *off* can also be turned *on*! Interest has become centered in the role of the immune system.

Until the appearance of AIDS, immunology was often considered a lesser and somewhat esoteric area of study. But during the last decade all this has changed. Evidence has mounted revealing that the mind has considerable influence over this crucial aspect of the body's defenses. Resulting investigations have even become a discipline unto themselves, baptized with the awkward title of 'Psychoneuroimmunology.' [13]

First, let's acronym that to PNI. Limited space prevents discussion of any depth. However, a brief summary is in order Why? Because the great majority of their conclusions coincide with the ideas presented here. For instance, they feel that the role of the mind deserves far more attention than hitherto bestowed upon it. Authority over the body is thought to be relatively direct and complete. This assumes integration and cooperation among lesser control systems. By contrast, traditional physiology has always viewed the neural, glandular and immune systems as if they were separate domains. This was a mistake, says PNI. The body functions as an integrated whole, not as a confederation of independent systems. What happens in one area is very likely to affect other areas. Body processes do not occur in isolation, one from another.

PNI observes that there is a constant stream of chemical chit-chat going on between brain and body. It takes place largely via an intercom net which extends everywhere the blood flows. This means down to the least cell. (Is it necessary to point out that this includes the germ cells?) It remains true that the neural system is responsible for rapid-fire messages to specific cell groups, predominantly muscles. But the vascular intercom carries all the general news plus vital 'to whom it may concern' data.The language used by the intercom is biochemical, and the meaning is in pictographs. That is to say, communication is stereochemical. It is a function of molecular shape or patterning -- the *form* possessed by the molecules. This is one case at least, where *form* and in*form*ation coincide. There are said to be as many as a hundred or more of these different molecular structures transporting information back and forth. They include hormones, neuropeptides, neurotransmitters, lymphokines, and a host of other related message-bearing chemicals. My guess is that their number is infinite. Consider, if you will, the endless varieties of antibodies which the immune system is able to manufacture.

This brings us to the components of the immune system itself. These are known to us as white blood cells. But as seen by PNI, they might be better described as a corps of elite personnel. They are agents of the brain as it were -- couriers, spies, and armed guards. One description pictures them as 'bits of the brain floating around in the body.' Their chief import-ance lies in their ability to recognize, remember, and neutralize alien intruders like bacteria and viruses. Because of this ability, some have referred to the system as an all-pervasive internal sense organ. It is everywhere alert to any help the body cells might need. This requires that it be highly complex with many specialized duties. Accordingly, some members act as look-outs (monocytes), others as killers (antibodies and T cells), and there is even a detail to dispose of the remains (macrophages.)

It should not be thought that these seemingly fanciful concepts were pulled out of thin air. Decades of experimental evidence exist. Some earlier studies date back at least to 1960. In Russia, one such study demonstrated that animals could learn (be conditioned) to alter their cholesterol metabolism. Another revealed that production of antibodies (clearly an immune responsibility) was also influenced by conditioning. And in the same year, in Buenos Aires, dogs were taught to lower their blood sugar level. All indicate mental action, probably enforced by the old brain, and extending down to the level of the cells themselves. In the forty years since, a wealth of experimental work has accumulated. Some of the major proponents of PNI are now ensconced in the National Institutes of Mental Health. I wish them well. [14]

What is to be learned from all this? I should like to suggest the following: (1) A major turnabout is occurring in the life sciences. Heretofore, the mind has been regarded as a mere artifact of the brain. Inasmuch as the brain itself was described as just another organ of the body, this left it in limbo Since the whole outlook had been contrary to both common sense and everyday usage, the public never believed it anyhow. (2) Basic cellular communication is being recognized as chemical. Even the nerves act chemically. Almost daily, it seems, new evidence appears suggesting that the brain may not be a piece of electrical gadgetry after all. Instead, it may be something enormously more complex -- the original and largest gland. (3) It is rapidly becoming obvious that the mind involves something over and beyond the more static brain structures called memories. These latter are almost certainly molecular, and the 'over and beyond' could therefore mean intermolecular energies. These are known to exist. In short, our picture of both brain and mind is being reshuffled -- and the consequences are disturbing to established dogma.

Regardless how theorists should choose to define it, the mind can be proved to cut into and edit the operations of the brain itself. It provides objectives and sets limits. As such, it explains why we are unable to recall thus and so, and why whole areas of the brain and body get declared off-limits. In these cases, the mind simply abstains from paying further attention to specific features of its cortical environment.

The key to this mystery is thought to lie in that enigmatic word *attention*. It has to be a separate process of the mental system. Many, including the noted biologist C. H. Waddington, have identified it with consciousness. [15] When you are attending to something you are conscious of it. And when you are not attending to anything at all, you are unconscious. That something which scuttles through your memory warehouse when you are dreaming is attention.

Later on, more will be said about attention. Before the strange fad of behaviorism stigmatized all speculation about the mind, it was recognized as the pivotal phenomenon about which all mental operations revolved. As early as 1908, Titchener observed, '. . . attention is the nerve center of the whole psychological system, and as men judge of it, so shall they be judged before the general tribunal of psychology.'" [16]

Chapter 2

Perhaps the Ghost Owns the Machine!

(Evidence that the mind has authority over all aspects of brain and body, and that this authority extends down to the level of the cell itself!)

"The extreme tyranny of mind over body is most dramatically demonstrated during conditions of trance, often called 'altered states of consciousness.' Without exception these result from profound voluntary inattention to the external world. Sensory input from the outside becomes restricted. Thus, when one is no longer attending to outer events, it is possible to concentrate almost wholly on internal bodily events. Control then becomes virtually absolute. The capabilities of people in these states are often difficult to believe even when authenticated -- and they have been fully authenticated.

India abounds with aesthetes who specialize in this sort of mental disconnectedness. So, let us off to India. The year is 1960. We find ourselves standing beside a deep grave-like pit, a strange coffin-shaped box, and a group of scientists. There is a figure in the middle of the cluster. He is Indian and his name is Shri Ramanand Yogi. He is wearing the usual loin-cloth. The upper half of his dark body is decorated with small white swatches plastered to the skin with collodion. They conceal electrodes. Wires dangle to the side. Believe it or not, he is being prepared for burial. He is going to be buried alive! His length of stay in the air-tight box is scheduled for ten hours! The scientists are present to document what happens. Question: what action does he take that enables him to survive?

Answer: when buried alive, the first thing to do is lower your body metabolism so as to conserve oxygen. This makes perfect sense. And this is precisely what yogins do. In the case of Shri Ramanand, oxygen consumption dropped from a norm of about 20 liters per hour to only 13.

Such action, of course, is further calculated to lower body temperature, pulse rate, and other vital signs. But contrary to popular opinion, yogins do not pass into any so-called 'suspended animation.' Electrical brain rhythms (EEG) continue, but become more like those occurring under hypnotic trance or the deep meditative state known as 'samadhi.' While in this semiconscious condition, external stimulation evokes little or no attention. Apparently, the subject is oblivious to all but himself. Quite literally, he is mentally detached from the external world. [17]

Voluntary comas of a comparable sort are rather common among lesser creatures. Black bears, for instance, are able to induce far more complicated bodily changes which enable them to hibernate for months. And hummingbirds lapse into a similar torpor every night. Otherwise, their high metabolic rate would soon lead to starvation. Among yogins, such voluntary slowing of body processes has been very well documented. And in all instances it has been shown that the conscious mind can take over control of body functions normally kept on autopilot regulation by the old brain.

Why is it that you and I cannot accomplish these same effects under everyday circumstances? If we could, it would provide us with a very beneficial technique for relaxing. Certainly the physiological mechanisms are available, as witnessed by the fact that yogins can do it. Moreover, the vast majority of internal organs possess sensors which relay information to the brain. So there are communication links. Eating a few green apples will convince anyone that he has sensors in his intestines. Why are they used only to alert us after we have foolishly over-dosed?

It is now generally believed that the reason we are unaware of the normal operations of our intestines or other organs is that the signals they emit are usually weak. They get drowned out by the overwhelming deluge of data coming to the brain from major senses such as eyes and ears. [18] We can't identify the internal processes of our bodies. In communication terms, they are masked by the 'noise.' The result is we can't attend to them. And any event which one cannot attend to goes unnoticed -- this by definition.

'So what?' asks the control engineer. 'It's only a simple feedback problem. All systems involve feedback, else they couldn't exist as systems. You physiologist-types call it homeostasis. You say that these inside sensory signals are feeble? Well, all you have to do is pick up the signal and amplify it. Then you feed it into a TV tube, or maybe some headphones so the person can find out what's happening inside. And voila! He'll be able to do something about it -- maybe.'

Strange as it now seems, this obvious solution did not dawn on the life sciences until the late fifties or sixties. It was then dubbed 'biofeedback.' Among the earliest to experiment along these lines was an ex-classmate of mine from the graduate school at Berkeley. His name was Joseph Kamiya. Joe knew about the changes in electrical brain rhythms (EEG) which accompany deeper states of meditation. Why not use biofeedback? This should enable the person to acquire control of his own EEG without the years of discipline supposedly required by yogins and zen roshis. The bottom line is this. Kamiya, as well as a number of others, were spectacularly successful. In many cases, it required less than 15 minutes for a person to learn how to control his own brain rhythms! [19]

This seemingly straight-forward accomplishment has far more significance than commonly realized. Let us pause and think about it for a moment. Brain rhythms are attributed to the metabolic activity of the individual brain cells themselves. The normal healthy cell carries an ionic charge on its outer membrane. It arises from the internal processes of the cell. These ionic charges build up to a max, then discharge spontaneously. One result is they tend to synchronize. Masses of cells beat with the same rhythm. Surely no physical attribute of the brain could be much more basic than this! Now, consider the fact that 'you' can readily tell your own brain, made up of billions of these cells, to change what it is doing! The implications of this observation should be down-right staggering!

Question: just *who* or *what* does the telling? What gives such orders to the very insides of the cells themselves? As evidence for the independent existence of a mind, I know of nothing that is more clear-cut and indisputable than this! The mind simply cannot be the 'workings' of the brain. Rather, it *controls* the workings of the brain. If one wishes lesser evidence that the mind is not synonymous with the brain, take a look at the effects of narcotics such as LSD, angel dust, and the like. They can totally scramble the mind while leaving brain functions relatively unimpaired.

What the public has always assumed is, in fact, true! The brain and mind are separate entities. The first merely provides structural facilities for the second. Though interdependent, they resemble each other no more than the acorn resembles the oak. For example, the brain is perhaps the most disorderly mass of protoplasm in the entire body. Whereas, the mind is exactly the opposite. Its tendency toward organization is its most prominent characteristic. Thus, all *observable* operations of the brain are only distantly related, if at all, to experienced processes of the mind. You can describe your sensations, thought transactions, and mental imagery without knowing anything whatever about brain functions. Operations of the mind are known and verified in entirely different ways than those of the brain. Differences are both qualitative and quantitative.

True, certain specific areas and nuclei of the brain have become specialized in particular categories of mental action. And one can identify the major tracts used for different kinds of information transport. But this is about the whole of it. All the finer details of brain structure and function are just what they appear to be -- matters of neurocellular growth. They bear no resemblance to any mental events. Take space and time, for instance. These are portrayed very faithfully by the optic system. Even the same rules apply. Velocity equals space divided by time for both the inner and outer worlds. But nothing even remotely comparable appears to happen in the brain.

This is not meant to imply that mental events have no structural counterparts in the cortex. Most likely, it simply means that their responsible agents lie at levels currently unobservable and therefore unknown. Their domain is probably that of biomolecular and colloidal chemistry, and *not* that of electrical distributions or neural architecture.

Whatever the case, it is self-contradictory to say that the brain could give orders to itself. And if the CNS is called 'self organizing' -- another popular phrase -- the paradox still exists. It is simply less obvious. Self organization during crystal growth is described by physical laws. This is understandable. But the same principles don't apply at the mental level. Direct applicability of such laws is obviously precluded by the infinite variety and complexity of mental activity. With reference to the brain, the phrase 'self organizing' implies a self which directs the organizing. The organization can be a growth phenomenon, true. But something has to be growing. And to dismiss the whole issue by merely declaring that the organism responds to external stimuli is hopelessly naive. For one thing, biofeedback stimuli are actually internal!

To return to biofeedback, it quickly became the 'in' thing. Its implications, even its therapeutic value, became secondary. It had *sales* value! Companies were organized to sell equipment to the public for 'how to' and 'self do' physical betterment. Amusing as this may seem, the overall program did accomplish one thing. It established beyond any possible doubt that people can learn to control virtually all the internal processes of their bodies. Previously, these had been considered fully and irrevocably automated. The list just about covers every process known to be regulated by lesser (sub-cortical) centers. It includes metabolism, temperature, heart rate, blood pressure, intestinal contractions, muscle tension, kidney and pancreatic functions, and so on and on. Available books and journal literature are now truly voluminous. [20]

So, whatever else it may be, the mind is manifestly a control system. And that which it controls (the body) is enormously complex. Therefore it is only logical that authority for most on-going bodily functions is relegated to lesser centers and subsystems -- mostly in the old brain. This has enormous advantages in that it more or less frees the mind -- isolates it from all the nitty-gritty details and noise of internal bodily activity. Were this not possible, its effectiveness as a control would be greatly impaired. Control systems have to be functionally separated from the operations being manipulated. If an army general were personally involved with the problems of every soldier, for example, there would be no discipline and certainly no time for strategy. The forest could not be seen for the trees. As noted earlier, such isolation is amazingly complete for the brain and cord. I would be remiss were I not to mention another equally spectacular source of evidence concerning the mind/body relationship. It illustrates what can happen when the body's control system (mind) is manipulated by some outside agency. The area is hypnosis, and the agent is the hypnotist. One is always hesitant to deal with hypnotic phenomena. They are held in even less repute than discussions of the mind, if that is possible. Moreover, in this case much of the ill repute appears justified. In years gone by at least, hypnotists were just as often frauds or worse. Fakirs of the East may have had some legitimacy. But these fakers of the West seldom did. The story of 'Bridey Murphy' from not too long ago, provides a ready example. [21]

Despite all the chicanery, there is no question but what genuine hypnotic phenomena exist. And again, some of them are so baffling they are almost unbelievable. The nature of the subject lends itself to deception, however, and one must be quite careful as to source reporting, reliability of witnesses, and other types of verification such as repetition of experiments by others. By and large, the reports published in technical journals by professional-level practitioners are thought to be trustworthy. Common phenomena used to test depth of trance are omitted here. These include induced sleep, pain and its elimination, hallucinations, and muscular rigidity. This is the stuff of popular exhibitions.

There are two types of evidence having particular bearing on our present thesis. Both have been verified either directly or indirectly. The first has to do with the use of hypnosis to study memory. One experiment will be mentioned. It was published by a well known professional and dealt with a famous subject, Aldous Huxley. Seated in Huxley's extensive library, with the subject in deep trance, it was possible to retrieve data from books 'which he had not touched for twenty or more years . . As I opened the book at random and read a half dozen lines from a selected paragraph. . . he identified the page number almost at once and then he would hallucinate the page and read it from the point where I had stopped.' [22] Findings of this sort, provided by Milton Erickson, would normally be questioned as almost impossible. However, they are not significantly different from experimental results reported by the brain surgeon, Wilder Penfield. These latter employed entirely different procedures with different objectives. It is doubtful whether one investigator even knew of the other.

As mentioned earlier, Penfield performed numerous open brain surgeries on patients who were awake and attending to events. Extremely fine micro-electrodes were used to stimulate points on certain areas of the cortical surface. Given such stimulation, it is stated that the patient involuntarily recalled the past with startling accuracy. This even included data which went unrecognized at the time, and which were later inaccessible to recall. The experiences were said to be as vivid as reality itself: memories of conversations held long ago, places visited, or instrumental music.'. . .it all comes back to him in great detail. He is suddenly aware again of those things to which he had paid attention in that distant interval of time.' From decades of such experiments, Penfield became convinced that (1) There is a mind which is relatively independent of the brain. (2) It operates with some type of energy thus far unexplained. (3) It evidences itself in the phenomena of attention. And (4) it is responsible for the programming of behavior. [23] It will later be recognized that these are exactly the same points emphasized in this lecture.

What does such fantastic performance imply, particularly that of Aldous Huxley? In effect, it suggests that one never really forgets anything to which he has ever attended, no matter how trivial. The sole exception would be forgetting due to loss of brain cells. Using this perspective, what is commonly called forgetting would be better described as inability to reference the desired memory structures. The memories themselves would still be present, but simply unavailable for recall under normal conditions of attention. It would be much as if a particular tax return were misplaced among the many billions at IRS. None of the usual computer searches could locate it. But it would nonetheless still exist.

Also, please pause a moment to consider what this suggests about memory storage capacity. Seventy years of waking hours, attending to first one thing then another, using all the senses, would create an astronomical number of. memories. It would be far more than the 10 billion neurons assumed to make up the brain, or even the number of junctions (synapses) between these. In brief, memories necessarily have to be molecular in size. There is no other way they could all be stored within the skull.

Back to hypnotic phenomena. The other class of effects which should be mentioned has to do with the skin. The late Alan Watts sometimes referred to the human as only an ego walking about in a bag of skin. But the skin is as far removed from the ego as physiological limits will allow. As outer garment it would surely have to be a loose bag. Unlike the horse which can twitch his skin any place he wishes, the human possesses few useable patches of subcutaneous muscle. (Muscles of the face are a notable exception.) This leaves the brain with only minimal neural access to local skin areas of the body. In other words, body skin would be about the least likely place to look for localized effects produced by action of the mind. Blushing, sweating, shivering, etc., are more generalized effects not requiring specific neural routes to particular skin locations.

Nonetheless, local skin effects are produced by the mind despite this extreme paucity of nerve supply. They can often be made to appear in skin areas where even sensory receptors are quite sparse. Let me illustrate with an example. Suppose we have a person in deep trance. He is presented with a fresh unlighted cigarette. But he is told that it is lighted! And the presumably hot glowing end is pointed out to him. This 'hot' end of the cigarette is then pressed against the skin of his arm. He will grimace, cry out, and evince every symptom of pain. This would be expected. What would not be expected, and which occurs in a surprising number of cases, is the effect on the skin. A blister forms, surrounded by the typical reddened patch indicative of an actual burn. In some cases, excision of the blister even reveals the same pathology as a true burn. [24] Does this sound far-fetched? Indeed it does. Others have thought so too. Thus, it has been repeated numerous times. And though it does not always occur (a difficulty intrinsic to experimental hypnosis), symptoms appear in a sufficiently high percentage of cases to render the phenomenon completely valid. It makes for problems. There is no way of explaining it by any existing theory. Since there are few nerves leading from the brain to specific patches of body skin, how does such complicated information get conducted? And even if there were neural messages to spot 'X' on the skin, how could they possibly carry detailed instructions to a particular group of cells? Current theory says nerves conduct only neuroelectric impulses.

To all appearances at least, it were as if the mind exercises complete authority over the behavior of the organism, and that this extends down to include the individual cell! (We made this observation before with respect to the EEG, remember?) The only conceivable alternative seems even more far-fetched. This is the thought that perhaps the cells themselves possess the ability to orchestrate the (phony?) burn symptoms, and to accomplish this upon receipt of a simple message 'burn,' somehow carried by the bloodstream. If this latter were the case, it would necessarily credit the cell with the capacity to discriminate and react to incoming information. That is to say, the cell would have to be endowed with at least rudimentary intelligence. And for all we know (which is precious little) both these explanations may be correct. Who can say?

Should the foregoing seem to be pure fantasy, it is no more so than several other types of hypnotically induced skin effects. If we are to believe the experimental reports, for example, Herpes Simplex (the common mouth sore) can also be made to appear under trance. But since there is no immediate means of establishing whether this is 'true' herpes, let us turn to a phenomenon more readily verified, viz., wart removal.

Robert Noll, A Michigan State University psychologist, had a problem. The problem: a seven year old girl patient. She had a total of 82 warts scattered on her hands and face, even on the insides of her lips! Medical help had been exhausted without significant results. She was then brought to Noll who suggested hypnosis. Treatment began under deep trance, and within two weeks half the sixteen facial warts were gone. After four more one-hour sessions during the subsequent few weeks, all 82 warts had disappeared. Needless to say, the cancer specialists with whom Noll worked were quite baffled. Ordinarily, it takes several years for warts to disappear without medical help. [25]

The well known author and physician, Lewis Thomas, mentions instances of these induced skin effects, including wart removal. He then states that of all the many things 'unflattened' by science, he would rather have an understanding of these phenomena than anything else he could think of. [26] So would I. Herpes and warts are both thought to be caused by specific viruses. If the mind can take action against viruses while following hypnotic suggestion, then it has to be influencing the immune system in a pretty direct and detailed fashion. Again, this implies transmission of complex information to individual cells. And nerves simply do not extend to each and every cell, particularly to mobile ones such as make up the immune system. Perhaps those people who started psychoneuroimmunology were not so far off-base after all."

Chapter 3

Anatomy of the Ghost ex Machina

(Mind is said to be a growing entity made up of molecule size memories which get activated by a coherent type of intermolecular energy. How closed feedback loops can lead to self-awareness.)

For some reason the lecture ended earlier than anticipated. So I threw the meeting open for discussion. Were there any questions?

"Yes." This came from a young lady in leotards. She had been lounging on some empty rear seats. "What I should like to know is just exactly what the mind *is*." she responded. "You mentioned its relationship to the brain, and you stressed its independence. But that's about all I got. I still don't understand much about the mind itself."

"I'm sorry," I replied. "I really wasn't trying to dodge anything. I merely wanted to sneak up on the subject gradually. But since you bring up the question of mind *per se,* I'll try to provide a brief overview. The first and most important thing to recognize is that it is a living growing entity. But unlike the body, it is largely an energy system. That is to say, it is not entirely made up of matter. It is partly moving energy which can assemble and rearrange itself. This enables it to grow in terms of increasing organization without increasing its mass or size. Such increasing complexity of organization is not peculiar to the mind. It is a characteristic of all living things -- for living things grow. [27]

Those organic phenomena which appear unorganized or highly irregular like coral reefs or sponges, usually are not organisms in the strict sense. They are better described as social assemblies of smaller organisms. The brain looks somewhat like a chunk of coral. Of all the body, it has the most disorderly structure. This is because it is primarily a social assembly of smaller beings called nerve cells. And these are all crumpled and crammed into the confines of the skull. Details of structure are therefore confused.

When one studies the normal mind, however, he discovers a situation exactly opposite to this! There is almost total regularity! Evidence of orderly functioning is everywhere! 'Deranged' people are insane. Thinking processes are always consistent. They are organized. It is not possible to think simultaneously of both 'A' and 'Not-A.' Moreover, when something does not mesh with the way you think or believe, it tends to disorganize you. It produces stress. This is why the lie-detector can pick up statements which are at odds with memory. All inconsistencies are emotionally disturbing.

On the other hand, if something does happen to fit with your beliefs, attitudes, goals and such, you will not only find it pleasant, but you will remember it. Indeed, D.0. Hebb even defined pleasure in these terms. He described the process as 'fundamentally a directed growth or development in cerebral organization.' [28]

Learning, thinking, in fact *all* our psychological processes involve memory. And memories, being molecular, are chemical structures. Just as the stereo-chemical shape of an odoriferous molecule determines its unique smell for the nose, so does the shape of a memory molecule determine a unique feeling. While rummaging through the attic trunk, suppose you come up with some treasured relic from the past. It will not only evoke memories, but these will be accompanied by a specific feeling -- one you may not have felt for years. For myself, I know, the smell of fresh leather or the handling of new hardback books have uniquely identifiable feelings dating back to childhood. Certain songs will also bring about similar reactions. In general, emotions have a chemical (hormonal) basis.

But let's get back to the structure of the mind. The process enabling the mind to grow is called learning. When one learns he *feeds* the mind. This is meant quite literally. And what is learned is never a miscellany of bits and pieces. These would be indigestible. It is the patterning or interrelatedness of things that appeals to us. Patterning connotes togetherness or belongingness, the hallmarks of organization. It implies meaning -- something that is mentally 'tasty,' something that carries information and has food-value for the mind. Thus, the more something is organized, the easier it is to learn. No principle of learning is better established than this. The same principle holds for the body. Proteins have the highest food-value and the most complex molecular organization. Simple minerals have no food-value and little organization."

I paused a moment to sort through some slides, then said, "So much for the philosophy. Suppose we return to the comparison between body and mind. Now, if someone will pull the drapes and flick off the light, I have a slide I'd like to show you. It was adapted from an earlier book of mine and it deals with exactly this issue. [29]

	Input	Symptom	Result	Excess
Body:	Food	Hunger	Growth	Satiation
Mind:	Patterning	Curiosity	Learning	Monotony

This is a simple analogy chart. Others have carried the comparison much further, even including digestion and assimilation. [30] Please note that like the computer, the mind feeds on information. But the information is structurally different from that used by the computer. It is not mere bit-by-bit pulses or charges. It consists of large complex patterns which might be better described as 'images in energy.' More about this later. The body also feeds on complex patterns, but these are material."

"What's the relationship between patterning and information? I always thought they were opposites!" This voice came from somewhere near the middle of the room.

"No, they are not opposites," I replied. "But explaining their relationship might get a little abstruse. However, if the rest of the class wants to bear with us for a moment, I'll see if I can make it understandable. To begin, the opposite of information is 'redundancy.' It may be thought of as 'no patterning' -- homogeneity. For auditory material or computer signals it is repetition of the same thing over and over again. For vision it may be likened to a scene which has no variation or change -- a blank slate as it were. As soon as any change occurs in this monotonous panorama, we have the beginnings of patterning. It also tells us something, however slight. So change has also been identified with information. As change increases we say the patterning becomes more complex. And accordingly, it provides more information. Every pattern has some degree of complexity or information. So either term may be used. But they are not wholly synonymous because they have different connotations.

What makes the subject so abstract and difficult to grasp is that changes are not 'things.' They are usually intangible relations between things. We are predisposed to see and think in terms of things. And because the interrelations between them are intangible and non-material, the entire concept is somewhat boggling. However, it can be shown that all 'things' are identical with the totality of their internal relationships.

This is why photographs appear realistic. Their internal relations, or the ratios and proportions of their imagery, have been retained. In the world about us, changes are occurring all the time. Changes are not entities, but they can be seen as relationships. These provide us with information. To say the mind feeds on information, therefore, is much the same as saying it feeds on change. When the changes become complex, they may be described as patterns. And since patterns are *forms, information* is literally *form*ative. The 'imprinting' of such patterning in the molecular structures of memory is called learning."

"Yak! That's a mind twister! You were right in calling it abstruse! I suppose this is why we are always interested in the new and different."

"Precisely. The novel and different are changes from the status quo, and are therefore food-stuff for the mind. Numerous studies have been done on curiosity, which you rightfully refer to as 'interest.' Those features of the outside world which cause us to attend to them, and which evoke curiosity, include: movement, incongruity, surprise, conflict, sudden intensity shifts, and alerting signals such as hearing one's name called, the phone ring, or the shout of 'fire!' All differ from the status quo. All are changes. [31]

Curiosity faithfully reflects the growth of the mind. It is particularly noticeable in early childhood, e.g., 'Daddy, what holds the clouds up in the sky?' Just as nature abhors a vacuum, so the mind abhors unanswered questions. They result in the same uneasiness as unfinished tasks. One senses something missing -- a vacancy in the growth sequence. The mind is uncomfortable unless it has completeness or closure. If not achieved, it feels deficient and insecure.

Thus, *the natural condition of the mind is to believe!* Uncertainty produces stress. Even highly improbable answers are preferable to no answers at all. And bad news is accepted with better grace than no news. If no answers are readily available, the mind will invent them! Primitive man deified features of his environment like the storm or sea simply be- cause he had to have answers, and there were no other explanations available. This is also why the average human doesn't waste too much time mulling over abstruse issues like these. He doesn't have to. He believes -- so he already 'knows' the answers. Call it a quick-fix if you like, but it nonetheless saves a lot of needless worry." [32]

" Is there anything that corresponds to starvation?"

He was grinning when he asked, so I wasn't sure he was serious. But I replied, "It just so happens that there is! It is called sensory deprivation. Patients are placed in environments providing no stimulation at all, sometimes even suspended in water at body temperature. When this is prolonged, it results in lapses of attention called 'blank-outs.' Hallucinations in different senses, feelings of bodily dissociation, and changes in the EEG have also been reported. What seems most disrupted by this total absence of information is the mechanism of attention."

"May we pursue this attention thing?" It was the young lady in leotards again. "I don't wish to seem unduly persistent," she said, "but just what could account for action of this sort? You know, what is it?"

"Suppose we return to your original question as to what the mind really is," I replied. "Then maybe it will become clearer. To begin, the components of the mind are of two distinct types. First, there has to be some kind of stable unchanging structures which persist throughout our lifetimes. These we know as permanent memories. They can only be molecular because, mathematically, they are so numerous they would have to fall into the molecular size range.

Secondly, this skull or warehouse full of permanently recorded sights, sounds, smells and so forth would be useless to us unless there existed some means of accessing and interrelating them. In and of themselves, memories are virtually inert. So there has to be something to do the relating -- something which seems alive and moving within the warehouse. Moreover, it is a discrete and unitary thing. This is known from the fact that it can only be in one place at a time. We can only be aware of one item after another. Whether thinking, dreaming, or simply looking, we are restricted to dealing with one thing at a time. All experience is serialized along the path taken by this 'something' we call attention.

The fact that we can attend to only one thing at a time has become such a popularism no one recognizes that it is paradoxical. Why should the cortex, the largest section of the brain, be so restricted? This is certainly not true for the housekeeping functions controlled out of the old brain. Breathing, temperature regulation, heart beat -- indeed hundreds of ongoing processes operate simultaneously. Only when *conscious* processes are involved, as in thinking, listening, or trying to recall something, does one's awareness seem to focus into a single moving point. This, in itself, suggests that attention may be what we have always called *consciousness*.

Perhaps the most compelling aspect of attention is its high mobility. It flits hither, thither and yon. We can sense the movement. So it has to be some kind of relatively free energy. But whatever it is, it is the stuff which strings together our thoughts, dreams and sensory experiences. It focuses on first one item, then another, like a flashlight moving in the dark, or the cursor on a computer screen.

Suppose you get hit on the head. This moving cursor gets knocked off track as it were. The light goes out. Consciousness disappears. Your permanent memories don't disappear, just this mobile spot of light. You see 'stars' because the constituent energy has been temporarily scrambled. During normal waking hours, however, this 'light' in your head has to come from somewhere. Yet strangely enough, no one seems curious about it. It is not light from the outside -- because light is not conducted through neural tissue. So it has to be the illuminating effects of attention!

I may as well admit that I am not fond of the term 'consciousness.' It has been over-used in too many ways. So I'll stick with the word attention. What exactly is it? What could behave in this fashion? It is clearly a focal point or convergence of some kind of energy. But it is not like anything with which we are familiar. It can only be an energy of mutual attraction. And in this respect it reminds one of gravity. [33] Unlike gravity, however, it seems dynamic! It only stays in one spot very briefly. It brings things together, and it hangs together. That is why you can attend to only one thing at a time. It also explains why the mental system tends toward organization, why diverse items get related, why images from the two eyes or sounds from the two ears fuse together, why the image you see matches the one in memory, and a myriad other facts.

Now, before I get accused of being on drugs and tripping off into the wild blue yonder, I should like to point out that *such an energy really does exist!* It is found between the large molecules of organic colloids. I'll not try to identify or explain it for the time being. But please note that the brain is a colloidal structure containing more water than the blood itself. So this is the perfect location for these energies. Furthermore, memories have to be molecular, and they have to get related. Thus, the entire picture makes sense. However, I'm getting ahead of myself -- slopping over into issues I wanted to save for later. For the moment, then, let's just say that the mind is an energy system. It is made up of permanent molecular memory structures which get related, 'brought to light' and recalled by a kind of intermolecular energy called attention.

The entire system might be visualized as a kind of three-dimensional map, a sort of cranial planetarium. Memories in the brain cells constitute fixed locations in the map. Between these positions a maze of pathways, streets and highways extend in every direction. Some areas are densely populated, others are open country. Somewhere within the volume of our planetarium-like map is this small cursor spot of light which moves from one position to another energizing or 'lighting up' each location in its turn.

The pathway is quite erratic. It does not scan in regular TV fashion. For example, it jumps with sensory input. Visually, we are aware of these jumps as saccadic eye movements.

When attention is focused on something, there is a small area of immediate interest *(Blickpunkt)* surrounded by a penumbra of lesser intensity *(Blickfeld)*. The Blickpunkt you are focussed on will always appear brighter and larger than it normally would. One well known researcher named Jean Piaget has aptly labeled the process 'centration.' The word goes well with 'concentration.' But it should not be thought that attentional focusing is an all-or-none affair. It can have different degrees of depth much as in hypnosis -- also an attentional phenomenon.

It is a commonplace that when one is not particularly interested in what he is doing, his attention is easily diverted. Contrariwise, he can be so absorbed in something, so detached from his surrounds, that it can possibly be dangerous. At one time or another all of us have been so buried in what we were doing, say reading a book, that we did not hear the door open or see the person who stood next to us. [34]

Interestingly enough, the focus of attention need not correspond to any structural features being perceived. It is not directed solely by the senses. It can and does move internally and independently of the senses. Thus, one can study an expanse of level ground and see precisely where he wishes to dig a well, or look at a rope and see where he wants to tie a knot. Indeed, his attention may be directed to an area at which he isn't even looking. It is quite common to fixate one thing while attending to something else 'out of the corner' of one's eye. If something moves in peripheral vision, it may be noticed well before one can shift and focus the eyes.

Needless to say, anything that influences thought processes will also influence attention. Thinking is the internal movement of attention from one memory area to another. This is why you can't attend to whatever is going on in front of you while thinking about something else. Such internal movement is particularly noticeable when dreaming. This is the unguided meandering of the cursor as it were.

Mysterious and fantasy-like as it all seems, there is no aspect of the mind more accessible to objective experimentation. The reason is that most of its activity is reflected in the brain waves or EEG. When the mind is at rest the brain pulses in a regular fashion about 10 times per second. The appearance of this 'Alpha' rhythm signifies that the cells are synchronized metabolically. But as soon as something attracts our attention, and I mean literally *attracts,* the EEG record flattens out. This does not imply that the attractional energy of attention is electrical. All it says is that the basal activity of the cells has been disrupted. The internal attentional energy, which is molecular and contributed mutually by the cells, is now mobilized and focused upon whatever it is to which you are attending. The most intriguing operation of attention is the programming of behavior. All voluntary behavior is necessarily programmed or 'planned' before it is put into action. Without such programming it would be random, full of mistakes and irrational. This organizing process takes place below the level of awareness. It identifies the successive steps to be taken well before the behavior itself. The result is a sort of 'outline for action' called a 'set' in English, and *'Einstellung'* in German. A closely related term is 'foresight.' It implies that behavior is simulated in the mind before being acted out. And this is precisely what happens. Normally it occurs so rapidly it goes unnoticed. But in cases of post-hypnotic suggestion one becomes acutely aware of its operation. Programs (suggestions) are implanted under trance. Subjects then do whatever was suggested immediately upon awakening --- often wondering why they feel so strongly compelled to do so.

To recognize how important it is to simulate (program) behavior in advance, consider the pianist. Without such prior organization, he could not possibly read the music while simultaneously playing the piano. And if he tried to direct each finger individually after reading each note, the effort would be ponderous. Instead, he reads the music in blocks or patterns well before the actual playing. The motor system of the cortex then notifies the cerebellum to activate the finger muscles sequentially. The final execution of the pattern follows almost without awareness, and feedback via the ears confirms the process.

Once a program is in operation behaviorally, or being 'acted out,' it requires only minor monitoring by attention. For example, we can jog in the morning while working out the day's schedule. Programs which are repeatedly used and always on tap, are called habits. Sometimes they can be performed almost wholly without awareness. Think how often we have 'followed through' on some simple habit without realizing we have done so!

Let me also mention something everyone seems to overlook -- the enormous impetus which programming provided for the evolution of the mind. Such spontaneous interrelating of brain structures preparatory to acting, was really a rudimentary type of *thinking!* Before it evolved, behavior was largely reflexive with little variability save what was invoked

by environmental change. Learning could occur only by 'trial and error' --
the random search-and-recognize which still characterizes many primitive
organisms. With expansion of the brain, however, creatures were able to
plan their behavior. The earlier haphazard technique was largely replaced
by goal-oriented activity involving insight. It became organized,
purposeful. This greatly reduced the error portion of such so-called 'trial
and error.' Various alternative activities could be tried out *mentally*, and
the unfeasible ones rejected because their consequences were foreseen.
The intention didn't have to be followed step-wise by the action itself. [35]

It is the flexibility made possible by this newly acquired, but
simulated world of 'what if . . . ?' which allows for day dreaming,
imagination, and all manner of fantasy. In its more elaborate constructions
it gives rise to long-term goals, manufactures ideals, and creates new
religions and theories. But in the nitty-gritty of everyday activity one
doesn't even know it is happening. He simply takes for granted that he is
not behaving aimlessly, that he is oriented and knows what he is doing. [36]

For the human with his massive brain, this new way of dealing with
life was not without its price. It took his nose off the ground -- deflected
his attention from the HERE and NOW. This often floated him in a froth
of fantasy. And though it provided a sense of humor, he also became the
only animal that worries, the only one so lost in thought that he wanders
into trees! He had a vague awareness of this programming going on inside
his head. But he couldn't explain why he thought what he thought, or did
what he did. He could rationalize afterwards, true. And he usually does.
But at the time he only knew it was the right thing to do. Call it hunch,
intuition, foresight, insight or whatever. It convinced him he had a free
will. As one wag put it, he was forced to believe in free will. He had no
other choice! So much for the philosophy. I've drifted off the subject
again. So let's go back to the basic mechanism.

As mentioned, such programming (called set) shows up in the brain
rhythms. When you intend to do something, the moment the intention
occurs it is noticeable in your EEG record. What is known as an
'expectancy wave' appears. You say you have 'made up your mind.' You
are 'set' to do it, and so you *expect* to do it. And once more, this is literally
true. Even the specific muscles you intend to use have been put on alert.
The proposed action can almost be predicted from the recordings of the
electrical muscle potentials (EMG). At the very least, you can detect which
muscles were to be used in the intended act."

I paused to load my pipe, and as I tamped down the tobacco, a chap
from the front said, "Sounds like an extremely complicated apparatus!"

"In one sense, yes. But in another, it really isn't," I replied, lighting up the pipe. "The memory molecules may very well be part of the RNA. We aren't sure. And the mobile attention feature could be a property of protoplasm in general. There are even some components of the brain which are liquid crystalline, and these can move very rapidly. This is something I'll return to later. In any case, and whatever the mechanism, it has to be something simple and primitive. It can't be anything as artificially contrived and complicated as a computer."

"Why not?"

"Because it is quite ancient. It is present in all creatures with enough neural structures assembled to make it detectable. And I might add that nerves and senses such as vision appear very early in the fossil record of life. The dragonfly, for example, has binocular depth perception. This requires fusion of the mosaic images from the two eyes. The fusion, in turn, presupposes energies of attraction. But like horseshoe crabs, the dragonfly is a relic from the dim past. He possesses almost no brain at all! [37]

To illustrate further, consider the minnow *Anableps*. All fish are somewhat primitive. Anableps swims the surface water. Each of his eyes has two pupils, one above the other. The waterline is kept carefully between them. Bottom pupils scan events in the water below, while top pupils watch what is happening above. Both systems use the same lens, but in different positions for focussing on different parts of the retina. There can be no question but what the mind (such as it is) shifts attention from one system to the other. [38]

Mental movement of attention is quite common among lesser creatures. In the course of evolution, it preceded muscular movement of the eyes. Birds like the kingfisher and falcon have two foveas in each retina. Either of them can shift attention between monocular and binocular at will. This could only be brought about by the mind. Rabbits, having eyes on the sides of the head, can see almost 360 degrees about them. But despite the visual range, they still can focus on only one item at a time. Anything else goes unnoticed unless it moves -- thereby creating a gradient of change.

The point of this foray into zoology is straight-forward. During evolution the shape, size and complexity of the CNS have undergone every feasible kind of variation. Wildly different means of implementing vision have evolved, especially among insects. Throughout it all, however, it is still possible to explain memory as molecular structures, and the interrelating function as some sort of mobile energy called attention.

Now, I'll grant that it may also be possible to account for this fantastic variety in terms of wiring diagrams. I don't know. But I can't see how any one such wiring diagram could ever relate to another. Details of nerve distributions are not the same in different brains. Only major tracts and centers are similarly situated. Between species it is worse. In short, the consistency and exactitude of mental operations suggest that they depend more upon the *matter* of the brain than upon its cellular distribution. Individual neuron arrangements are probably just what they appear to be -- features of growth.

Along these lines, some researchers at MIT recently 'cross wired' sixteen newborn ferrets. They took the nerves from the eyes (which normally go to the optic lobes of the brain) and routed them over to the brain areas supposedly responsible for hearing. Following recovery, there was no way they could determine whether the ferrets actually 'heard' the visual patterns presented to them. But it was discovered that the electrical responses of the auditory cortex were exactly the same as those expected at the optic lobes, I. e., it were as if the nerves had not been switched! It was suggested that all parts of the brain operate the same way -- meaning that details of nerve distribution don't matter much . [39] It was the same conclusion reached long ago about lab rats by K. S. Lashley. He called it the 'equipotentiality of the brain.'"

I paused and looked about the class. "Since the period is about over," I said, "suppose we see if there are any further questions."

It was the young lady in the gym suit again. Apparently she was quite alert. "Something I am still not clear about," she remarked, "is why memory necessarily has to be molecular. I should think this would require considerable proof to back it up. If the nervous system carries information by means of neural impulses, how could these impulses ever interact with anything as small as a molecule?"

"You are indeed right," I replied. "One up for you! The impulse is many orders of magnitude larger than any molecule. So there seems no way in which memory could be set up or subsequently referenced by impulses. As to questions of memory size, suppose we examine the popular view. This states that the brain acts like a computer. Memories get recorded at the synapses where neurons join. Supposedly they are recorded in bits. It doesn't matter whether one specific memory is at one given synapse, or whether it is somehow scattered as a kind of mosaic among many such synapses. The problem remains the same. Let's look at the numerical side of the dilemma.

Suppose we accept the standard estimate of about 10 billion neurons in the human cortex, or 10^{10}. Guesses about the average number of synapses or junctions they make with other neurons vary anywhere from 50 to 1000 -- depending on the theory being promoted. So let's give them the benefit of the doubt. We'll take the exorbitant number of 1000 each. This then makes for a maximum of 10^{13} synapses. And the synapse is the least neurological locus at which information could be stored using this outlook.

Unfortunately, 10^{13} recording sites is not enough. In fact, it is only one ten-millionth of what would be necessary. The mathematician, Von Neumann, is reported to have calculated the amount of information in adult memory at 3×10^{20} bits. I don't know how Von Neumann arrived at his figure. [40] My own estimate, using TV scanning concepts, came up with 5×10^{23}. But even this now seems too conservative.

Once a figure gets this large it becomes like the national debt. A billion more or less doesn't matter much. The point to be made is this. The concept is hopelessly inadequate. Visual input can neither be received by the senses nor stored in the brain as computer bits. I agree that the idea looks beautiful in theory. After all, the neuroelectric impulse is an on/off affair much as in the case of the computer bits. But theory notwithstanding, visual information has to be received as complex organized patterns (images). Numerous experiments establish that it is retained in memory as patterns. And nobody recognizes, recalls, or dreams of anything in bits! [41]

As a final argument, please note that each of us is able to see and recognize some very complex pictures. Virtually all features of the pictures are in memory. This is shown by our frequent awareness of even the most minor alterations. Now, given this point, suppose we calculate the 'bits' present in just one such picture. Morowitz recounts a case in which this was done. [42] The informational content was derived for a well known painting by the French artist, Seurat. And it was discovered that the artist would have had to choose his color coding out of $10^{1,000,000}$ possibilities! To appreciate this number compare it with an estimate of all the snow flakes which have ever fallen on earth. This is said to be only 10^{35}. The number of electrons in the universe is somewhat greater, having been 'calculated' at 10^{79} Figures of this magnitude are so speculative they completely dumbfound the imagination." [43]

"They *are* boggling," she conceded.

"Computers are very useful machines which are employed to imitate some of the simpler brain functions," I pointed out. "But the brain itself is *not* a computer. Quite the contrary. The computer is a tool devised and used by the mind -- actually a sort of extension of itself. Hereafter, I'll try to stick to the underlying logic of concepts. The motto will be 'Keep it Simple!'"

"It doesn't sound simple to me," she countered. "Anyhow, what do you mean by 'simple'?"

"As mentioned," I replied, "many very primitive creatures have excellent vision with almost no 'computer' to process the input. But more importantly, Mama Nature is conservative. When She wants to improve something, She never discards the original. It just stays where it is and atrophies. Look at the vermiform appendix! She is an antique collector!"

"And?"

"Well, She already had equipment which worked beautifully for racial memory, namely, the genes. So why should She go to all the trouble of whomping up something entirely different, something alien to everything else in biology, just to take care of acquired memory?"

"Then you feel it would be an 'imperative of Nature' for memory to be molecular."

"That puts it nicely. I don't see how it could be anything else, either logically or mathematically," I replied.

Just then another arm was raised. "Yes?" I inquired.

"I can get along with memories being large organic molecules," was the comment. "But I still have trouble with this jumping something-or-other called attention. Would you care to clarify this a little further?"

"Gladly, if I can do so without getting into technicalities," I replied. "So, I'd like to by-pass questions about what makes attention shift, or what the energy might be. Are there other aspects of the concept troubling you?"

He gazed thoughtfully at the floor for a moment, then said, "I guess what bothers me most about the whole idea is that it would appear to fragment our inner world. Why doesn't it make the way we experience things totally unrealistic and therefore unusable?"

"To be perfectly frank," I answered, "our mental world *is* unrealistic in many ways. Suppose one considers vision. No matter what theory is held, the visual world has to consist of a series of still-shots, one after another. And these are seldom taken at rates that would make them appear continuous as in the movies. Saccadic eye movements slice the world into successive images. This is because the mind can only deal with 'things' or patterns -- organized stuff. It would not be possible for it to track all points in the continuous flux of events. Therefore, 'thingness' is necessary to convert the continuum into stationary useable packages. Outer events, whatever their 'real' nature, get broken into chunks having assigned beginning and end. These are commonly interpreted as cause and effect. So we have the further illusion that there must be a cause or reason for everything, including the existence of life itself. Everyone balks at the idea that life simply *is*. This 'stream of consciousness,' as William James called it, is a solitary single-track progression. [44] But the outside world assuredly is not strung out in this manner. For example, it might be a world in which everything happens all at once everywhere. We don't know. And worse yet, we *can't* know! Our share is only a trajectory of spots in time.

And speaking of time, it also seems possible that this one-thing-after-another flow of the mind could account for all our temporal experience. Only the NOW can really exist. But memory provides us with a past, and anticipation (programming again!) projects a future. Neither exist. Both are manufactured in our heads. Moreover, each of us has a sampling of this outer world which is unique to him. No one else can see it through his eyes from his position, classifying it and storing it into his own personal pigeon-holes. Everything we know occurs in this fashion. The mind operates on a complete linear ordering of all point-events. Thinking and dreaming take place this way, and language follows the same rules. Nothing makes sense if you say it or read it backwards. [45]

"If it is a single-track progression as you say, then how can I hold a conversation while driving a car? This would seem to require two tracks. I perform quite a few acts conjointly, or at least it seems that way to me."

"Have you ever heard of what the computer people used to call 'time-sharing'?"

"Vaguely, yes."

"Same thing. You flip back and forth between those programs called 'sets' too rapidly to notice. As soon as one becomes repetitious you let it run and flip over to the other. People seldom are wholly in what they are doing at any given time. So far as I know, the only true cases where two different events can be attended to simultaneously, are in split-brain patients. I won't explain these except to say that they are surgically induced abnormalities in which the attentional mechanism seems to become divided, one half for each hemisphere of the brain. [46]

While we are on this question of realism, I should like to mention that our memories are also somewhat unrepresentative. Not only are they separate chunks related sequentially, but they are never updated. One simply receives another and more recent edition for his library. Thus, in my dreams or reveries I remember my friend as he *was*, or see myself in earlier years -- neither of which is true. Memories are fixed and enduring.

So one also acquires the additional illusion that nature is static. He is sadly unaware that all things are a becoming, a growing, and a changing.

To summarize, our lives are not reality, but rather, our ideas of it. Unfortunate as this may be, it is unavoidable. Outer reality has to be broken down into more stable 'things' if it is to be sorted and classified. And this is always a necessary first step whenever we organize anything. Furthermore, the creation of organization is, in effect, the life-work of organisms. Things *are* their functions. And the function of the mind is to organize. The disorganized is irrational."

I glanced at my watch. "Sorry," I commented. "I really didn't intend to lapse into all this philosophy. We still have time for one more question."

Again -- the girl in the leotards. "You have already stated that you don't care for the term 'consciousness,'" she said. "But it is commonly used and is part of the public vocabulary. Would you object to explaining just why you don't like it?"

"Not at all," I replied. "As you know, words are mere noises unless you can identify their meanings -- what they refer to. And consciousness has too many meanings. It has been used in so many different ways it has become a buzz word. One is never sure what is meant. The general public looks upon it as a sort of mysterious non-physical entity -- more or less synonymous with the 'self.' The clergy usually interpret it as 'soul.' And the scientists either ignore it or else toss it into an overstuffed bin labeled 'unknown brain processes.' There are even those who see it as something which arose at the time humans became social animals. That is to say, all prior creatures were unconscious!

One writer contends that consciousness is little more than an illusion. Others are a bit more specific. For example, it has been described as having the same relationship to the brain that computer programs have to their hardware. This makes a little more sense because it suggests an on-going intangible control function. However, computer programs are rigidly predetermined. Whereas, consciousness is exactly the opposite. The thinking narrows a bit further when it is said to be a sort of internal feedback system allowing one part of the mind to influence another. And so it goes. There is no consensus whatever. [47]

Suppose we take a moment to pursue this feedback idea, but reduce the entire issue to its fundamentals, namely, the brain cells themselves. After all, these cells are small living creatures in their own right, and they are highly sensitive. I would like to show you a slide. (*See Figure 2.*)

This slide depicts three interrelated neural cells. Let us say they are located in the brain. All communication is one-way, as shown by the arrows. The cell labeled 'A' can only be aware of what goes on in 'B.' In turn, B only senses what happens in 'C.' And to complete the cycle, C detects events occurring in A. When arranged in this fashion, they form the simplest possible neural network. Looked upon individually, no one of them can react to anything except its immediate environment, essentially the cell impinging upon it. In and of themselves, there is no reason to assume that any of the cells possess what might be called 'self-sensitivity' or 'self-awareness.'

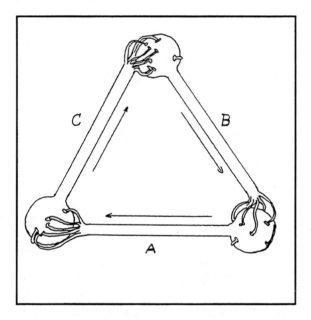

FIGURE 2. Highly formalized drawing of the simplest possible neural network. Arrows indicate direction of information transport.

But wait a moment! Something has happened -- something added by the way in which they became organized! If A is aware of changes in B, and these were induced by C, then it is also getting information about C. The two information sources (B and C) can be distinguished because all nerve cells are slightly different chemically. And since the reaction of C depends upon events in A, the cycle of communication is complete. It is providing A with information about *itself!* Should A initiate some action, this would be relayed through C and B, and become known back at A.

In brief, the group has acquired feedback. It has become a unified system possessing properties not present in any of the individual cells. When something affects one cell, it is sensed by the whole system! Though separate cells have only sensitivity like a plant, the total has achieved self-sensitivity like an animal! Multiply this by billions and one gets some idea why the human has such an immense ego.

Figure 2 is highly simplified. But the concept behind it is far from simple. It states that *the appearance of feedback can lead to self awareness.* This is not meant to imply that consciousness is simply feedback between brain cells. Neither does it require that the feedback be neuro-electric. It merely demonstrates that self-awareness can arise when communication links become so organized they are mutually self-informative. The resulting organization is what defines a *self!* This self is necessary to identify everything else (e.g., non-self). When provided with memory internal to the system, it can learn and grow. In other words, it becomes. *alive!* Prod it and it may say 'I didn't do that! You did it!'

Without knowledge of themselves and their effects, creatures could not correct for their mistakes. They could only behave randomly. Thus, it is not without reason that the baby's earliest behavior is directed toward finding out about himself, tweaking his ears, playing with his toes, etc. Feedback about himself is a necessary prelude to any meaningful interaction with the environment.

Defined in these terms, and viewed as a product of organization, self-awareness turns out to be an emergent social phenomenon among cells. The phrase 'emergent social phenomenon' seems to suggest something which appears spontaneously out of nowhere. In general, people are loathe to think that something can be made out of nothing. Nonetheless, this is precisely what happens when the property which emerges is non-material and without detectable mass. We are used to dealing with things that are material and have mass. And this is the primary reason we have been unable to define life or mind. They are matters of organization (changes of state) and have no mass."

How it all Began

Chapter 4

Thrown together, or Grown together?
(Chance or Symbiosis?)

(Chemical evolution suggests that life was virtually inevitable. The enormous complexity of the cell, and why its development required 80% of all the time life has existed on earth.)

The dean had to use the auditorium that evening. This meant our guest speaker would have to make do with one of the larger classrooms. It was just as well, I told myself. The topic was "Origins of the Cell." It sounded rather dry and pedantic. Only the biology students and faculty were expected. But we were wrong on all counts. The place was loaded. Following the introduction and a few moments casual chatting with the audience, he began his talk with some comments on evolution.

"We are told that the earth has been around for some four and a half billion years, give or take few million. However, the first nucleated cells capable of reproduction did not appear on the scene until about one and a half billion years ago. In brief, it took three billion years for the cell to evolve. Once here, however, everything else including dinosaurs and man required only half that time. This should tell us something. But what? Many wonder why it took so long. They argue that the earth, as well as the molecular ingredients of life, were peculiarly predisposed toward the development of complex organization. In other words, the appearance of life was *not* improbable. It was almost inevitable!

Unfortunately, we can't point to any particular spot in the history of organic development and say 'this is where life began.' Looking backward through time, it would seem to be a continuum in which the organic slowly fades into the inorganic. Much the same components are involved in all phases. There is nothing unique about the elements making up organic matter. The only real difference we biologists can find between the living and the non-living is the great complexity of organization present in living things. So let's look at the earth in these terms. Question: What potential does it have as a place where complex organization could have arisen?

The first thing we note is that the surface of the earth is alive and dancing with rhythmic energies from outer space. Rotating orbital bodies create gravitational pulses. The heavens are luxurious with them. The moon is one of the more obvious of these. And though its influence upon our bodies goes largely unnoticed, it swings the earth's surface with strong recurrent tides. In the tidal waters where life is thought to have begun, this introduced both regularity and ecological variety. The rising and setting of the sun are even more pronounced. The steady beat of day and night, not to mention the seasons, coaxes virtually every living thing into adaptive rhythms. Synchronized with these are temperature fluctuations which alternately speed up and slow down chemical processes. [1]

Finally, there is the music of the stars. Though of small amplitude, these energies provide a background symphony of pulsing light -- electromagnetic radiation of every sort. Some are even called 'pulsars.' Further, much of this energy comes in wavelengths making it particularly effective for the microscopic levels of life. This is why we can see a portion of the electromagnetic spectrum. It affects the rhodopsin of the eyes. It is also why certain wavelengths of ultraviolet light are lethal to bacteria.

'So the earth pulsates to rhythms of various amplitude and frequency,' you say. 'So what?' To answer this 'so what' it is first necessary to realize the vital relationship existing between rhythm (periodicity) and order (organization). One creates the other. Or more accurately, one is simply a different aspect of the other. *Rhythm is to time what order is to space.* One denotes function, the other its corresponding structure. [2]

To illustrate, suppose we examine an ordinary checkerboard. It is organized into alternate red and black squares. This pattern immediately identifies it as a man-made artifact, a product of the mind. But if we let our eyes sweep across it, the patterning gets translated into an alternating rhythm which occurs visually. The checkerboard is structure in space. The perceived rhythm is a corresponding function which can occur in time. Indeed, this one-to-one relationship between organization and rhythm is what creates our TV picture out of pulsating electromagnetic wave patterns.

I could wax quite philosophical about all this. I could note that reproduction of like patterns in space is called order or organization. Reproduction of like patterns in time is called periodicity or rhythm. But there is no separate space and time. There is only space-time. And the reproduction of like kind in space-time is called *life!* In all instances there must be likeness of patterning, a togetherness of parts. If the coming together occurs between inanimate objects, we speak of energies of mutual attraction. If psychological, we call it need or desire. If in a social context, it gives rise to grouping effects and is known as friendship, affection, or even love -- depending on degree. How do we know that these are not simply different facets of the same phenomenon?

So much for the over-extended metaphor. What about the material aspects of organic things? Do they contribute to life's highly complex organization? Indeed they do, and uniquely so! These are the hydro-carbons. The 'hydro' refers to hydrogen -- the most common element in the entire universe. Combined with oxygen it makes up water. Life began in the seas. The seas cover most of the earth. And logically enough, 99 out of every 100 molecules of our bodies are water molecules. In structural terms, the body is a colloid, a gel-like mesoform which is neither solid nor fluid, but an intermediate state. It has something of the solid to provide a degree of permanency, and something of the fluid to prevent rigidity.

The more water is studied, the more enigmatic its properties appear. For example, it seems to have two melting points. One is at 0 degrees C where it passes from a rigid crystal (ice) into a quasi-crystalline state containing what have been termed 'cybotactic fields.' These phase changes are minute, ever-shifting, internal areas of temporary organization. The second melting point occurs between 30 and 40 degrees C when heat agitation eliminates all traces of this transient internal organization It has been suggested that body temperatures of warm-blooded creatures became stabilized in the neighborhood of 37 degrees C simply because it enabled their cells to devise a variety of quasi-crystalline water structures for specific needs. It is well known that when large organic molecules are dissolved in water at this temperature they surround themselves with different kinds of pseudo-crystalline ice formations.

The curious physical properties of water derive largely from the fact that water molecules are asymmetric. And again, this asymmetry is some-thing else they share with all the molecules of living matter. They do not form simple $H-O-H$ linkages, but rather $_{+H}{}^{-O^-}{}_{+H}$ structures. This means that cations (positive) and anions (negative) will tend to rotate water molecules in opposite directions. Cations will hydrate organic colloids, whereas anions will not. Such minute electrical differences determine the salting-in and salting-out processes essential to cellular osmosis. Thus, water is not only pseudo-crystalline at body temperatures, but also has unique electrical properties making it peculiarly suited to the ionic processes of life. [3]

But let us get on to the more interesting carbon component of these hydrocarbons. Though not so common as hydrogen, carbon is nonetheless plentiful. Its most outstanding characteristic is its tendency to *organize!*. It seems almost compelled to join with a variety of other elements to create complex molecular patterns. The resulting carbon marriages are truly prolific. The different kinds of compounds it can make are potentially infinite. The number of possible protein molecules alone has been estimated to be as high as 10^{2700}! By contrast, all other elements in all possible molecular arrangements are probably less than 50 thousand [4] Half a century ago, Beutner became so impressed with this morphological versatility he remarked that life, in spite of all its complexity, appeared to be little more than just another of the many properties of carbon. [5]

It would not help to dwell on the atomic features enabling carbon to be so versatile. Suffice It to say that its atoms have a kind of independence, a freedom to choose how and with what they will associate. Linkages are not so rigidly predetermined as with other elements. As a result, carbon can help make up long serial chains of atoms, curve in upon itself to enclose space, or proliferate into extensive lace-works having intricate and detailed patterning. Most importantly, complicated and asymmetric molecules can be assembled just as readily as simple symmetrical ones. This latter capability is almost unknown among compounds which don't contain carbon. The result is exactly what one would expect. Organic matter began as a synthesis of complicated asymmetric carbon-bearing molecules. These could proliferate or *grow* in almost unrestrained fashion. Such growth, freed from the usual molecular limitations, is what defines life.

To supplement the argument, consider that the seas in which life originated were probably much warmer than at present. Consequently, chemical reactions would have taken place about two and a half times faster for every 10 degrees C. And since water covered the larger part of the planet, most of the elements would have been present to some degree either in solution or suspension. Add to this the scenario of the hydrocarbons. These were uniquely flexible, given to creating complicated patterns, and eager to form all manner of possible structures. Moreover, there was constant urging from both local and extraterrestrial energies to do so.

My guess (and it can only be a guess) is that these early seas were a sort of broth made up of macromolecules of every size and description. The countless numbers of different proteins and other molecular structures necessary for the cell, could have been already present, just waiting to shuffle themselves into a viable whole. The basic building blocks of life, for example, are the amino acids. And these have even been found in meteorites from outer space. [6]

No, the two or three billion years commonly allotted to chemical evolution, would seem more than enough to create all the molecular components of life, and then some. So why did it take so long? There could have been several reasons. But the truly sticky factor was most likely the need for these first living molecules to be self-replicating. They had to continue with reproduction. Without it, everything had to start over from scratch. This self-replicating feature may well have originated with the single strands of RNA rather than DNA. Retro-viruses are based upon RNA and are known to mutate at extremely rapid rates compared to DNA-based organisms. Thus, an RNA-based structure could have evolved with a far higher error rate and provided more variety. Laboratory alterations of certain protozoan RNA have already been made to copy parts of themselves. [7]

Recent evidence even suggests that self-replication may have been possible at levels still smaller and simpler than RNA. At least two viruses, both disease producing entities, have been discovered to possess no detectable DNA or RNA at all! Actually, they are proteins a hundred times smaller than the usual virus, and are seemingly immune to both heat and radiation. These latter attributes might have stood them in good stead on an early earth. Since current theory requires ribonucleic acids for reproduction, these are real puzzlers. [8]

Given all these possibilities, it seems indeed strange that anyone should consider the origins of life improbable. Nevertheless there are those who do. They usually argue that life's beginning was 'nothing short of miraculous.' Reasoning is almost always based on misconceptions about the nature of probability. Thus, the conclusions are invalid for mathematical reasons. Calculations of this sort commonly assume that at the time life occurred all elements were present in the same proportions, and that anyone of them was equally likely to combine with any other.

This makes for ease of calculation. But none of it could have been true.[9]
Besides, probability can only be used for *pre*diction, not
*post*diction. The arrow of time is built into the measure itself.
Mathematically, it cannot properly operate in reverse. Backward
prediction embodies a predetermined goal, like answers in the back of a
math text. To speak of probabilities when the outcome is known, is
almost irrational. The answer is always 1. Thus, most events
automatically become highly improbable when viewed in retrospect. Take
automobile wrecks for instance. Despite their everyday occurrence it
appears extremely improbable that someone named Jones would have
impacted with somebody named Smith precisely at noon on the corner of
Main and 15th Streets. Nevertheless, he did. The true probability was
1.

Lynn Margulis of the University of Massachusetts, presents a very
cogent argument that oxygen-using cells such as comprise our bodies,
were a later development. [10] They date back only about one and a half
billion years. The theory claims they arose by means of symbiosis. This
seems eminently logical. Living things have always been interrelated into
various overlapping ecological systems which are largely symbiotic. For
these advanced cells (eukaryotes), this meant that some of the earlier and
simpler non-oxygen users (bacteria or prokaryotes) merged to become
primitive O_2 users. The resulting alliances then made for a single
organism having capabilities beyond the scope of any of it member parts.

Please note that these later and more proficient cells were not solely
individuals. They were simultaneously *societies* of individuals, each member specializing in some particular aspect of the cell's internal functions.
Our own bodies bear witness to this. Each of the trillions of cells contain
various organelles such as mitochondria and centrosomes. These
constitute 'organs' or separate beings, depending on viewpoint.

Take the mitochondria for example. They retain their own membranes, have their own DNA, replicate themselves, synthesize their own
proteins, and are individual specialists in their own right. They produce
energy for the cell. The centrosomes, by contrast, have no nucleus.
However, the work they perform is much more fascinating. To all
appearances, they officiate as midwives during the birth of a new cell.
This occurs by fission and requires total disruption of the cell's normal
activity. A highly complicated operation follows. It ends with
reorganization into two separate and presumably identical entities. Other
than general procedure, little is known about it.

It should not be overlooked that every one of us begins life as a single celled organism of this very type. Just because our cells grow in masses and are not separately visible does not mean they are no longer individual living beings. The individuality of the cell did not disappear mysteriously when it and its family became a particular human. Much like the honeybees -- also descended from a unified source -- they are still self-contained entities within a larger body. Whether cells or bees, individuals simply work for a common cause. It is a trade-off. Largely superfluous freedoms are given up for the security and kinship of the whole. To lesser extent, we do the same thing daily for our own societies.

With the advent of modern microscopy, and particularly the scanning electron microscope, the cell ceased to look like a mere blob of colloidal cytoplasm. It turned out to be an amazingly complex creature. Among other things, it was found to be comprised of many thousands of different proteins engaged in an equal number of different tasks. Now, many of these tasks are step-wise in specific sequences. And they have to be synchronized with others. So it is mandatory that some sort of control or coordinating function be present. It is not possible to conceive of them as wholly automated.

Let's compare the cell with its society, the human. To begin, both are enclosed within a highly sensitive skin. For the cell, this outer membrane is capable of identifying molecules by their *shape!* This stereochemical shape of molecules, I might add, is their only uniquely identifying feature. Composition is not necessarily unique because of isomers -- and we know that the body distinguishes between isomers.

The significance of such discriminative chemical perception should not be dismissed lightly. It is the ancestor of *all* perception, and it is still the sole means by which all biological processes take place. Often overlooked is the fact that stereochemical shape is patterning. Thus, no matter how one words it, *the cell is capable of pattern perception!* And whether molecular or otherwise, patterning conveys information. Put more precisely, patterning *is* information. Like the identity between order and rhythm, this relationship between form and in*form*ation is seldom recognized.

To get back to our analogy, recent findings have further revealed that the cell has an internal skeleton. This lattice-work, described as 'micro-trabecular,' is made up of interlocking filaments and tubules. Each tiny 'bone' has a diameter of about 6 millionths of a millimeter. It supports the internal organelles mentioned earlier, and enables the cell to move. [11]

Now, brace yourself for this next observation. The cell also sports *muscles!* These allow for amoeboid movement and consist of the same contractile actin molecules found in our own muscles. At Cold Spring Harbor Laboratory on Long Island, isolated tissue cells were watched as they migrated across a glass slide. The movement was not random. It appeared logical and orderly -- much as if the wee beasties had some sort of rudimentary awareness. They often followed a maze-like grid, traveled in straight lines, and made right angle turns. However, progress was quite laborious. It required days for them to traverse a slide. [12]

Independent unicellular creatures like amoebas and paramecia are common objects of study. Their activities are often fascinating. As an amoeba approaches a food particle, its leading edge becomes concave and two arm-like pseudopods are extended on either side. These pincers then close to engulf the food. Body orientation and placement of the pseudopods are precise. Do you suppose the amoeba plans this strategy? Remember, it has no nerves, and its brain is only a clump of DNA.

Compared to amoebas, the paramecium is almost a genius. Mental prowess may be due to rudimentary nerve-like structures called neuronemes. These extremely fine fibrils are thought to synchronize the motion of its cilia. It darts hither, thither and yon beating its tiny oars in perfect unison. If it finds no food, it is too smart to continue groping around like the amoeba does. It simply takes off for greener pastures.

Efforts to train protozoans began in Russia early this century. It spread to this country where it has continued on and off ever since. During the 50s, whole series of elaborate learning experiments were performed. These may be summarized with the statement that almost everyone who has tried teaching paramecia has reported success. But most of them have also reported that the little fellows forget rather easily. As might be predicted, such experiments meet with resistance from those having a bias against learning in preneural creatures. Resolution? Simply change names! Instead of learning, it is now called 'sensitization' or sometimes 'habituation.' [13]

Seen from the vague vantage point of theoretical neutrality, this particular hassle seems somewhat amusing. Why is it that single neural cells, whether located in monkeys or mollusks, may be conditioned without creating objections? [14] And what about the rather extensive learning and remembering required of certain white blood cells when they encounter and neutralize unfamiliar microbial aliens? (And I might add that there is argument about this one also!) [15]

It should be remembered that cells are living things, and all living things adapt to environmental change -- else they don't survive. This includes the bugs that give us flu or TB. Their environments are our bodies, and they have adapted to our use of antibiotics. We realize this, but ignore the implications. If the adaptations persist it means *learning*. The mathematical probability of any *chance* mutation proving beneficial to the adapting organism, is virtually non-existent.

When one is asked to define an organism, it is commonly stated that: (1) it must be capable of reproduction, and (2) it must be able to live successfully apart from others of its kind provided it has the proper environment and nutrition. The cell scores well on both points. Sometimes there is the further stipulation that it must also be capable of independent behavior. It cannot be merely a cog in a maze of gears. Independent behavior presupposes awareness and implies learning. Nowhere in the body is this latter feature better illustrated than in the immune system. These small cellular organisms are divided into at least four and possibly six types according to their occupational specialties. And in this respect, they remind one of the caste systems of ants and termites.

Though the brain can communicate chemically with leukocytes, they are not under its immediate control. For the most part, they travel with the blood stream and attack any foreign invader encountered. When they meet with an alien organism, say a bacterium, they immediately relay this information to a helper 'T' cell. This individual then initiates certain defense measures. The alien is chemically 'finger-printed' and profile information is added to the rogue's gallery so that similar criminals may be recognized. Specific antibodies then lock into and immobilize him. The brain is notified to raise body temperature. Still different members designated as 'killer T cells' are called upon to destroy those body cells taken over by the aliens. Any open wounds bring in an additional brigade to stimulate production of fibrin. This closes the gap and shuts off bleeding. In brief, the immune system constitutes a highly coordinated and complete internal maintenance and guard corps. It is vital because the cellular society has no other means of protecting its citizens.

No one today, familiar with the literature, would argue that nerves are necessary for learning. There is considerable evidence that learning occurs in primitive multicellular marine creatures which have no nerves. These are also readily conditioned. In some, like coelenterates, learning may be localized. That is to say, it is specific to one part of the animal's body. A particular tentacle may become educated with no evidence that the remainder of the animal has gotten the message. Further, a broad spectrum of complex behavior exists in creatures without intact neural conduction routes. One can only conclude that it must arise from some unknown type of chemical communication within and between cells. At least this was the conclusion reached by Jacques Loeb back in 1900. In his opinion, nerves merely enhanced the speed of a capability common to all protoplasm, namely, the transmission of information. [16]

Whether cells can learn, and to what degree, evokes interest for a variety of reasons. To cite just one, our genetic theory tells us that all instructions for embryonic growth come from changes and/or activation of specific genes in the DNA of developing cells. An almost identical view prevails for evolution theory. Here the development is that of a new species. This is also attributed to changes in the DNA. Given that such changes occur, no matter what causes them, and whether meaningful or not, they are retained by the cell. If the cell is considered a living individual this means learning. But if the cell is a robot, and its DNA no more than an information-laden tape deck, any changes can only be noise. Chance re-shuffling of the noise is then proposed as an explanation of the presumably slow and erratic course of evolution. But for the embryologist it leaves the consistency of these developmental changes quite bewildering.

'Why bother with all this hypothetical mish-mush?' many embryologists would ask. 'There are enough unanswered questions about animals whose nerves are intact!' It is very easy to find complex behavior which regulates itself independently of neural routes. Sometimes such behavioral adjustments even run contrary to all prior usage of the body parts! And they occur *without* learning.

For instance, consider the centipede. For this creature, walking is a complicated business. It involves closely synchronized movements of the legs accompanied by changes in body posture. Now, let's suppose some of the legs are lost in various locations. No problem! The pattern of motion remains undisturbed. The sequencing of limbs is immediately reprogrammed without so much as losing a step! This is true even with major losses of legs requiring extreme distortion of the body and radically different placement of the remaining limbs.

Such muscular versatility is not peculiar to centipedes. Similar readjustments are also common in the cross-amble style of locomotion used by crabs, spiders, and certain insects. Despite removal of any number of legs, the *pattern* of motion is not affected. Remaining legs simply coordinate themselves into a new sequence. It were as if the creatures had a kind of model of the necessary motion in their heads, so to speak, and felt compelled to maintain this fixed behavioral pattern regardless of the circumstances or the neural routes involved. [17]

Sorry to get off the subject like this. So let's return to the cell. If each of our trillions of body cells is a living organism in its own right, and not simply some sort of pliable building block, one would expect it to have some means of identification, a 'self' distinct from that of the others. In short, individuality should make it different in some respect. Otherwise all are properly considered the same. Now it is obvious that liver cells are not the same as brain cells or muscle cells. But do cells of any given type differ among themselves? Suppose we look into this 'identity crisis' which theory foists upon the cell.

First, if you will recall, the potential number of chemically different proteins is almost infinite. Every cell which ever existed could easily possess a slightly varied chemical signature or identifying name tag. Minor chemical diversity of this sort would not necessarily mean rejection as 'non-self' or chemically alien. We have a tendency to equate differences with argument and hostility. Cells do not have such tendencies. They are preeminently social beings. Nerve cells particularly will synchronize their behavior under a variety of circumstances. The urge to join, to belong, to work together overrides almost any minor incompatibilities. For example, it is claimed that isolated cells taken from vastly different organisms, even belonging to separate genera, are eager to coalesce with each other, sharing chromosomes and becoming one entity.

Run a sponge through a sieve so that it is completely pulverized and it will reassemble itself. So it is said. I have not tried it. But at the University of Colorado something quite similar was tried with the brains of mice. All the component cells were meticulously teased apart, placed in a culture solution, then shaken for several days. Following this thorough mixing, the cells nonetheless began to gather together, form synapses, grow myelin sheaths, and demonstrate normal activity. [18] Spectacular as such experiments may be, however, they do not fully answer our question. Whether sponge or brain, there is no way of knowing whether the same cells come together in their original arrangements. It says something about the total, but not the individual.

More to the point are the many transplants involving regeneration of nerves. These have been done with creatures such as frogs and salamanders. It may seem like a mean thing to do, but an extra limb may be grafted almost anywhere on a salamander (say his back) and hooked up at random to the local nerve supply. After healing, the limb behaves in much the same fashion as if it had been normally positioned, even though it now paws the air meaninglessly. In other words, its muscles would seem to be called into action by some sort of chemical signal or 'name,' regardless what part of the nervous system transmits the message from the brain. [19] Since our current theory states that all neural impulses are much the same, this gives rise to a multitude of unanswered questions..

In still other experiments the eyes of frogs were removed and the optic tract severed. The eyes were then rotated 180 degrees, reinserted, and allowed to heal. After about a month the frogs were able to see again. Vision was normal except for one slight inconvenience. Their perceived world was *upside down!* This was easily demonstrated. If a fly were presented below the midline of vision, they aimed upwards for it. If above, they struck downwards. This must have been frustrating for the frogs. But I can see how it might have been equally so for the theorists!

When the frogs were autopsied later, it was found that where the severed ends of the optic tract had regenerated during healing, there was a large tangled knot of nerves. Apparently each of the thousands of small neural fibers had found and reconnected themselves in proper order! That they had done so was shown by the consistency of post-operative vision. This leaves one with no other recourse than to assume that each neuron had some sort of unique chemical identity, and that it could use this chemical difference to guide itself accordingly. [20]

Numerous experiments of this type, using various species, have been going on for decades. In general, researchers have concluded that all nerve cells at least, have separate chemical name-tags. The billions that make up the brain are thought to acquire these distinctive labels early in the process of development. Thereafter, they are used to recognize other neurons according to function or specialization. The specific chemicals, though unknown, are doubtlessly proteins. They diffuse and extend with the axons of the cells as these grow and proliferate over what, to them, are often extensive distances. The resulting total makes for an elaborate network of information-laden trail-markings not unlike those used by foraging ants. It enables the growing fiber to find and follow prescribed routes to specific junctions and sites in the brain.

One cannot help but wonder about such intricate lattice-works of chemical pathways. The suspicion is that they might somehow be involved in that mysterious exchange of information known to exist between cells. Such communication obviously occurs, but there is yet no inkling as to how. As we look at ever smaller entities through the electron microscope, it is apparent that life does not always get increasingly simpler the smaller it becomes. Seen under the microscope it is still enormously complex. This implies much local control and communication of which we are wholly ignorant. It can only be chemical because much of it lies below the level of nerves. Cells depend exclusively upon chemical sensitivity, whereas our awareness of chemical differences is so poor it is almost non-existent.

How much individual behavior is the cell capable of? We don't know. And perhaps it is better that we don't. It could be far more than we assume from the arrogance of our position. It could even include modes of sensing and awareness that are lost to us. For example, how are we so sure that the ovum must obligingly accept the first spermatozoon suitor who finds her? After all, she is an individual! There is a sense in which it might be said that we do not exist as such. We are being lived by the trillions of cells of which we consist. From the cell's point of view, we may be nothing more than an abstract term for the many interdependent roles played by the cellular citizens of a well regulated society.

As one thinks it over, he cannot be certain. But my guess would be that the cell is *not* aware that it is part of a still larger organism. Most likely, it only knows that it gets orders (divine revelations?) from somewhere. It feels irresistibly compelled to follow these instructions. Causal links between hormonally delivered commands (chemical) and cellular reactions, are far more consistent and predictable than those presumed to account for human behavior, namely, stimulus-response links.

On the other hand, suppose there *is* awareness of kinship to some unknown infrastructure, something we recognize as ourselves. This would be consistent with the facts of organ rejection following surgical transplants. The immune cells at least, can readily distinguish between those organic entities which 'belong' as against those which are alien. And finally, please note that chemical individuality is not restricted to our cells. It applies to we humans as well. Each of us has a distinctly different odor -- a chemical name-tag as it were. Our dog can recognize it from among any number of others, even when we are not present. Question: Do you think it possible that there might be some higher level of organism to whom we humans all seem alike? Could our own identities be in question, much as we have doubted those of the cells?"

The lecture was over. I sat in thought for awhile, then joined others who were gathered around the speaker in the hall outside. Several of us had questions. One was a member of the anthropology department. He knocked his pipe out on the heel of his hand and said, "You certainly have some interesting angles on the cellular mystery! I find all of evolution fascinating. By the way, I know it's not germane to tonight's topic, but I wonder if you would give me your opinion on a related issue?"

"Of course -- if I can," was the response. "What is it?"

"It has to do with the sudden expansion of the human brain during the Pleistocene period. In a way, it reminds me of the Cambrian explosion in which all life proliferated suddenly. I never could understand the reason for it -- why it came about."

Naturally we were listening. At one time or another most of us had wondered about the same question. The speaker looked thoughtful for a moment, tugged at his beard, then replied, "Your mention of the Cambrian period is interesting. As I see it, there were two major break-throughs which occurred during the course of evolution. Both were associated with communication. The first took place shortly before the Cambrian. It was about this time that the cells developed a chemical language. This was what made the sudden burgeoning of life possible. It enabled cells to communicate meaningfully, fostered symbiosis, and led to multicellular life. The chemical procedures were already present, of course. But it was the innovative use of organic molecules as messages, or behavioral modifiers, which brought about cellular specialization and permitted colonial organisms to develop. These were the forerunners to true multicellular creatures.

The second break-through was somewhat similar and bears on your question about the rapid expansion of the brain. It occurred much, much later, and in my opinion was very closely associated with the invention of a verbal language. This also had a very serious impact on life. It expanded human communications well beyond what was possible by chemical means such as pheromones. Other animals, it should be noted, are still largely restricted to chemical techniques. Verbalization broadened man's social horizons and made the larger brain necessary.

As to why it grew so rapidly, let's pause and think about the numerous ways in which the human differs from other creatures. We recognize the advantage of language. But we tend to overlook the fact that man is also unique in various other ways. The most important of these, for example, bears on his survival. Though seldom mentioned, he is the most vulnerable of all animals in his size range. He has no natural armor like the turtle or the armadillo. He doesn't even have fur. Neither does he have any means of defense. There are no horns, fangs or claws, as among other predators. And certainly there are no chemical defenses like those of many reptilia. Worse yet, despite his helplessness, he has no ready means of escape. He lacks the wings of the bird or the agility of the deer. So one has to ask himself, just what *did* he have? He must have had something that enabled him to prey upon others rather than be preyed upon. As I see it, the only possible way of surviving such odds was to out-smart the opposition. This was his only escape from the dilemma in which Nature had placed him. He had to outwit the enemy with various ruses, devise weapons, set traps, and use trickery and deception. In brief, his survival depended almost exclusively on his mental prowess. He had nothing else to recommend him -- certainly not any physical abilities. Supporting this argument is the fact that the body did not change significantly during the same period. It was only the brain that grew. In other words, the burgeoning of the brain may have been just a matter of its high survival value. Had he depended on his legs, they might also have enlarged.

Sometimes there are questions why specific parts of an organism, say the brain, should develop while the remainder of the body continues relatively unchanged. It has happened numerous times. One can point to the exaggerated fangs of the saber-toothed cat or the fantastic antlers of the Irish elk. But so far as I know, there is no reason to assume that evolution has to be constant, much less proportionately so. [21] Thus, from Homo habilis to Homo sapiens, there was little modification of the body. But the brain enlarged to such extent that it also altered the face.

To put it briefly, man's weakness was an asset. Evolution became *mental* evolution. The ice ages which occurred between 115,000 and 10,000 years ago provided the final competition. It was near the end of this period that Cro-magnon man appeared. And I believe that everyone here will agree that he has become the master predator. [22] Those creatures preyed upon are usually herbivorous and have eyes on the *sides* of their heads. Whereas predators all have eyes in the *front* of their heads. In this respect the human came well-equipped. Man did not reach the top of the food chain by attending to side and rear. He focussed on frontal events.

The major riddle, and the one which most intrigues me, is not when or how the brain evolved to such magnitude. It surely cannot become significantly larger without corresponding changes in the size of the birth canal. The provocative question, as I read it, is why this increased capability showed up only in his tool-making or *engineering* advances. It would appear that the remainder of his behavior, especially his *social* behavior, has not changed significantly during all recorded history. Furthermore, the most basic questions concerning life, mind, and matter have all remained highly theoretical -- just as they were in ancient Greece. Only his tool-making has evolved, certainly not his social graces. And this fact, I might add, could well be his undoing."

Chapter 5

Dilemmas of Dogma: Impossible Robots!

(The fact that cells communicate chemically implies a prototype intelligence qualitatively different from our own.)

Walking home from the lecture that evening, I fell in with a colleague who was returning from the basketball game. "You missed a good talk tonight," I remarked.

"And you missed a good game," he countered. "What was the talk about?"

"The cell. What I found most interesting was a suggestion that the cell is a living organism in its own right, a small individual much like ourselves. In his opinion this implied that it has some degree of intelligence, that it is not just an automaton as commonly pictured. I've been giving it some thought, and the more I mull it over the more I tend to agree. The cell simply *has* to have at least the rudiments of a mind. Logic demands it. There is no reasonable alternative."

He cocked a quizzical eye at me. "How so?"

"Well, let's go back in history. Not so long ago everybody believed in what was called 'preformation.' They thought that at the time of conception, either the sperm or the egg contained a small figure of a human, a sort of miniature or homunculus. Call it a human to the 10^{-12} th power, say it was a 'picohuman.' When it developed into a baby all it had to do was grow larger. It came already preformed."

He grinned. "That was kind of simplistic and naive, wasn't it? Besides, the microscope says it isn't there. They can't find it."

"Right. But suppose we compare this idea with the present-day view. After all, we still begin with a single cell which assembles itself out of that same sperm and egg. Everything living begins this way, even plants. All we have done is replace the homunculus with a clump of DNA."

"Oh no we haven't," he countered. "There is plenty of evidence that the DNA codes for all the proteins -- and the body is made up of proteins."

"O.K., then why don't we just develop into a mushy pile of protein molecules? Call it Homo sapiens blob. Why a baby? Do you suppose the DNA tells the proteins, 'Look! You are such and such kind. You belong over there with the others! And be sure you don't gather too many like yourselves. I don't want any cancers around here! Oh yes, and also be sure you twist yourselves into the shape I told you. Otherwise, you won't be able to join up with the others.' Do you suppose that this is what happens?"

He chuckled. "Very funny. That's just about the opposite of what's believed. It is strange, though. There's really not much known about epigenesis. As you're aware, that's jargon for all the morphological changes taking place during development. Nobody seems to have much of an explanation. So far, all the theories I've read attribute developmental changes to special chemicals of different sorts. Some suggest chemicals that determine which cells stick to which, others chemicals that modify the DNA itself, and so on. What's your opinion?"[23]

"To begin, I think calling the process 'epigenesis' is somewhat mis-leading. It suggests that the 'genesis' part is solved, and the 'epi' implies that we are now probing still further. Actually, none of it is solved. As for special chemicals, these were claimed to be responsible at least fifty years ago by Needham. [24] He called them 'organizers.' Others have used the term 'morphogens.' So far, they have only complicated the problem. One has to explain what these special chemicals are, where they come from, and how they go about creating an almost endless progression of changes -- all of which are related. Besides, I doubt if it is humanly possible to identify them all. We have only skimmed the surface."

"Oh? May I ask why?"

"Because chemistry is the language of the system. Within the brain, and between cells, communication is in stereochemistry -- hieroglyphics of a sort. It is something like printed Chinese, but more elaborate. And to call it a 'code' wouldn't change anything. Codes are simply encrypted language. I guess what I am driving at is that organic chemicals are created to fit the need and are potentially infinite in number. The fact that some of them are quite common, like insulin or testosterone, only says that certain needs and functions are quite common. What we identify as hormones, specific enzymes and such, compare with frequently used words and phrases. Those encountered less often, like antigens and antibodies, could be foreign words and their antonyms. [25]

Methods for transmitting this chemical information in the body are similar to those used in human societies. Data carried by the blood-stream reaches all cells. It compares favorably with 'to-whom-it-may-concern' information disseminated by radio, TV, and other media. Prominent here would be the hormones released by ductless glands. More specific information devised for some particular body area would be transported by nerves. These are now known to function neurochemically. And in fact, they even bear some physical resemblance to the telephone and computer networks we use. Chit chat within and between cells, conducted locally, would not be unlike that between people -- save for its being chemical.

If embedded in the cortex, stereochemical structures could even account for memories! They would then qualify as printed and stored language. Ideas occur when this chemoverbiage gets strung together -- new compound, new idea! In brief, special chemicals are probably as diverse as what happens in the brain and body, because that is why it happens. Molecular biologists have translated some of these hieroglyphs, but they are only beginning to understand the grammar.

Morowitz, a molecular biologist, notes that though this assortment of organic chemicals is truly immense, it probably could be meaningfully organized (decoded or translated) with the aid of computers. As he envisions it, one might make some sense out of the clutter by trying the same methods used by Mendeleev and those who followed him. As you will recall, these efforts resulted in the periodic table." [26]

"Heavens to Elisabeth! Let's forget about the special chemicals! What else is there you could think of?"

"I don't have a solution to the problem, if that's what you're asking. But I am convinced that Nature always achieves her effects by the simplest possible route -- minimal expenditure of free energy, etc. And it strikes me that current theories are overly complicated. There are too many loose ends. Individual cells evolve and change as they pass through successive generations during embryological growth. Rough calculations tell us that it takes only about 44 generations to arrive at the newborn, and perhaps 4 or 5 more to achieve maturity. So the important feature is not the particular chemicals, but rather, the serial organization of the process.

I have often wondered what brings about this continuous patterning of growth. And I still can't help but suspect that the sequence itself somehow relates to the longer-term growth and sequencing of evolution in general. After all, the human *is* a part of the living scene. So why shouldn't past history show up during his development? Despite ridicule and arguments to the contrary, there is some supporting evidence for this 'recapitulation' as it's called. I merely bring it up as a possibility that part of the changes may be historical. I won't pursue it. But in my own mind, neither evolution nor embryogenesis can possibly depend upon chance."

"Why are you so dead set against chance?" he inquired.

"Well, let's just consider the human development question and use a little of their backwards probability. As I recall, somewhere or other, Sir John Eccles estimated that the DNA code is capable of creating $10^{10,000}$ different selves. I would consider this extremely 'iffy.' But if true, it would mean that the chance of any one particular baby coming along would be only one in $10^{10,000}$ -- almost infinitely small. In spite of all this, it is obvious that people usually resemble their immediate forebears. Sometimes one is even able to recognize his relatives by appearance alone. This would seem impossible using these assumptions. For example, the chance that you and your brother would be alike would be unbelievably minute. But regardless of the questionable math, there is simply much too much consistency in the process to allow for chance.

Suppose we examine just one step in the developmental puzzle. At each of the many cross-roads where the embryo's shape must change, there either has to be (a) decision-making by the cells due to alter, or else (b) some external agent has to modify the process. That is to say, either the cell decides what to do, or it is compelled to do it. And just consider what that word 'compelled' means. In final analysis any compelled, or 'fixed' program modifications, would backspace the problem into the extreme past -- for the modifications certainly are not random. If cellular behavior were to consist wholly of robot-like reactions to fixed programming of its DNA, as commonly assumed, then why isn't adult behavior similarly programmed? Nothing noticeable has been added at birth, and maturity is only 5 mitotic generations away."

He smiled wryly. "As you know, there are those who believe that adult behavior *is* largely programmed by the genes -- that we are just large cumbersome robots fulfilling their will. [27] I find this rather hard to swallow. On the other hand, I can't go along with your idea of decision-making by the cell."

"Why not?" I asked. "Look at it this way. Those chromosomes appear suspiciously like what one might expect if the cell had brains. And if they are cellular brains, then this would account for the enormous time required for them to have evolved. After all, the chromosomes of the human consist of over 3 billion pairs of nucleotide bases! No human has ever devised anything even remotely approaching the intricate complexity of their structure. Conceive, if you can, the microelectrical fields which must exist in something made up of so many billions of atoms!

Indeed, it may be impossible for the human to achieve such complexity, for they devise *him*, and this includes *his* brain! He is a result in the event chain, not a cause. Why can't the cell be intelligent? Just because it is microscopic is no argument. Space-time is completely relative. Things can be just as small as the cosmos is large.

Besides, you can't use piece-fit-to-piece, cog-and-gear thinking when dealing with living organisms. They are basically non-mechanical. And the same goes for flipflop-switch-and-wire thinking. To consider the cell a complete automaton, incapable of making any decisions, ignores the intricacies of its own internal processes such as mitosis. In addition, it creates logical paradoxes for embryology. As mentioned, either the cell decides what to do, or something tells it what to do.

This latter option means that all development has to result from some totally inflexible predetermined program. And if such were the case, the program would have to be much more complicated than the baby itself. Otherwise, there would be no way of correcting for the unpredictable variations and emergencies brought about by local differences of growth -- the road hazards on the way to becoming a baby. So, the ever-popular idea of programming, coding, etc., is largely illogical. It dodges the problem by simply relabeling it."

"Horns of a dilemma!" he said,. "I don't care much for either option!"

"Maybe the hangup is semantics," I offered "-- the way intelligence is defined. As I use the term intelligence, or what we call mind, it is not an all-or-none type of thing. Humans vary from idiot to genius, and it's common knowledge that different species of animals have different degrees of intelligence. If it exists to some extent in all creatures, why shouldn't it also occur in the cell?"

"Let's go back to the programming bit," he interrupted. "What about identical twins? I should think they pretty well establish that both developed according to the same fixed and pre-set pattern."

"Not as I see it. Twins are virtually identical simply because identical cells would make the same decisions given the same circumstances. In fact, identical twins show amazingly similar behavior all through life. [28] And presumably, postnatal life is not completely controlled by genetics. I would be much less inclined to expect this close similarity of behavior if the twins resulted only from trillions of separate, small, mindless robots stuck with the same road map. Intelligence is necessary to handle the hazards encountered during the process of growth. To extend the analogy, suppose one were given the task of . . ."

"Wait a minute!" he interrupted. "Here's a coffee shop. That game made me hungry. You can expound your wild ideas just as well over some Danish and coffee, can't you?"

I nodded, and we entered and took a booth. The Danish, it turned out, was slightly stale. As I picked away the crustier spots, he said, "Now where were we? -- something about road hazards, I believe."

"Yes," I replied. "To get back to the analogy -- pass the sugar, will you please? -- suppose one were given the task of building some very large and complex cities. Account would have to be taken for streets, bridges, sewers, water supply, food distribution, power lines, and other features too numerous to list. No two such cities could possibly be made to look exactly alike, nor would they function in exactly the same manner. Each would have to be modified to fit the terrain as well as all the unforeseen conditions which would arise.

But assume that such planning were undertaken. It was then proclaimed that all this was to be accomplished solely by robots acting in complete subservience to some sort of fixed program, each being programmed with precisely the same set of instructions! The whole idea would be considered ludicrous. Any instructions which would fit one set of conditions wouldn't necessarily fit another. Worse yet, the robots would have to cooperate. This would not only require communication, but decision-making and possibly even mutual problem solving. No conceivable program could be devised which could foretell and deal with all possible exigencies!

Now, read cells for robots, DNA as programming, and the baby as city. Unrealistic though it may sound, this scenario closely resembles the orthodox concept of how the human (brain included) arose from a single cell. And it should be noted that the human, or any other animal, is much more complicated than any city. Even such localized tasks as the formation of scar tissue requires cellular cooperation to close the wound. How can cells at locus A know they should proliferate in directions to join with cells at locus B? The location, shape and extent of wounds is totally unpredictable.

To me at least, it would seem infinitely simpler and more logical just to assume that the cells themselves have some degree of awareness or mind. It is not a new idea. It was suggested back in 1952 by Lapicque.[29] It follows from the fact that cells communicate chemically. Why communicate if they can't use the communication? Perhaps their so-called instinctive programming is one of a more general sort not spelled out in detail. For example, it could be open-ended instincts about what to do, and not any specific step-by-step program for doing it."

"That brings up a question I meant to ask earlier," he commented. "I remember having heard you use the phrase 'open-ended instincts' before. And just now you implied that there was some sort of intermediate state -- something between automated (mindless) instinctive behavior, and normal behavior that is mindful. Just what does 'intelligence' mean in this case?"

I laughed. "Obviously, I do not mean that cells can do calculus. If they could, the human would not be such an incalculable mess. For instance, he wouldn't still have a vermiform appendix, an unsupported abdomen, or flat feet. [30] What I mean is that the cells have enough intelligence to operate effectively within the constraints of their environments. And I might add that this is about all most humans can do. The environments of the cell are simply more constant and homogeneous than those of humans. Duplicate their environmental conditions in a petri dish and they can live very well outside the body. The same is true of a man on the moon. The space-suit is a petri dish.

Let me put it differently. We can never know the extent of the cell's intelligence because it is not only dissimilar from ours, but it deals with a different world. The world of the human is made up of human things. It changes slowly. That of the spider consists of spider things. Change is more rapid. But the world of the cell has the most plasticity of all. This is the molecular realm where everything exists in its most variable state. It's a panorama of stereo-chemical forms and their differences, not a world of images, sounds, and feelings like ours. Outside their own sphere of molecules and their manipulations, the cells would find every-thing alien and utterly incomprehensible. Nothing can be understood unless the memory contains some related past experience with it. Whether paramecium, house cat, or Einstein, no organism can compute beyond its data base.

Besides, intelligence is not something uniquely human to be judged in terms of human culture. To see the other side of the picture, look at the white blood cells. These have a highly varied milieu providing a vastly larger data base, so they behave intelligently -- even by human standards."

"O.K., O.K., I get your point. But let's go back to what you call 'open-ended instincts.' Just what the devil are they?"

"It's a concept I borrowed from Bierens de Haan," I said. [31] "It is best explained by use of examples. Take the spider. The webs of the different species are so distinctive they can be identified by their patterning alone. Because the webs are complex, however, and must be built under a variety of conditions, no two are exactly alike. Thus, they can't be understood as products of simple rote movements of a serial nature. Rigid mechanization of this latter sort wouldn't allow them to be custom-fit to different locations. Web-weaving, therefore, cannot be completely instinctive as that term is commonly understood.

For the spider, what seems to be inherited is (1) the impetus to spin a web, plus (2), a generalized schema of what the web should look like. In other words, the spider carries around in her head a kind of mental 'template' to which the web must correspond. It can't be any program of specific movements, one after another. Tonight's speaker mentioned that much the same sort of behavior occurs in the cross-amble style of walking used by crabs. This also conforms to a pattern and is independent of how the pattern is accomplished muscularly.

The concept of open-ended instincts has many possible applications. For example, it could explain the structures built by beavers, the nests of birds, or the protective cases created by larvae of the caddisfly. These latter are constructed from whatever happens to be handy: twigs, sand, bits of leaves, or almost anything. But despite the variety of materials requiring different manipulations, the resulting cases always have the same *pattern*. It is obvious that the pattern determines the behavior. The neural routes to particular limbs don't matter. Earlier German psychologists referred to such a conceptual blueprint as a '*Suchbild*,' or search model." [32]

"It's a fascinating idea," he acknowledged. "As you indicate, it deals with the grey area between fixed instinctive programming and what we know as learning. In a way, it more or less fills in the presumed gaps between our thinking and that of many lesser creatures. I assume it also allows for learning at the cellular level."

"In my opinion, it does," I replied. "I would describe learning as the acquisition and storage of *patterns* -- not the stringing together of little bits and pieces. And it should be remembered that the most important of all patterns occur stereochemically as molecular shapes. But as tonight's speaker noted, there have been scores of experiments on single-celled creatures, as well as on individual neural cells -- and the learning issue is still considered up in the air. My guess is the difficulty stems from using learning situations which are definable in human terms, but which are not within the decision-making repertoire or purview of the cells themselves.

Suppose we consider a situation where the decision-making obviously would be meaningful to the cell. Let us assume it's a starving bacterium, and that it must 'mutate' in order to survive. I mention this because of recent investigations dealing with precisely this predicament. Experiments were conducted at the Harvard School of Public Health. Others were done independently at the University of Rochester. In both cases this type of problem was presented to bacteria. And in both cases results strongly suggest that cells will *choose* to 'mutate' in adaptive fashion under such conditions -- thus allowing for survival. [33]

"That makes sense -- at least for the bacteria," he admitted with a grin.. "But it certainly runs flat against accepted dogma. Not to change the subject, but I have a different question. Since you are convinced the cell learns, I presume the resulting memory ends up in its DNA. If so, what role does the gene play in all this?"

"Glad you brought it up," I said. "That term 'gene' is really confusing. The concept has suffered a deluge of publicity with all manner of implications, especially since the advent of genetic engineering. As a result, the public now visualizes the gene as a discrete, independent and clearly definable 'thing,' an entity in its own right. The DNA molecules of the chromosomes, on the other hand, are viewed as little more than genetic repositories, mosaics or patchworks of genes. So far, the order of gene arrangement appears meaningless. This is quite perplexing from an evolutionary standpoint. One wonders how such a disorderly hodge-podge could ever have come about. What would be the logic behind such total absence of arrangement?

As used by professionals, of course, the word 'gene' is more of a functional term, a simple matter of labeling. It refers to any segment of the DNA which can be shown to identify with a specific protein or hereditary effect. The segments themselves are not necessarily independent or even similar. The same may be said of their functioning. Interactions among genes are fascinating by reason of their very complexity. Some control others, turn them on or turn them off. Dominants suppress recessives, and recessives combine to suppress dominants. Those from the mother may differ from those from the father. Still others act only in groups and are designated as 'polygenes.' Some are even said to 'jump' from place to place.

In addition, the greater mass of the DNA is called 'surplus' because no particular genetic effects have yet been identified with it. It would almost seem that a gene is largely what it is described as being. Though there are 'markers' in their sequences, these are not absolute. Moreover, the whole picture changes almost daily, sometimes becoming better known, but just as often bringing up still further questions. The mysteries are numerous -- virtually equal to the facts."

"What kind of mysteries?"

"O.K. Suppose we ignore the term gene because of its conceptual difficulties. Instead, let's take an over-view. Let's talk about the total DNA and the numbers of chromosomes. Assume that the orthodox view is correct, and that this DNA is really no more than a tapedeck of instructions used automatically by a robot cell. One would then expect a greater amount of recorded information in the cells of more advanced species. That is to say, as creatures became more intricate structurally or behaviorally, their cells should have required more DNA to record the increased complexity. This simply is not the case. The salamander, *amphiuma,* has 20 times as much DNA as we have. And some unicellular creatures such as certain rhizopods, have 1500 or more chromosomes compared to our 46. In fact, so far as chromosome numbers are concerned, the human is somewhere in the middle of the list. Ridiculous as it may sound, even the potato has two more chromosomes than the human! [34]

Furthermore, if mutations in the DNA were a matter of chance as commonly assumed, more chromosomes should mean more mutations. And if we admit that mutations fuel evolution, then the crayfish with its 200 chromosomes should have evolved almost five times as fast as the human. Instead, he has been stuck where he is, impervious to time. The horseshoe crab, ant, dragonfly and cockroach are in a similar predicament. All are very ancient. The cockroach, for example, goes back at least 250 million years. Why haven't they either evolved or become extinct? Why are they stuck in a time-warp? [35]

Turning to the other side of the picture, one encounters similar problems. For instance, all humans are considered the same species because they have approximately the same DNA sequencing. However, chimpanzees also have over 99 percent of the same sequencing. Question: why isn't the chimp more like the human? [36]

Add to this the fact that all species possess large quantities of DNA not currently known to be associated with any genetic effects. This creates still further puzzles. Is it merely unidentified genes, or does it play some different role? Note that we still haven't accounted for the control center or 'brain' of the cell itself. The cell is extremely complex. It has to have one. And if not in the DNA, then where is it located?"

"How much of this so-called surplus DNA is there?"

"No one really knows," I replied. "It would vary with the species. But for the human again, the usual estimate is that it could account for about 100,000 genes. Of these, only about 2,000 have been identified with specific functions, or 2 percent. In any case, there is plenty of DNA. It has been calculated that if it were all uncoiled from the nucleus of the cell, it would stretch almost 9 feet and contain more information than 200 Manhattan telephone directories." [37]

"Gadzooks! What do you think is responsible for it all?"

"I haven't heard any reasonable explanation," I confessed. "But if I were to turn my imagination loose, I would suggest that perhaps part of this 'extra' DNA may represent past history of the species. It could be records of proposed changes which did not materialize, or possibly those which have been replaced by still further changes. Should this be the case, it would now be nothing but gibberish. I mention this possibility because there is no known mechanism by which the DNA, acting on its own, could erase or edit information once it is recorded. Current theory pictures it as a sort of library of molecular templates, quite stable and non-reactive. Over many millions of years, this would accumulate into an enormous data base.

Oh -- I should add that there are reports of an enzyme which has been labeled 'reverse transcriptase.' Presumably, it enables the reading of information from cellular RNA back into nuclear DNA. It would seem that the information flow is not always and necessarily from DNA$\Rightarrow$ RNA$\Rightarrow$ proteins, as once thought. This enzyme is particularly interesting in light of the numerous experiments linking RNA to acquired memory. But I don't see how it could explain the surplus." [38]

"How would this affect your assumption that the chromosomes also constitute a kind of primordial mind?"

"I don't see any problem," I assured him. "Recorded past history is a part of every mind. Another word for it is memory. A goodly portion of the DNA could be just such primordial mind, as you put it. By this hypothesis, the cell itself would be considered the basic organism. What we refer to as genes remain specialized areas of the DNA, but would be looked upon as more like 'cellular glands' -- at least those used by the cell to devise commonly needed proteins. Still others would be blueprint files for transmissible hereditary effects. To extend this far-out theorization, the 'thinking' portion of the chromosomal mass would probably be allocated to some part of those silent or 'surplus' areas. As suggested, these could retain memories of the genetic past. Being such, they would be used much as we use memories of the past during our own thinking.

Before trashing this whole idea as pure fantasy and totally outrageous, remember that these nucleic acid molecules are truly gigantic. Each contains many billions of atoms making for countless point-charges of energy, polarization differences, and extremely complex intermediate fields of all sorts. Any folding, motion, or deformation of the molecules would in-crease this potential energy patterning almost to infinity. [39]

Man-made computers, you will recall, achieve something very similar to thought processes by use of much simpler energy patterns. However, I would not look upon the chromosomes as computers. They might resemble tremendously complex computer chips. But if they were chips, they would have to be millions of times more effective than the simple rigid types we now know. I like to think of them as possibly being pure intelligence -- 'pure' because they would be intelligence reduced to the constituent energy patterning itself."

He grinned, then commented, "Maybe the cells have too much brain!"

I ignored the remark and continued. "As I believe I stated, cells have this irrepressible urge to combine with other cells. They are preeminently social creatures. So now, visualize half a trillion of these pattern-bearing organic super-chips -- all assembled together within one skull. Then interrelate them with elaborate neural and chemical networks. Each is capable of communicating with the others, because each cell has its own chemical signature or call-number. Such a mechanism, I submit, might perform suspiciously like the human mind.

I recognize that this picture looks like straight science fiction, over simplified, and far-fetched. But that is one way of painting it in light of what is known. Every living thing begins life as a single cell and ends up as an organized society of cells. Thus, *the key to the enigma has to lie in the cell itself!* It is the basic unit of life just as the atom is a unit of matter.

I can't seem to forget that this cell took much, much longer to evolve than all the rest of life put together. It suggests that perhaps such an enormous time span may have been necessary because it is much more complex *functionally*. As a structure, it is admittedly small. But in terms of functional complexity it could be gigantic. It is entirely possible that we represent its most ambitious effort. Our much vaunted brains could be simply a consortium of specialized cells called nerves. And since their specialty was communications, they got together and decided to run things. They weren't shuffled together by chance. They decided it."

"Wild, man! Completely wild! As you see it, then, what really evolved was *mind!* From the very outset, the body was only a vehicle. Bodily changes were merely adaptations commandeered by the mind."

"That puts it in a nutshell," I conceded. "Even orthodox followers of Darwin admit that evolutionary modifications of the body started as shifts in behavior patterns. [40] The animal elected to change its habits for one reason or another, most likely environmental pressure of some sort. Natural selection then adapted the body to facilitate the new routine. But the animal's brain had to have directed these initial changes in behavior. The body didn't decide them. All behavior is directed -- by definition. Random activity is not called behavior.

So any way you look at it, the mind had to precede everything else. And why not? Mindless chance only creates randomness. And randomness is disorganization, again by definition. The body creates nothing. Even sex, which is highly instinctive, requires mediation by the mind. The body itself has neither sex nor personality. Ask the coroner. He uses the pronoun 'it'."

By this time we had reached a point where the sidewalk turned into his home. He proceeded by himself a short distance, then pivoted about and stared at me. "You know what all this sounds like, don't you? It sounds like vitalism, spiritualism, and mysticism -- all rolled into one package!"

"Well, it isn't!" I retorted. "Some time when we both have a day or so, I'll explain what the word 'mind' means. It's a matter of chemistry."

"That's exactly what my daughter says about her new boy friend," he replied with a grin.

"Well, maybe she's right!" I shot back, and continued on home.

Chapter 6

The Many Faces of Evolution Theory

(Bones, bunkum, and bothersome theories -- including the heresy that evolution may be just what it appears to be, namely, cellular innovation which may still be in progress.)

Our biology seminar called "Advanced Theory" met the following Wednesday. As it happened, this allowed plenty of time for the recent talk to have been hashed and rehashed. As I entered the classroom there was a lively discussion going on in the rear. I waited what I thought was a reasonable time, then asked, "Is this a private argument, or can I get into it?"

A hush fell on the group. One of the graduate students looked up and smiled. "Sorry, sir. We were just going over a point made by the speaker last week. We think he miscalculated."

"Oh?" I asked. "About what?"

"About the relative time it took for cellular life to evolve. When compared to all the rest of evolution combined, he said it took about twice as long for the cells."

"You think that was excessive?"

"No -- just the opposite. We think he underestimated. As we see it, life was unicellular right up to the Cambrian period somewhere around 570 million years ago. That's when the first multicellular creatures appeared. And no matter how we juggle the figures, this means that single-celled life forms made up about five sixths of all life history. Everything else occurred in only the remaining one sixth."

I made a few hasty calculations. "I'll be damned!" I commented. "You are right! He must have figured from the point at which oxygen-using cells appeared. That makes it *really* awesome! The one-cylinder jobs occupied over 80 percent of all the time life has existed! That should tell us something about the complexity of the cell! I'd like to pursue the issue, but we are running behind schedule. And we have not yet discussed how these separate cells began to socialize, or the beginnings of multicellular life. All of it is highly speculative, of course. The truth of the matter is we don't know exactly when multicellular life began -- because these early creatures had no hard parts, no skeletons to leave in the fossil record."

Pawing through my briefcase, I came up with some notes. "The war of the worlds," I announced, "did not occur on TV. Nor did it involve any extraterrestrial aliens. It took place right here between the world of small things (microscopia) and the world of large things (macroscopia), between the unicellular beings and their societies -- the multicellular beings. Moreover, it is still raging. The people win some and the bugs win some. It is chemical warfare, painful and destructive. So we should at least take a quick glance at the situation. It doesn't pay to totally ignore your enemy.

We use the term 'belittle' and we tend to 'look down' on creatures smaller than ourselves. This may be why we regard the cell as a sort of inert   gelatinous building-block totally devoid of any identity or intelligence. We do this even though the facts of healing, regeneration, and embryonic growth seem to mandate at least some degree of intelligence. It would appear that our ego recognizes only one identity, its own. No organisms above us! And nothing significant below us!

Insofar as our own body cells are concerned, we can get away with such arrogance. They are family. But it is a mistake when dealing with certain other members of microscopia. Some of them are downright vicious! The great plagues of Europe are now history. However, the malaria plasmodium is still killing 2 or 3 million people every year. And it is just one of our many enemies. There are others fully as dangerous. Fortunately for us, these vicious types are a small minority.

Let's look at some figures. There are less than 5 thousand species of mammals. Compared with these, there are some 200 thousand known species of microbes. Most are neither harmful nor helpful. Like many people, they just are. Moreover, a goodly number of them are allied in mutually beneficial symbiosis with multicellular plants and animals. Best known of these latter, perhaps, are the bacteria inhabiting our intestines or those of the termites. Thus, some are vital. Our lives depend on them.

Something often overlooked when considering microscopia is their social behavior. Bacteria are extremely social, indeed sexually so! They get into one another's genes quite freely. Worse yet, they disregard the common taboos against breeding with members of a different species, genus, or even phylum! There is no sexual discretion, much less sexual selection. For them, God is love plus opportunity. The process is called conjugation, and it is a term well taken. One bacterium will sidle up and press against another. A pore-like opening appears between them. Through this opening the donor then inserts a ring of DNA called a plasmid. It is hereditary material and becomes a part of the recipient -- later passed on to its descendants. [41]

Such loose behavior has extremely broad implications. Some microbiologists have even suggested that the microbial world might well constitute one immense, loosely structured, but highly active organization in its own right. [42] Each member is potentially an on-line relayer of genetic information from any and all who pass its way. If one further extends this picture to include those parasites called viruses, the entire biosphere becomes involved. Viruses subvert the DNA of cells and can thus alter genetic data in multicellular creatures as well.

The whole thing is beginning to look as if microscopia might well be one large invisible communications net which blankets the planet and provides constant chit-chat between all cellular aspects of life. To reveal some idea of its magnitude, scientists recently reported measurements of more than a billion viruses per teaspoonful of earth's waters, whether from seas, lakes or bays. Compared to the microorganisms, all the remainder of life was said to be a negligible quantity. [43]

Now, consider the following: (a) Cells have this irresistible urge to get together, whether they are the same species or not. (b) Chemical communications necessarily exist both within and between them. And © symbiosis is widespread throughout all levels of life. Given such conditions, no one should be surprised that cooperatives formed among cells. These soon consolidated into multicellular organisms which then grew to dominate the biosphere."

A hand popped up. I nodded, and a bespectacled youth asked "Is there any good example of otherwise separate unicellular organisms communicating chemically?"

"Many instances could be cited," I replied, "but probably the most spectacular are the amoebas which make up slime molds. Despite their unappetizing name, these are just ordinary looking amoebas -- distinct one-cylinder jobs. They go merrily about their business eating and dividing, with no evidence of any social relationships until their food supply becomes low. Then, something dramatic happens. Certain of them act as leaders. A chemical call-signal identified as *acrasin* is released. Other amoebas home-in on the signal and crowd around the leaders. The total assemblage congeals into a sausage-shaped body about 1 mm. long. This then moves worm-like in the direction of light and heat. About a week later, following migration, it contracts into a ball and grows a stalk. The top of the stalk produces small spheres filled with spores, and the whole life-cycle starts over again. [44]

There has been considerable study of these and similarly fascinating creatures which inhabit the twilight region between individual being and social being. Smaller creatures fuse to become larger ones. And in some species, following certain role fulfillment, they may separate to become small individuals again. As might be expected, most are marine creatures like the sponge or siphonophores. All use chemical communications between separate members or member-parts." [45]

"Is this how the Cambrian explosion got started?" someone asked.

"No one really knows," I replied. "But certainly it is logical to assume that these colonial creature/societies preceded true multicellular types. A wide range of such intermediate forms may still be found. The opportunities existed then, and the advantages were enormous. Multiple cellularity allowed for greater specialization, giving rise to greater efficiency. More offspring could be produced. Larger size was possible, as well as greater variety of shape. Furthermore, when considered as a composite individual, cells could be replaced -- providing a much longer life."

"Somehow, all this seems contrary to Darwin, doesn't it?"

I grew serious for a moment. "I have been trying to avoid that issue," I finally explained. "But since you brought it up, I may as well be blunt about it. Yes, it runs contrary to some aspects of Darwin's theory, specifically the idea that life is an ever on-going fight, that survival and reproduction basically result from success during competition, and that this is the primary mechanism of natural selection.

The cell, by its socializing to create larger organisms, argues for Kropotkin's theory. [46] This stated that not conflict, but *cooperation*, was the true driving force behind evolution. It was the exact opposite of the dog-eat-dog survival by bloodshed, emphasized by many of Darwin's interpreters — most particularly T. H. Huxley.

Dinosaurs were past masters at the kill-and-eat game. And though they existed a million years, they failed to extend themselves socially through joint cooperation. No matter what finally killed them off, they apparently could not make the next step and become cooperative social animals. Negativism is not an effective approach to anything -- including your enemy. As for the human, sadly enough, it is simply a matter of attitude.

A glass of water may be seen as half full or half empty. Unfortunately, Neo-Darwinism emphasizes only the empty half of life. It is fundamentally pessimistic. In essence, it states that life is merely a question of surviving long enough to reproduce before becoming food for something else. The picture is made even more bleak by modern mutation theory. This further insists that any improvement can only occur by chance.

But let's get back to Kropotkin. Cooperation, symbiosis, altruism, love, and similar terms, all refer to a general attraction which exists between organisms of like-kind. It is said to provide greater survival value than sheer individual strength, belligerence, or the felt need to reproduce. Indeed, it promotes reproductive success. Reproduction is rarely an act of seize-and-rape. Even among the wildest animals it is a cooperative function.

Most importantly, cooperative behavior is necessary for any kind of organization to arise. As such, it involves action of the mind. By contrast, conflict usually occurs without serious thinking and is most often associated with disorganization. And disorganization is what characterizes insanity. It is the antithesis of rational action. Unquestionably, both conflict and cooperation played a role during evolution, and they are definitely still with us! But the constructive features responsible for the development of life had to have arisen from this almost universal *integrative* tendency. We recognize it at the cellular and biosocial levels. But Kropotkin extended it to a general principle applicable to all living things.

There are many aspects to this propensity for togetherness. For example, it is responsible for the most fundamental property of life, what we know as *growth*. It might even be described as a primordial creative urge. Biological growth is creation by the cell. Invention, art, language, new ideas, indeed all culture, is creative growth by the multicellular mind. Only cooperative creative behavior promotes growth. And it alone is accompanied by a *joie de vivre* -- a feeling of expanding elation. This is true whether it is the creation of a child, a new idea, a work of art, or simply the exuberance of youth. I like to look upon it as the sensation of growth -- a feeling that comes with extension of one's horizons or enlargement of the self. Otherwise, it would have no relevance for the self. The philosopher Nietzsche wrote to his friend, Peter Gast, 'Listen to an idea I have had. One ceases from loving oneself properly when one ceases from expressing oneself in love toward others.'" [47]

The arm went up again. "If this is true," he asked, "how do you account for all the hatred? Not just individuals, but whole cultures have fallen because of hatred."

"To begin," I said, "it is doubtful whether any culture has ever fallen because of hatred. War is always sold to the public as 'self protection' -- usually to rationalize greed. Those who assailed Rome did not necessarily *hate* Rome. They attacked only to further their own ends, mostly loot. Alexander 'the Great' was essentially on an ego trip.

Look at it this way. The mind operates on an energy of attraction. This brings things together and organizes them. Thus, it can and does give rise to greed. But hatred is irrational. It is an expenditure of energy in channels contrary to one's own interests, and so, is counter-productive. I can think of no instance in which hatred has led to anything creatively new or valuable. It only promotes action against. It repels, pushes things further away. It pulls nothing together. So it gains nothing.

One never fights *against* anything! He can only fight *for* something, to advance his own goals or to protect whatever he feels is threatened. Thus, *the so-called 'fight for survival' ignores the desire to survive!* The first commandment of life is self-survival -- the love of life. Neo-Darwinism emphasizes a secondary negative result, not the primary causal force of evolution. Among wild animals, for instance, hatred is virtually unknown. The predator kills only for food. He does not hate the creature he kills.

So much for that. It sounds too much like a sermon. Let's get back to your initial question. This primal tendency to cooperate, to believe, to belong, to grow, is one of the many reasons for thinking that mind is responsible for evolution. All are features of an on-going organization or growth -- else why should cells have ever socialized or set up symbiotic relationships in the first place? Or why should the immune system protect the body, the mother protect the young, or the stag protect the herd?"

"If all life is a growth process, is it possible to look upon the Cambrian period as the childhood of multicellular life?"

"That's one way of putting it, yes. But I think this sudden prolifer-ation of multicellular life which occurred in the Cambrian is best under-stood when viewed against the broad context of evolution in general. Somewhere, I have the steps of the process listed, at least as I see them."

I again rummaged through the briefcase and this time came up with a slide. The blinds were pulled, and I stuffed it into the projector.

VERY BRIEF HISTORY OF LIFE

1. *Emergence* of large non-reproducing organic molecules of every possible composition. (Chemical bonding.)

2.. *Discovery of Self-reproduction.* Emergence and planet-wide spread of primitive self-reproducing cells (prokaryotes) which do not use oxygen. Sources of food: minerals, water and sunlight. Waste product: oxygen.

3. *First Over-population Crisis.* Pollution of earth, oceans and atmosphere with oxygen. Rusting out of oceans and surface minerals. Mass extinction of prokaryotes with low O_2 tolerance. Most survivors go underground.

4. *Discovery of Oxidative Metabolism.* Emergence and planet-wide spread of oxygen-using cells (eukaryotes), brought about by symbiotic alliances among certain of the earlier prokaryotes. Life begins to feed off other life. (I love you so much I could eat you!)

5. *Second Over-population Crisis.* Oxygen-users create symbiotic social alliances with one another, producing colonial multicellular creatures . Specialization occurs. The Cambrian explosion: rapid experimentation in size, shape and cellular role specialization. Mass extinction of inefficient multicellular designs.

6. *Emergence* and planet-wide spread of successful multicellular life forms. Progressive evolution of plants and animals. The brain expands. Man becomes dominant.

7. *Third Over-population Crisis.* Use of fossil fuels and artificial materials lead to non-biodegradable wastes (Stone Age, Iron Age, Garbage)! Pollution of earth, oceans, and atmosphere. Ever-increasing extinctions.

I pulled back the blinds, turned off the projector, and cautioned, "please note that the dates on these events have been omitted because they represent spans rather than points in time. There is much overlapping." I paused, then added, "Regarding the final phase dealing with the current overpopulation crisis, I should like to quote J. B. Lamarck. This is meant for the benefit of those who read only his critics. Almost two centuries ago Lamarck predicted, 'One would say that man is destined to exterminate himself, after having rendered the globe uninhabitable.' [48] I have slightly more faith in human ingenuity than this, but he could have been right. Certainly, mass extinctions are already well under way."

One of the students at the rear of the room had a question: "I don't wish to change the subject, but your citing of Lamarck brings up a problem that's been troubling me."

"The floor is yours," I replied.

"I haven't read Lamarck fully," he went on, "but I agree that he has been grossly misinterpreted. However, his critics do present an argument which appears to apply equally well to your own position."

"Oh?" I asked, "what's that?"

"First, let's make sure I understand your position. This states that embryonic growth and evolution both involve mentally directed variations, and *not* chance mutations. Is that correct?"

"Essentially, yes." I replied. "And I would go further and say that there really is no such thing as chance. It is only a cop-out term for lack of information. If we were somehow God-like and knew everything, there could only be two probabilities -- one and zero. All fractional values in between (chance) merely reflect our uncertainty, our lack of information. As I see it, probability is not a measure of anything. It is an estimate of some 'true' but unknown state of affairs. If there is no such 'true' state, the estimate itself becomes meaningless, and all causality goes down the drain. Thus, to call mutations 'random,' or chance, merely says that we don't know what causes them. [49] Given this point, what was the problem?"

"The difficulty has to do with the rate of change," he continued. "It is argued that evolution should have been much, much faster if it had been directed by the mind. If cellular mutations are meaningful variations to begin with, and natural selection is only environmental confirmation or rejection of these, why wasn't the process more rapid? Is the cell a slow learner?"

"First," I responded, "many of us would not agree that evolution has been all that slow. Development of the original cell was understandably laborious. But the rest of life from trilobite through dinosaurs to man, has taken place in only the last 570 million years. The total number of all species which have ever existed has been estimated at a minimum of two billion. [50] That averages out to almost one new species every three months!

Moreover, the process has been gaining speed all the time. We went from ape to man in the last five million years, and all civilization is no older than 15,000 years. Considering the enormous variety and complexity of living things, this seems much too rapid to be explained unless it were somehow selective rather than random.

The whole picture, of course, is fuzzy. We have only fossil bones with which to work. And bones alone can't tell us what was responsible. All the important tissues, the 'software' which initiated the changes, have disappeared. Certainly the bones didn't initiate anything. So one is now in the same position as some alien trying to understand a computer from inspection of the empty metal case. There is no access to the components, no wiring diagrams, and no idea whatever about the software programs.

Secondly, as to the learning capacity of the cell, I would characterize the cell as a rapid learner! At least the brain cells are. They learn just as fast as we do, because that's what happens when *we* learn! After all, our brains are made up of these cells. When something gets recorded in our memories there has to be rapid molecular-level change occurring somewhere in the brain cells. The resulting growth of the mind is responsible for our mental life and behavior -- the activity of our cellular society.

When it comes to altering the body itself, however, the situation is much different. The brain is a governing consortium of nerve cells! Thus, bodily changes are not solely a question of the survival of one germ cell containing mutant DNA. If determined by the mind, it means changing the society's constitution so to speak. In this latter case, there would have to be agreement among ten billion brain cells! In other words, the proposed structural change would have to accumulate in enough of the brain cell population to reach a level where it could influence the more independent germ cells. These germ cells are a part of the glandular system subject to the old brain. Though not wholly isolated from cortical influence, they are not directly in the chain of command.

In a way, this provides a safety measure. If they were easily influenced, there would be no hereditary tradition in the cellular society. Evolutionary variations would fluctuate wildly with our desires and beliefs. Nothing could be worse. But to some degree this may have been just what happened during the Cambrian explosion. The variety which occurred at that time was incredible. There could have been little tradition in these new cellular societies, much less any immune system to enforce it.

To summarize, evolution directed by the mind would be necessarily slow, consistent, and ever better organized. Only on extremely rare occasions, if ever, could it be a matter of random mutation. Bear in mind that the goal of the DNA is to replicate itself as nearly perfectly as possible. Much as in human society, new cellular ventures and aberrations would come face to face with orthodoxy -- most likely enforced by thought-police which we know as white blood cells.

I might add that the situation is pretty much the same for the Neo-Darwinian theory. This now accepts the idea of random mutations. Nonetheless, most Neo-Darwinians assume that changes in body structure are always preceded by changes in behavior, i.e., they do not appear out of thin air as one might predict from random action. If such is the case, and regardless whether or how natural selection works, the behavioral changes would still have to influence the germ cells somehow in order to get recorded and become transmissible. *Weeding out the non-adapted would not explain specific adaptations in the germ cell DNA of the survivors!*

To appreciate this problem, pause a moment to consider the orthodox view that DNA is a code which undergoes random mutation. Because of the almost infinite number of possible permutational arrangements of its billions of nucleotides, any *meaningful* sequence would almost never occur by chance. Meaningful mutations (if they *do* indeed occur) would seem to suggest *intent,* or *purpose* -- the action of intelligence at the cellular level. It is felt that this issue of chance mutations has not been thoroughly 'thought out' by its advocates. It needs serious study from the standpoint of the probabilities involved. So far as

I know, in all the experiments thus far conducted (mostly with fruit flies), there has never yet occurred an induced mutation which proved beneficial.

Suppose a meaningful mutation *did* occur in the course of human events. Present-day theory says it would have to take place in the germ plasm -- testes or ovaries. It is extremely doubtful if it would affect more than a small fraction of one DNA molecule, or occur in more than one cell. This particular deviation, in this particular molecule, in this particular cell, would then have to be transmitted unchanged via meiosis, and finally coitus. If it were a sperm cell probability would further drop as a function of the number of sperm. The entire process would then have to be multiplied by a long series of other contingencies, namely, the probability of (1) a viable conception, i.e., genetic compatibility; (2) carrying to term and reaching adulthood; and (3) achieving further viable impregnations. And this assumes that one mutation, acting alone, would produce a transmissible effect -- something which seems dubious in itself. [51]

One time when I had little else to do, I tried estimating all this using some data from primitive tribes. And in making the estimates, I bent over backward to favor the orthodox view. Nonetheless, probabilities were grotesquely small -- something like firing a random rifle shot in the air and hitting a wild canary. The exercise was interesting, but figures won't be cited because they were felt to be both meaningless and untrustworthy.

That evolution occurred, there can be little question. As to *how* it occurred, questions are not only endless, but mostly unanswerable. [52] To cite a bit which I believe came from Gertrude Stein: 'There ain't no answer. There ain't going to be any answer. There never has been an answer. That's the answer.'

Moreover, for all we know, evolution may still be in progress. Regardless of the theory chosen, it still seems highly illogical to assume that all living creatures are in stasis -- frozen, as it were -- impervious to time and universal change. Suppose some Nubian slave from ancient Egypt, circa 4000 BC., were somehow transported to M.I.T. Objective: to acquire a PhD in physics. Current theory says he would have no problem if he had been reared in a well-to-do home. I strongly suspect that this is simply more 'politically correct' sheep-dip. [53]

Everyone admits that our existing culture is undergoing increasingly rapid development or evolution. This would seem to suggest some sort of corresponding changes in the brains of those who create and live in the culture. Else how could the developments have come about? Experiments with lab rats at least, offer evidence that an enriched environment produces chemical changes in the brain. [54]

In addition, extensive data recently collected from 'developed' countries show a startling increase of I.Q. (20 points) in the mere interval between 1952 and 1982. Independent studies done elsewhere also reveal gains of 5 to 25 points. The argument that such tests are 'culturally biased' is not valid for these studies. The greatest increase actually took place in the so-called 'culture free' tests. [55] Thus, whether evolution is still occurring is not going to be settled by dogma, political or otherwise. Indeed, it isn't likely to be settled at all!"

I glanced at my watch. "We have time for about one or two more questions -- provided they don't take too long," I remarked.

The arm that was raised this time belonged to an attractive young lady who had been twirling the pull-cord on the window blind. "I am majoring in entomology," she announced, "and I am at a loss. If the basic cell is intelligent, especially nerve cells, why doesn't this show up in insect behavior? They have quite a collection of nerve cells. Why do they act only from blind instinct?"

I started to laugh, then caught myself and apologized. "I'm sorry. But your question reminds me of a statement made by the famous humorist, Will Cuppy. He observed that if an animal does something, say it is an ant, they call it instinct. But if we do the same thing for the same reason, they call it intelligence. He wouldn't buy the argument that an ant doesn't know what it is doing. He wasn't so sure that humans really know what *they* are doing. Most human behavior is patterned by habits and rituals not unlike that of ants. So it is often performed without full awareness, and is neither more nor less predictable than that of the ant.

It is true that we frequently can't explain why insects do what they do. But almost as often, we can't explain why humans do what *they* do. Perhaps if we were able to see things through the eyes of the insect, its behavior might make as much sense as that of the human. In short, what I am saying is that we anthropomorphize. We judge them by our own standards. We 'belittle' them, even refuse to recognize that they can learn. Nonetheless, ants can be taught to run a maze, despite the fact that such activity must be utterly meaningless to them.

Let's try to be thoroughly objective about this issue. Let's judge the ant's intelligence solely on the basis of its behavior. That's what behaviorists try to do with humans. If we do this with ants, we note that ants conduct slave raids on neighboring species, engage in child labor, get involved in warfare, use chemical sprays to rout the enemy, practice thievery, and engage in all manner of deceptive ploys including ambush and assassination of queens. Does this sound familiar?

On the constructive side, of course, they also raise milk cattle (aphids), farm fungi, undertake huge construction projects, are fond of pets, willingly cooperate in joint activities, and treat members of their own group with much more consideration than we do. There is constant helping, grooming, feeding, and meticulous care of the young -- all coordinated by an endless exchange of chemical information. [56]

If anything, termite societies are even more impressive. In proportion to their size, some tropical species construct nests which surpass anything built by humans. They may be fifty or more feet in diameter, over ten feet tall, and house literally billions of inhabitants. Careful attention is paid to good building principles: chimneys and ducts for ventilation, proper orientation to sunlight, air conditioning, and roofs with eaves for protection against the rain. Passages are often beautifully arched, with a rounded dome-like suite for the queen and her attendants. And the entirety is laced with spiraling galleries, corridors leading to various rooms, and nurseries for the young. Those situated in dry areas may even have deep wells dug to supply fresh water. And to top it all off, their social structures are just as intricately organized as their architecture!

Question: is all this rigidly encoded within the DNA of each individual ant and termite? Or does the organic total, comprised of countless tiny brains, somehow possess a sort of collective mentality? I cannot help but suspect that the latter may be true. But whatever the case, their behavior is certainly not governed by any fixed and previously coded programs, as instincts are commonly described. No two territaries are exactly the same size or shape. Neither are they laid out in precisely the same fashion. Each of them shows evidence of adaptation to terrain and other conditions. Moreover, individual behavior reveals the same variety. If this behavior were entirely reflexive, what could be the source of all the obvious adaptation? There has to be intelligence operating at one level or another.

Suppose we accept the standard assumption that the behavior of social insects is entirely fixed and individually programmed into each tiny brain. One would then expect at least the rudiments of a program to begin with even one individual. This does not occur. The little beastie simply wanders about aimlessly. These were ants. One by one their number was increased to five. Then, it dawned on me that they had nothing to do. So, a small piece of hamburger was introduced on the scene -- and this blew the work whistle! They milled about for a moment as if sizing up the task. Then some set to pushing, others to pulling, and the project was underway! Since the behavior switched from random activity to coordinated teamwork, they had to have known what they were doing. Whatever did the switching, it influenced the group as a whole.

Grassé, a French scientist of social insects, describes a similar experiment with termites. He placed about a spoonful of them in a dish with earth and fecal droppings, their natural building material. At the outset, there was only random behavior. Pellets were casually picked up, carried a distance, then dropped haphazardly. However, when two or three of these building blocks accidently piled together, they must have been interpreted as the rudiments of a column -- because the activity then became organized. They set to work in earnest. Given that another column was under construction nearby, they finished them both, then topped them off with an arch. [57]

Thus, whether ants or termites, it would seem that two conditions are necessary for behavior to become meaningfully patterned:. (1) They must achieve a certain critical population density. And (2) there must exist a potential task, or the recognizable beginnings of one. The relatively rapid appearance of mutual orientation and cooperation indicates that thinking is introduced from one source or another.

It is suggested that what happens with ants or termites may well be analogous to what happens with the three neurons which were diagramed earlier *(see Figure 2)*. The neurons became integrated into a system via feedback. This interacted with their genetic memories, and this was what organized them. In the case of the social insects, the feedback loop (or loops) would doubtlessly be chemical. Chemical communications have unique advantages. They persist for some time, are transmitted in the dark, go around corners, and have an intensity gradient that allows for tracking. Communication between cells is chemical, as is most of that between animals from protozoa to primates."

At this point the bell rang. However, I knew the room was not scheduled to be used the next period, so I continued. "I have only one more point to make about insects, and I'll be brief about it. Grasshoppers, spiders, and humans have something in common. At birth they are small replicas of the adults they will later become. They gain in size but remain about the same shape. The young can be identified for what they are.

Such shape constancy does not exist for a large percentage of insects. These undergo metamorphosis. It would seem that insect life reached a kind of impasse with the advent of an external skeleton. The disadvantages need not be detailed here. They are obvious. However, the situation was considerably worse for the worm -- having no skeleton at all! This also was pretty much a dead-end structure. It greatly limited the design changes necessary for evolutionary change or growth. There was nothing to which they could hook the muscles! What to do? What to do?

Let us engage in some fantasy. Let us suppose that the neural members of this worm-cell society recognized they were up a blind alley. If so, they would have had only one recourse: *back track* -- go to the beginning and start over again! Fantastic as it sounds, this appears to have been what happened! We now know the process as metamorphosis.

The transition from caterpillar to butterfly begins with a surprising amount of gymnastics just to rig and suspend its chrysalis. But once enclosed and protected from the elements, it passes into a comatose condition. Caterpillar tissues and organs are broken down and recycled. Raw materials from this dismantling are then reassembled into entirely different structures and organs. Further, this has to be accompanied by a kind of 'operations manual' detailing their use. The rebuilt creature almost always has different shape, organs, locomotion, diet, environment, and enemies. The final product (butterfly) is totally dissimilar to the worm.

Ordinarily, evolution theorists carefully sidestep this problem of metamorphosis, and understandably so. There is no earthly way in which it can be explained as a series of small chance mutations, each followed by natural selection. It is a massive, intricate, two-stage process accomplished by the cells themselves. Many thousands of steps are involved, both destructive and constructive -- with no survival pay-off until *all* are completed! From start to finish, it takes place within the confines of the chrysalis, entirely isolated from environmental conditions reputedly making for natural selection. Indeed, it would appear impossible for natural selection to have had any influence whatever! Using mutation theory to explain metamorphosis would be very like trying to explain the Taj Mahal as a product of centuries of earthquakes in and around Agra. If it were just the butterfly, one might dismiss it as some unexplainable quirk of Nature. But the 300,000 known species of beetles also undergo metamorphosis! [58]

Resolution? Here's my guess (and it *is* a guess!) During the disassembly of the caterpillar, followed by the assembly of the butterfly, one set of structures had to remain intact. These were the original neural cells of the caterpillar brain. This has been suggested indirectly by experiments. Chemical information (hormones) taken from the brains of insects, have been used to manipulate the different intermediate stages of their metamorphosis. [59] In brief, it had to have been the insect *mind* (however laughable that term may seem) which dictated all the different changes through which it went. I admit that such a conclusion sounds totally ludicrous. But unfortunately, it appears to be the only conclusion available. Then again, what could be more unbelievable than the fact that people develop out of single amoeba-like cells?"

Journey into No*"thing"*ness

Chapter 7

Why Everything Outside is Really Inside (and may not be there)

*(It is **we** who create the "things" of the outside world because we can only perceive relationships, and these are intangible and void of substance. Lucky us! Physicists tell us this is the stuff outside-- so we are actually tuned in on reality itself!)*

"It is not a question whether we can trust our senses," I told the seminar. "We have to trust them. We have no other choice. They constitute our only windows on the outside world. Of course, this doesn't imply that we have to be naive about the matter."

"What do you mean by 'naive' in this case?" a student asked.

"I'll give you an example," I replied. "There is an old riddle that points up exactly what I mean. It states that a large tree falls in a forest, but there are no creatures around to hear it. The question is whether the tree makes any noise."

The class grinned. "That *is* an old one," the student chuckled. "Naturally there wouldn't be any noise -- just a lot of disorderly pressure waves in the air. But these wouldn't be noise. To be turned into sound they have to be heard. What we hear is only our interpretation of changes in the air pressure waves. It happens in the brain."

"Exactly," I responded. "Now, let's suppose there is a fire in the forest. Is there any heat?"

"None whatever -- only oxidative chemical changes plus increased motion of the surrounding air molecules."

"No bright orange-colored flames?" I enquired.

"No colors of any kind. There would be some changes in the wavelengths of the light. The waves would tend to become longer. But these wouldn't be any color whatever. Color is what happens in our visual system when it receives light of different wavelengths. But the light in itself doesn't have any color."

"You have this down pretty pat," I congratulated him. "So what would you say actually is taking place out there in the forest?"

Now I had him, I thought. He studied for a moment, then admitted, "I don't know."

"A beautiful answer," I laughed. "The truth is *nobody* really knows. As the philosopher Immanuel Kant put it, the things in themselves can never be known. With some exceptions, today's scientists would agree that these 'things in themselves' which we call the outside world, do indeed exist. However, they are probably made up of mere swirling energies of different densities and distributions. That is to say, they are only patterns in energy."

"But we can really see stuff out there!" one of the girls protested. "Isn't that proof that we can know about things outside?"

"It depends on what you mean by the word 'things,'" I replied. "Some 'clumps' of energy are so concentrated, so compacted, we recognize them as different from their surrounds. They become figures against their back-grounds, so to speak. But aside from these differences of patterning, particularly how they contrast at the edges where changes in density occur, there is little else we can say about them. The attributes we depend upon, and which we know them by, don't exist except in our heads. The things themselves are soundless, colorless, shapeless, and without roughness, warmth, taste, or any similar properties. This is the reason animals had to develop senses in the first place. In order to survive they had to adapt to an inorganic world, one almost totally unlike themselves. Some even developed senses we don't have, and their perceived world is different from ours.

It is difficult to comprehend, but the mind can have no direct contact with outer reality. For one thing, it is isolated inside the skull. So there can be nothing inside except perceptions, records of past perceptions called memories, our reactions to them called feelings, and the interrelations between them -- called ideas, concepts, beliefs, and so forth. All are inside.

It follows that there is no possibility of the mind dealing with anything except parts of *itself.* Whether what is seen is actually representative of reality, or whether an idea is true, can only be judged by how consistent it is with other mental constructs already present in memory. In short, we do not see things the way *they* are. We see them the way *we* are. It is illusory to assume that we compare external objects directly, one with another. [1]

This 'unknowability' of things is essentially what Einstein meant when he pointed out that 'physical concepts are free creations of the human mind,' and not something primarily determined by the outside world. Sir Arthur Eddington, another famous physicist, expressed it even more emphatically. He stated that what we know of the physical world is 'entirely abstract,' that it possesses 'no actuality apart from its linkage to the mind.' As he saw it, this restored the mind to its proper place in nature -- a place far more logical than simply looking upon it as some sort of unknown 'complication found in the midst of inorganic nature at a late stage of evolutionary history.' [2]

The idea is not a popular one. Almost everybody is repelled by the thought that he has no outer world separate and apart from this 'highly decorated' representation in his head. The very existence of himself demands that there be a non-self -- the tangible world of 'things' outside. Like all other creatures he must deal with these things outside if he is to survive. And he must have total unwavering confidence in what he sees, hears, and smells. So, Nature devised a means of bridging this chasm between self and non-self.

The mind uses what might be called 'projection.' In actual practice it were as if the senses were projectors. Data coming from the outside are 'highlighted' in the sensory mechanism, and then get projected back outside again! At least that is the way it appears. For example, the charm and loveliness of a girl, the dress she is wearing, etc., all seem to belong to the girl. They are not seen as being some sort of sensory processing in one's head, some assessment we make. But everyone else has his own projector, and some may not see her so! Indeed, a few might even find her homely!

The chair on which I am sitting is not literally in my head. There's not enough room for it. Neither is the book I may be reading. What is sensed is inside *me*, not outside with the chair or book. It is a construct of the mind. Thus, 'I' do not see a flower, nor do 'I' hear a melody. The seeing and hearing are these structures and events themselves. Otherwise, the 'I' becomes the little man who sits inside my skull and evaluates whatever comes in. Perception has to be a *direct* awareness of the patterning of energies from outside. It can't be something coded, something run through a computer, or something which has to be interpreted by a sort of small intracranial alien. Sensory codes, for example, would require decoding.

Admittedly, this distinction is difficult to grasp. But it's crucial to understanding the mind. There is no way in which a person could be inhabited by any 'I' or 'me' separate and apart from the act of knowing. There can be no middle-man between the mind and the outside world. When you see a flash of light, the flash *is* the light. In the same manner, the thinking *is* the thought, and the act of hearing *is* the melody heard. While you are hearing or reading something are you aware of someone doing the hearing or reading? In addition to the events themselves, can you find a listener or reader?

To use still other examples, you can imagine or dream of almost anything. But you are never aware of the dream structures themselves, i.e., how they are constructed in the brain. Similarly, you can remember events of the past. But you have no idea what these molecule-sized memories look like. For all anyone knows, they may not even be separate items. They could be only parts of some continuous structuring process corresponding to experienced time. Certainly this seems to be the way they are recalled. At some point one simply gets transported into the past. Then he travels back toward the present, occasionally taking in side events en route. There are no noticeable gaps. As experienced at least, it is a continuum.

It would seem that during mental activity we are only aware of the action, and not any structures doing the acting. To my way of thinking, this is rather direct evidence that the mind is an energy system in its own right, relatively independent of the brain tissues giving rise to it. If it were not, we would be aware of the constraints imposed by these tissues. Surely we are aware of body parts such as arms or eyes when these move. But more to the point here, it says that the mental activity *is* the experience. This explains why the objects of perception must appear outside. They have to be some-where, and they can't be seen as existing inside.

Our contacts with the outside world occur solely via our senses. They have no easy task. Their duty is to receive and transcribe the *patterning* of the input. This is meant literally. The patterning is kept intact, but is written into energy 'X' used by the brain. Engineers refer to the process as transduction. With one exception, all major senses are what is known as transducers. Does anyone here know which is the exception, which sense picks up patterning directly and does not act as a transducer?"

Nobody offered a guess, so I said, "It's the sense of smell. It is a chemical sense and is actually part of the brain. It has no specialized

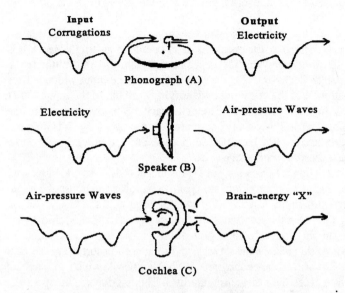

FIGURE 3. The three transducers used when hearing the music printed on a phonograph record: (A) Piezoelectric crystal with needle; (B) Loud-speaker with magnet; and © Cochlea of the inner ear. *Note that the only feature which remains constant throughout the entire procedure is the **pattern**!*

receptor cells like the retina. It consists only of free nerve endings. These respond directly to the *shape* of molecules and transport this pattern-data unaltered to the brain. There are no way-stations or synapses as in other senses.

Some of our most poignant memories are aroused by smell. It is a vestigial chemical sense closely allied with feelings. Being vestigial, there are almost no short-term memories of odors. They are all long-term, permanent, and reached only by recognition. Panoramas of bygone scenes may be visualized. Whole symphonies may be recalled from memory. But it is rare to recall even the simplest of smells. They are immediately recognized, but not so easily brought into awareness and manipulated. They belong to a more primitive world preceding that of words and abstractions. This is why one cannot accurately describe a smell. The best he can do is say it smells 'like' something or other. All creatures except man rely heavily on this primitive sense. In fact, chemoreception was the *original* sense. The new brain quite literally evolved from the olfactory lobes.

But let's get back to vision and hearing. These are highly developed systems. Nonetheless, their basic mode of operation is still the same. It is always the *patterning* which is picked up and faithfully transmitted to the brain. Why? Because this is the only feature of the input which carries information! It is the one unique identifying attribute of the input. Other features are only properties! They can vary, be more or less. But the patterning does not lie on any continuum of 'more or less.' It is unique!. To understand how it happens, suppose we take a quick look at how inorganic transducers manage to do it.

In this slide we see a series of transducers -- devices which pick up patterning (form, organization, etc.) from one source and transcribe it into a different medium, usually some type of energy. In the figure shown, there is a phonograph record depicted at the top. It has been printed with one long spiral groove. In the bottom of this groove there is a continuous sequence of tiny hills, valleys, crags, and what not -- a sort of mechanical pattern. The arm of the phonograph (A) holds a needle which goes up and down as it rides over these irregularities. This produces corresponding pressures on a crystal which, in turn, modulates the flow of electricity in exactly the same proportions. Thus, the pattern in the groove gets written in electricity. Since the two patterns are exactly alike, the crystal is called a transducer.

The modulated (patterned) current now flows to a magnet (B) which vibrates the diaphragm of a loudspeaker in proportion to the 'juice' it receives. This loudspeaker system is another transducer. It takes the pattern carried by the electricity and translates it into a corresponding series of air pressure waves. When these configured air pressure waves reach the ear, a third and very complicated transducer known as the cochlea (C) comes into play. This reproduces the same pattern into energy 'X' used by the brain.

Please note that the only thing remaining constant throughout this entire maze of changes is the *pattern*. It is this patterning or organization which provides us with information. It is our only source of meaningful experience with outer reality. [3] Fortunately, the process is extremely accurate. I shall not speculate at this time about the nature of energy 'X' except to state that I believe it to be almost certainly chemical. For a variety of reasons it can't possibly be the neuroelectric impulse now generally assumed to carry information in living systems."

"Why not?" asked the same student.

"As I mentioned, there are numerous reasons. Most have to do with how the impulse behaves and where it goes. However, the most prominent reason is that the impulse energy is ionic. It is made up of electrically charged atoms. Since the charge always has the same electrical sign, it is mutually self-repellent. All parts (ions) push against all other parts. This means it can't be modulated to carry information. The best it can do is upset the ionic balance on some other neuron with a still different charge. Thus, the impulse is not 'conducted.' It is only a spreading electrical disturbance. Any signal fidelity would be almost zero. [4]

By contrast, everything we know about the mind and senses testifies that their operations are exactly the opposite. They are not scattered and chaotic. They are extremely accurate, possess high fidelity, and suggest attractional rather than repellent energies. Attraction makes for organization. It connects things, holds them together, and makes for growth.

The operation of attractional energies in vision was probably first noted by the Gestalt psychologist, Kurt Koffka. [5] But they are readily demonstrated in virtually all perceptual processes. For example, whenever we look at an unorganized array of items we tend to see them as grouped into various clusters. They appear related according to how close together they are. Those closer to each other are seen as belonging to the same group. We classify stars into constellations for this reason. Such grouping effects are extremely common and are attributed to the attraction which arises between items in the sensory display. We Gestalt people called it the 'law of proximity.' Here, I'll show you what Koffka meant by proximity and attraction.

Look at the following Figure 4. This slide contains three shapes. The middle one (B) looks like a tile-work of nine squares. But suppose the inside lines are moved closer to the outside ones as in the right-hand figure (C). It is then seen as a picture-frame. Contrariwise, if the inside lines are moved closer together as shown at the left (A), the figure becomes a cross. All parts of the figures otherwise remain the same in each case. One must therefore conclude that their grouping is due to mutual attraction of parts. As the lines come closer together their inter-attraction intensifies, as with magnets.

Elementary organization of this type occurs constantly in all the senses. It implies that attractional energy is used to organize what is perceived. It provides a figure-ground effect by 'pulling' the figure together. Much the same action occurs when the image from the left eye fuses with that of the right eye to produce depth perception. And in this case the attraction can not only be felt, but has even been measured. [6]

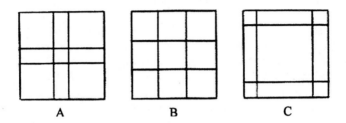

FIGURE 4. The effect of attractional energies on what is seen
as figure against ground.

In final analysis, all perception is perception of *relationships* like
those existing between the lines of Figure 4. Reasons for this conclusion
will be given later. The point here is that you can't have an apparent
relationship between items that repel each other -- as would happen with
impulse ions. By definition, any relating has to be a matter of attraction.
It has to form a bond, else it doesn't relate. There is no such thing as a
negative bond!.

Sensory relations giving rise to visual figures, are due to differences
in the immediate input. We are aware of them as contrast effects, and they
occur largely at contours. If no differences exist the input is uniform and
nothing is perceived. This is a general rule and is not restricted to the
visual perception of contours. A somewhat different example happens
with one's experience when riding an elevator. When the ON button is
pushed, you notice the movement upwards. This is the difference of
acceleration. Once in motion, however, there is no sensation of movement
because velocity is uniform. There are no changes to sense. In fact, the
most common measurements in psychology are thresholds, known as 'just
noticeable differences' or JNDs.

Constancy, homogeneity, uniformity, and similar conditions do not
register. There is no change, no patterning to be detected. A whistle blown
steadily for a protracted period soon disappears from awareness. Not the
stimulus, but the *change* in the stimulus is what provides information.
This was mentioned earlier when discussing curiosity. The senses react
to changes in the input. But changes are not things! They are *differences*
between things or events. And they are represented in the sensory system

as intangible energy relations. This is quite fortunate. Otherwise, perceptions could not be representative of the outside world made up of just such intangible energy relationships. [7]

Most perceived relations are in motion. Gestalt psychology began with Max Wertheimer's demonstration that translatory motion can be seen even though nothing of a corresponding physical nature exists. [8] We take for granted that there is no actual motion in the motion pictures we watch. Physically, there is nothing but a long series of still shots. The motion occurs in our visual systems. It is a product of elaborate ever-shifting clusters of relations. Being attractional, these are what bond the action together.

What is recorded in the eyes is precisely what the stimulus conditions dictate. "Sensory perception is *veridical*," Egon Brunswik used to say. You can trust it completely. The brain may juggle its input data -- even misinterpret it totally. But the data themselves are dependable. The senses don't lie to the brain.

By and large, the brain's interpretation is also veridical. Let's suppose we are watching an old cowboy movie. Occasionally the wheels of the stage-coach will be seen to revolve *backwards!* Such visual anomalies are evidence that the relating activity occurs in the retina with extreme rapidity. The resulting images, fully organized, are then faithfully transmitted to the cortex for recognition. There they are interpreted *literally.* The significant fact is that the interpretation is irrational in this case! Were the perceived images somehow assembled cortically (as commonly assumed), the wheels would have been seen to continue forward! The mind is consistent. It would not concoct something contrary to common sense! The same argument applies to virtually all so-called visual illusions -- such as seen in Figure 5.

When operating normally, the cortex accepts and interprets data as they are reported to be, even though it may be *aware* that the interpretation is false! In brief, our visual pattern transmission has extremely high fidelity. What we see is *not* primarily a construct of cortical processes. Karl Stumpf (1848-1936) contended that the study of sensory relations was so important it should be made a science in its own right!

Nonetheless, it is commonly thought that we Gestalt people were the only proponents of such wild ideas. Not so! Both Ernst Mach and William James had previously argued that we perceive relations directly. And more recently, K. S. Lashley continued to insist that relations were the fundamentals of perception, and that they could not be broken down into non-relational processes. [9]

One fascinating sidelight of all this is that it involves a major premise of relativity theory. Indeed, the word relativity means 'relatedness,' and perception of relations is the *only* position compatible with the theory. Long before Einstein, Wilhelm Wundt, the founder of experimental psychology, observed that nothing is ever seen in an absolute sense. [10] It is always apprehended relative to other things. In brief, it is the differences or relations between them which become known. The psychophysical principle called the Weber-Fechner law is essentially a statement of this point. It says that equal *ratios* appear equal psychologically -- *not* equal magnitudes. [11]

Time and time again experiments have shown that what we really perceive is a complex or 'cluster' of relations. In short, we perceive *patterns*. [12] And just as often, it has been ignored. There is a logical reason for this avoidance of obvious fact. People are stuck with the conviction that they see 'things,' but not space. Nonetheless, one can't have an 'is' without an 'isn't', a figure without a ground, or a *some*thing without a *no*thing. They are two sides of the same coin. To have 'A' one has to accept 'Not A.' There is a common quip that time is what keeps everything from happening all at once. Similarly, space is what keeps everything from being all the same thing. 'Thingness' and space are not mutually exclusive except when we theorize. In the real (and perceived) world they interact.

To illustrate what is meant, the so-called empty space in and around any simple drawing will become structured by the contours of the drawing. These create stress gradients tending to pattern the surrounding areas in a very predictable fashion. In the above figures taken from Rausch, [13] three parallelograms illustrate the argument. In each case extension of the longer lines would intersect the external dots. However , the dots appear to be displaced in the direction to which the figure is skewed. Figure C, not skewed, shows no such displacement. Over fifty years ago I measured the effects of this structuring of 'empty' space and found it to be very like what happens in the fields set up by electric currents. [14]

It is simple enough to prove that one sees open space despite arguments that the retina is not stimulated by it. Were it not visible, one would find it impossible to visualize billiard shots, aim guns, or catch a pitched ball. Moreover, this ability is *inherent*. It is not learned. A feigned poke at the eye of a baby chick will bring about avoidance responses. And the human infant will react defensively to what appears to be an impending collision. Both demonstrate an innate ability to perceive

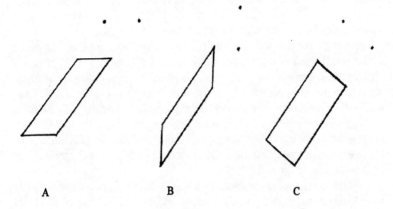

FIGURE 5. How contours distort surrounding space.

translatory relations over presumably empty space. [15] As seen, at least, life is a movie

Few, if any, have bothered to explain the logic behind this perception of the relations which arise from physical differences or change. To highlight their importance, therefore, suppose we consider some elementary physics. Temperature differences cause heat to flow from a hot to a cold body. Pressure differences are responsible for the flow of water in pipes. And electricity only moves when there is a difference in potential. In all instances, the differences may be written as ratios, i.e., *relations*. And I could go on and on. However, you get the idea. All movement of energy, whatever it may be, occurs only by reason of differences. It is a general principle relating to the second law of thermo. And it may be the most important principle of life. In the biological world, much as in the physicochemical, absolute constancy is absolute quiescence -- *death*. Like our sensory systems, life itself exists only by reason of its many differences.

Allow me to give an example how perceived differences or relations influence behavior. Assume you are in the forest mentioned earlier. You are standing perfectly still, making no noise. A deer may approach you, perhaps even nuzzle you if the wind is in the right direction. But if you make the slightest move, or if the wind shifts, the deer is gone like a shot!

While you were immobile, you were merely part of his environment. But when you moved it produced an intensity difference in his visual field, a gradient of change as it were, and this alerted him to danger.

Reactions of this sort are not peculiar to deer. Nor are they restricted to vision. They pertain to all creatures and all senses. Awareness of change has enormous survival value. As noted when discussing curiosity, change is our sole source of information. It is food for the mind -- the stuff of patterning. Very often it signals life, friends or enemies. Homogeneity, equality, constancy, or uniformity tell us nothing. Differences provide the most critical features of life. It is fortunate that the organism can perceive these differences directly. This brings us to our next slide. *(See Figure 6.)*

When one looks at the two chairs shown below, they are immediately recognized as having the same pattern or shape.. But they are of different sizes. Both consist of the same number of different segments. Two of these segments are labeled in each case. The contention here is that the chairs are seen to have the same shape *solely* because $X/Y = x/y$ for all dimensions. In other words, all corresponding features of the chairs would result in equal ratios. The total of such relations is what provides them with their identity of form. Thus, in addition to the black/white contrast which enables us to see them, we have to be seeing something else not physically given. This something else is their *relative proportions*, i.e., their interrelations (ratios). These constitute their form. The mind recognizes the chairs as being the same. The recognition is rational (by ratio). This is what rational means.

One's ability to perceive forms is innate and demonstrable shortly after birth. It is not 'reasoned out' from contour data. Even insects recognize form. So it has to be perceived directly. Relatedness of this type explains why the whole is more than the sum of its parts. The whole is parts *plus* organization, and this *plus* is what we recognize. If one were to of mind might have their beginnings when an aggregation of items becomes 'trans*formed*' into an organized whole. Why? Because this is what provides it with identity and makes it an entity in its own right. It becomes a 'thing,' and is seen as such. In short, it acquires the inorganic equivalent of a 'self.'

Again, this central feature of perception has tremendous survival value. It enables us to see shape or form independently of size. Were this not the case, the enemy seen at a distance (smaller) would not be recognized as the same enemy seen closer (larger). The child who learned to read with one size of print would be unable to read with print of a

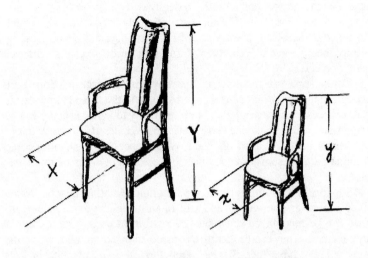

FIGURE 6. Identical shapes have the same relatedness.

different size. The melody learned in one key would go unrecognized in a different key or tempo. And understanding spoken words would be virtually impossible. Voices differ in tone, inflection, tempo, and similar secondary characteristics. In other words, we would be stuck with *absolutes*! We could not survive in a relative world!

Such simple issues seem childishly obvious and biologically crucial. So it is not surprising that perception of proportionality has been experiment-ally verified countless times in a variety of ways -- even using creatures such as fish! [16] In the jargon of psychology it is known as transposition. (Don't ask me why!) It is integral with the perceiving process itself. Unfortunately, however, there is no earthly way in which it can be explained by existing theory. The reason? Because it demon-strates that the shape or form of a thing (its organization), constitutes a direct and immediate experience.

All other properties of a stimulus may be varied except its form, and it will still be recognized. Vary its form, on the other hand, and it becomes strange. Thus, form is retained in memory independently of other features such as size, color, brightness, or substance formed. Attributes of this latter sort are secondary. In short, what I am saying is that *form can exist independently of substance or size!* Otherwise, it could not be remembered and recognized independently. It is *not* a property of any thing. It is the 'thing' itself! This is an extremely important point which was noted by Meinong as early as 1891. [17] And please, let's not quibble over its being merely 'perceived' form. Our entire world is what we merely perceive.

Further proof of the argument is shown by the fact that forms are recognized though the perceived patterns come to the brain from entirely different sensory systems. Patterns presented by touch or hearing can be recognized visually, and vice versa. One can even identify numbers traced by a finger on the skin of his back! What conceivable meaning could stimulus parts or sensory codes possibly possess in cases of this latter sort?

Suppose one considers auditory perception. Melodies may be 'transposed' however one wishes and still retain their identity. Once-heard tunes can be recognized regardless of instrument used, tempo, key, or other features. They can be identified despite the fact that all the original notes and rests have been changed. Only the *interrelations* need be kept constant. Strange as it may seem, these are what constitute the melody. They are the *pattern*. Notes are not 'parts' of a melody. They have no significance except for the role they play as nodal points indicating changes in the relative patterning. [18] It is the patterning (form) itself which is perceived, remembered, and recognized. This is the material with which the mind works!

Like depth perception and many other vital phenomena, transposition is largely bypassed by present-day theorists. It is inconsistent with their theory. It requires that the senses operate in terms of patterning rather than volleys of impulses. The experimental work of Gestalt psychologists, gathered over half a century, is almost wholly ignored because of its incompatibility with preconceived opinion! And I might add that there is not a shred of evidence for the opinion. It is strictly assumption.

Our current hangup on the separateness of 'things,' including our urge to reduce everything to common denominators, is almost pathological. It means that we miss (or misinterpret) much of the real world about us. This world is made up of relations, not things, bits, and pieces. There is abundant physical evidence that material things themselves consist almost exclusively of just such relations.

So much for how the house rolls dice! I have a story to tell. It is a travelogue based on the question whether any 'thing' really *does* exist in the world outside. The setting is Columbia University where I did graduate study in an era now long gone and far away. Personae are Professor John Dewey and graduate students. Curtain!"

Chapter 8

Strange Perspectives from Inner Space

(The exotic nature of reality -- why the existence of everything depends upon our perspective, and how the mind organizes the outer world so it can become known.)

Wags from the more ivied halls of academia are fond of noting that the campus of Columbia University is no more than an extension of New York City streets. Looking across this paved expanse, one can easily bring to mind that venerable and arcane philosopher, John Dewey. He would be wearing a grey knit sweater decorated with spark holes from his pipe. A steam locomotive is envisioned: step-puff, step-step, puff-puff. But let's go inside. It is a warm Spring day and a light breeze ruffles the papers on his desk. Dewey lays his pipe on the papers, points to it, and asks a student, "What is that?"

Flustered student: "Why it's a pipe of course, Dr. Dewey."

"Oh no it isn't," responds Dewey. "It's a paper-weight." He then picks up the pipe, stands it erect in the window, and lowers the sash.

"Now what is it?"

This time the student is not so easily trapped. "It's a window prop."

"Correct! It's a pipe only when someone smokes it. A thing *is* what it does. Things don't function or *have* functions. They *are* the functions. Remove their activity, their usage, and they are as meaningless as a clod of dirt. In fact, if one could immobilize their atoms and molecules, eliminate their activity, they wouldn't even exist."

Was Dewey overstating the case? Are we simply hung up on Gertrude Stein's rose? Is a pipe is a pipe is a pipe is a pipe? Does my screwdriver really become a crowbar when I use it to pry open a paint can, then turn into a stylus when I use it to scratch a line, or a chisel when chipping off paint? Is there no actual "screwdriverness" except when screws are being driven? In brief, wherein lies the identity of a thing -- anything? What about shape, the *form* of a screwdriver or pipe? Certainly this is what we use to recognize them. Isn't this unique?

"Well, yes and no," Dewey would answer. Their shapes make them uniquely identifiable as objects. But they would still be meaningless without knowing what they are used for. Meaning derives from function. With enough difficulty one could drill a hole in the screwdriver and use it as a pipe. It would then actually *be* a pipe.

And don't forget orientation say the quantum physicists. Every time we attend to something, we interact with it. That is why a form depends on how we look at it. Tip a square up on one corner and it is still a square geometrically. But to us it becomes a lozenge or a diamond. It appears different from a square because we peer differently at it. Pictures are notoriously difficult to recognize if hung upside down.

Shape, form, patterning, orderliness, and organization are all related. All are recognized, and people agree about them. All of them are of extreme importance to both physical and living matter. But not one of them can be defined or measured except in terms of size or some other superficial property. Neither can they be analyzed in terms of their parts. Four straight lines of the same length, scattered randomly, do not constitute a square. As will be demonstrated later, the squareness resides wholly in their inter-relations, one part with another. The same is true for the shapes of all things, for all things have some degree of organization -- else they can't exist as things. Given such facts, how is it possible to define 'form'?

When trying to "eff" such ineffable questions, one fact becomes obvious. We are hamstrung by our individual perspective of things. If not, the square would still be the same as the lozenge. This perspective varies with our position, size, and possibly even our mood. Thus, it might help to consult with the well-known Alice of Wonderland fame. Alice was able to get around this perspective problem, at least so far as size was concerned. You may recall that she had a mushroom with some rather remarkable properties. When she ate from one side of it, she grew larger. And when she nibbled from the other side she grew smaller. Presumably, the mushroom (and fortunately also her clothes) changed size with her.

Suppose I borrow this mushroom from Alice. On my way back to class at Schermerhorn Hall, I pause on the corner of Amsterdam Avenue and leisurely watch the traffic. Absentmindedly, I take a bite out of the mushroom. It happens to be the reduction side, so I immediately begin to shrink. But there is no way I can recognize that I am becoming smaller. Since everything is judged relative to me, what I really see are the radical changes now occurring on Amsterdam Avenue. The sharp edge of the curb is no longer sharp. It is becoming rounded. The smooth surface of the sidewalk is no longer smooth. It is becoming lumpy with small hills and valleys. Across the street the intricate design of the facade on the larger building is growing more and more vague and shapeless. From this reduced point of view I am unable to see the total, much less recognize the relationships between features of the building.

Even more remarkable perhaps, is the fact that everything seems to be slowing down! What was once a busy corner is gradually becoming motionless. Automobiles have enlarged to such extent that distances between front and rear bumpers appear interminable. They crawl along so slowly they are little more than harmless parts of the landscape. The pigeon in the sky (an immense dark area), is a frightful apparition in slow motion. The massive wings scarcely move. Time itself has ground almost to a halt!

I realize that I am now in the world of insects, the largest class of animal life on earth. There are more species of insects than of all other animals combined. These are creatures possessing a vast array of sizes, shapes and habits. And it suddenly occurs to me that their actual life-spans may be just as long as those of larger creatures like ourselves. [19] Since time enlarges with space, lifetime would have to expand also. But enough of this time question. On this once busy street humans are now few and far between. Even when their outlines can be recognized, they float ponderously above, almost as unchanging as the clouds they resemble.

This insect world is a dangerous one, possibly more so than the legendary world of dinosaurs. Gargantuan ants grapple with one another, each some three stories high. The noise is deafening. Everywhere large ferocious monsters are on the prowl. Many are carnivorous: here the mantis, there the spider. And since I am not armor-plated like the huge beetles clanking by, I can only escape by taking another bite out of the mushroom and shrinking even further -- hopefully out of the size range seen as prey.

In a moment or so I find myself on a minute crystal embedded in the dusty matrix of cement. Ordinarily, it would have been microscopic. But being currently down-sized, it now looms on all sides as a massive smooth crag with sharp edges and precipitous heights. I glance about me. It is truly a desolate scene. There are no buildings, autos, insects, or anything else I can recognize. All familiar shapes are gone. They belonged to a world which no longer exists. And strangely enough, all had vanished in the same way. First they became enormously extended and less dense, followed by transparency, then disappeared entirely. Obviously they had consisted only of relations -- and these relations were now invisible.

It is almost impossible to believe that I am still on the same street corner. In the most real sense, the world I once knew has become totally non-existent! All those familiar things owed their being solely to their patterning as this had been seen by me. They had been products of organization, not "stuff," but the *patterning* of stuff. And since they depended on *my* perspective, they had also been creations of my mind.

It is quite eerie here on the corner of Amsterdam (if that is where I still am) -- almost frightening. Nonetheless, I tell myself, material objects must exist! Things can't simply vanish into nothingness. They had merely become tenuous, diminished in density until imperceptible. But what I missed most was their patterning, their form. With it of course, had gone all functional aspects such as use. And this is what had made them meaningful. Are they still present in the larger world from which I came? Yes, I must assume they are still present for others in that world. But as for me, they are imperceptible, unknowable, and even unimaginable.

Perhaps Dr. Dewey had actually *under*stated the case. In final analysis it would appear that all things are events -- not just at the atomic level, but at *all* levels! Except for the roles they play in our lives (their functions), what we call "things" may be of doubtful existence. Our permanent memories are molecular. But we can't find them, and we know them only by their functions. Now I was really in a mental bog! Was it possible that there is no such thing as matter, no "stuff" which we consider organized or patterned? Could it be that only the intangible relations exist?

I recalled a Swiss physicist who had declared that the scale of observation actually *creates* what we see. As our microscope focusses on a piece of rope we note a succession of spiral strands, long irregular fibers, plant cells, and finally cellular organelles. If our visual world were microbial like mine now is, how could we know of the rope? How could we say anything about it? Does it indeed exist in any meaningful sense?

All such speculation is vaporous, I tell myself. Surely thingness or reality must lie somewhere besides in the mind. You can't have organization without something to organize. Or can you? There was only one way to answer this question. I had to go within matter itself! I had to become even smaller. The mushroom! Another nibble and I began to feel myself sink into the crystal which slowly opens beneath my feet.

Again, I am in the midst of order. And what fantastic order it is! Here in the crystal organization is so absolute and monotonously exact it is stupefying! Everywhere the view is the same in the same repetitive fashion. Endless corridors extend between rows of atoms carefully aligned. This is obviously the molecular world, I muse. The smallest living things have long since vanished. Even as I sank into the crystal I watched a huge phlegmatic protozoan become increasingly larger and more tenuous. And finally, it also changed into a gas cloud and was gone. Like everything else, it seemed to be only relationships, organization -- certainly nothing solid.

The rigid accuracy of this molecular realm, totally fixed and completely predictable, quickly becomes maddening. It is far more than can be stomached comfortably. Again, I felt I had to get out! Not much is left of my mushroom. But I take another small bite. And sure enough, down I go once more! Upon regaining my composure I glance hastily about. At last! I am in the final depot on the line! It is the atomic world! But it looks like nothing so much as an explosion in a warehouse full of Christmas tree ornaments. Objects of different size, shape, and color are flying every which way with no rhyme or reason! There is no organization or predictability at all! What a difference!

Going from one extreme to the other induces stress, I realize. So I find myself a seat on a large slow-moving neutron (to avoid getting electrocuted) and mull over the situation. Everything I see is unbelievably opposed to the exact order of the molecular world. It makes no sense -- like stepping from the Louvre into Bedlam, or going from a symphony to a boiler factory!

Just then, a deep sepulchral voice booms out of the confusion. "Yo! -- You there!"

To say I was startled would be the understatement of all time. "Me? Who. . . who is it?"

Back comes the entombed voice: "I am the god of unformed matter. My soul is eternity!" [20]

"What do you want of me?"

"I want to look at that mushroom you have been munching."

"Here!" I extend my hand and the mushroom promptly vanishes.

"Aha! Just as I thought!" the voice chortles. "It is hallucinatory -- one of those that produce the narcotic psilocybin. No wonder your subatomic perceptions look like a fireworks display! Here, let me help you sober up a bit. Then you can see this world as it really is. It is what you people call the 'geometrodynamic viewpoint.'"

There was a snapping sound much as if made by fingers, followed by a moment of disorientation. The neutron upon which I had been sitting suddenly disappears from under me. I pick myself up and look around. But all I can now see is a vast emptiness of extremely thin liquid. It is something like a cross between fog and fluid -- and it extends everywhere.

"What is this material?" I ask.

"It is not material," the voice responds. "It is Urstoff or ylem. It has also been called ether. But a more accurate phrase would be latent energy. I use it to *form*ulate matter. After all, I *am* the god of unformed matter. You want to see a proton?"

Out of curiosity I nodded, and a finger descended to swirl a tidy little whirlpool in the Urstoff. There was something odd about it. Now I saw what it was. It didn't seem to slow down. It kept right on spinning!

"And here's an anti-proton." Another small whirlpool was set spinning in the opposite direction. "And a neutron." This one was spun at right angles to the others. (Remember -- we were in a volume of the Urstoff.)

"And while we are at it, let's add a lightwave." A slight dab created a ripple which spread continuously outward and kept right on spreading.

"If it weren't for this Urstoff," he mused, "that lightwave wouldn't have anything to wave in, would it? Magnetic fields would have nothing to bend or distort, and there couldn't be any gravity at all! The reason the lightwaves continue and the whirlies keep spinning is that there is nothing to slow them down, no friction. Friction is a property of matter or densely packed energy. It doesn't exist down here. And the energy itself, regardless how it looks, is only motion in the Urstoff.

Heat is a good example of what I mean. It's a term for the motion of molecules. When the motion speeds up or slows down, you say things get hot or cold. You admit that matter is a function of temperature, and that heat makes the difference between solid, fluid, and gas. And you also admit that heat is only motion. But for some reason or other, you can't see anything fundamental about motion. A equals B, and B equals C, but A doesn't seem to equal C! That's not very rational, is it?" [21]

He tapped a little whirly called a photon and it went spinning merrily away. "See," he said, "no friction. That's why it acts like a particle."

"But I thought light was considered to be both wave and particle," I commented.. "How is it possible to explain something like that?"

He chuckled. "You mean *they* can't explain it. So they are stuck with a paradox. But actually, it's very simple. Suppose I did something to interrupt that whirly called a photon. It would uncurl or unwind itself. Then it would be a ripple like honest waves are supposed to be. If it hit an obstacle, though, it might curl up again. That's how one turns into the other.

As you can see, this Urstoff is pretty handy -- explains almost everything. Whirlies can be fashioned or put into motion any way I wish. They can be made big or small, and spun in any direction at any speed. That's why people are running around sorting through hundreds of different so-called particles." He paused, then chuckled somewhat louder. "Just wait till they try finding particles that correspond to those mile-long radio waves! That will be funny to watch!

Oh -- something else," he added. "If you look closely at that whirly called an electron, you'll see that the edges sort of fade out and disappear in the Urstoff. It creates a stress pattern referred to as a field effect. If large numbers of them were spun in the same direction, the field would extend well out into the Urstoff. Then it would be called an electromagnetic field. We make magnets this way. Large lumps of matter do much the same thing except it's called gravity. These stress patterns can't be seen, but they're everywhere. They don't have any mass, so they don't classify as matter. And since they don't do anything, they are not functions. They are action at a distance. That is why your physicists are often uncomfortable with them."

Fascinating! I told myself. But I wanted to be sure I understood it. "Let's return to the electron, may we?"

"Of course." He used his finger to twirl another, then said, "Look at it closely."

I bent over and stared at it.

"Do you see anything floating around in the current?"

"All I see is this little vortex in the Urstoff."

"Naturally -- there's no particle there! As a result, your quantum physicists have to describe electrons as energy blurs which exist everywhere they could possibly be at the time. They are not 'things.' They are events! Nothing but the motion exists!" [22]

"Let me see if I have all this straight, may I? First, there is this Urstoff, ether, latent-energy, or whatever. It is non-material, almost zero density, but is capable of acquiring patterning or form to become matter. Secondly, there is the motion or energy itself. And this is what does the shaping or organizing. Given enough motion, the Urstoff turns into matter. What else? Did I miss something?"

He stared at me for a moment, then growled, "You certainly did!

You are just like everyone else! You ignored the form or patterning. It's insulting! I *am* the god of unformed matter -- so why do you think I'm here? Form can't appear out of nowhere. Motion doesn't organize matter, and things don't 'acquire' patterning. Motion is only energy. It goes where the pattern demands -- much as when water spills on the ground.

I don't know why, but everyone seems to either ignore it or get it backwards! They assume that organization is a property of what they call 'things.' Actually, it is the *form*-ative nature of organization that gives existence and identity to all these so-called things. Take a look at diamonds and graphite. Two more different substances don't exist. One is hard, translucent, and used to cut objects. The other is soft, opaque, and used to lubricate them. Nonetheless, both are pure carbon. Only their differences of organization make them what they are!

Organization or form provides identity with endless variety. It is said to be the only property of things which can be varied infinitely, and in each variation be unique. That is because it is *not* a property of things. Things are a property of it! No one shape is any number of times the shape of anything else. Form cannot be added to, subtracted from, multiplied or divided. Unless it is very simple, it can't even be described.

Why do you think the ancient Greeks placed such emphasis upon form? Form is the essence of existence. It is mind-stuff. It can't be measured or broken down into common elements for analysis. It has no common elements. Forget the ridiculous idea that everything can be broken down into smaller and smaller parts. Parts, particles, subparticles (quarks), subquarks -- and what then? No matter how small, if they are to be considered particles there has to be space between them. This means they should be divided still further. There's no end to such thinking. No wonder their quest is elusive. It is illusory!

It is this tinker-toy outlook which is childish. It is backwards -- the cart before the horse. Since the whole is always more than the sum of its parts, why don't people try to find out what this *more* is? Instead, they divide, fractionate, and pulverize. And the further they divide, the further they get from reality. Organ, organism, and organization even have the same root meaning. Take them apart and they are destroyed. They are the 'more' that is referred to. They exist only because of their togetherness, the outer aspect of which is their form. Change the size, color, duration or intensity of almost anything you see, and it will still be recognized. But change its organization or form, however slightly, and it becomes strange.

In simpler stable states, organization allows for the continuing existence of matter. Disorganize it and you have an atomic explosion.

When present as serial patterning it conveys information. When occurring in music it is tone and harmony. Make it disorderly and it becomes noise. At the level of biomolecules it is always the shape or form of the molecule which determines its functions. Given a large complex of such organization, it can even be called mind! It definitely is not a property of matter. No way! Matter, living or otherwise, is a product of organization. It is always emergent and always *form*ative. It comes first because it provides the necessary frame-work for everything else!"

I felt like I had just flunked my orals! But gadzooks! Why get so upset? Why the tirade? Gods are supposed to be cool and collected! However, it did start me to thinking. Can mind actually be equated with emergent organization? Or is organization merely a property of whatever is being organized -- something contributed by the individual when things are perceived or thought about? If this latter is true, as virtually everyone seems to believe, then why is organization so critical and so utterly different from all other aspects of matter? And if it should turn out to be only a property of 'things,' and these things themselves are only mental constructs, are we not back where we started?

So much for the geometrodynamic viewpoint. Does it represent a true picture of the subatomic world? Who can say? There is no way of testing any of it, including the orthodox view. If you want the truth, we don't know. Not knowing is something few theorists like to admit. It seems degrading to them. If they don't know, they usually rationalize. But there is nothing derogatory about admitting you don't know. It used to be called honesty!

Our fanciful episode must be discontinued at this point. The *Perils of Pauline* come to mind. In this silent movie serial of a bygone day, one session ends with the train rushing down on our heroine. And there she lies, helplessly strapped to the railroad tracks! Our situation is not so perilous as Pauline's. Nonetheless, a change of venue is advised to avoid bogging down in the mental mud of some very abstruse subatomic physics, and possibly even the Big Bang!

Whatever the theory espoused, one fact seems fairly certain. Material objects are themselves simply energy networks consisting of spatial relationships or force-fields. These, in turn, can only be Urstoff of one sort or another. Matter, when analyzed, is over 99.999+ percent space-time or Urstoff. The perceived solidity of things is even flimsier than the circle of light seen when a lantern is whirled in the dark. Right now we are standing with both feet planted firmly on no*thing*ness. Fortunately, the feet are made up of about the same magnitude event-structures.

Suppose we had nibbled from the other side of Alice's mushroom. This would have enlarged us and changed our perspective in entirely different ways. Space-time is wholly relative. There is nothing uniquely "true" about our present position, size or duration. If we were enlarged, what we now know as "things" would take on many of the same features currently ascribed to atomic and molecular events. We already know numerous large scale rhythms that exist. Some electromagnetic waves are miles long, and some astronomical pulsations are centuries apart. As we grew larger, these would become ever shorter in periodicity (wavelength), and their intensity would increase proportionately. A wholly new and strange world would doubtlessly come into being.

Organization and rhythm are merely different ways of looking at the same phenomena. Structure is the geometry of function, so to speak. In a larger world, therefore, shapes and objects would emerge out of what are now invisible and non-material energy relations and their force fields. The seemingly stable spiral nebulae would be seen for what they may well be, viz., rapidly swirling vortices of fiery energy. A totally new and different world would emerge. One should ponder such possibilities before categorically denying the existence of minds or other structures beyond our limited purview, and this is true whether they are great or small!

In the everyday world which we experience, test in the lab, and can verify, nature is rational. It is sane and orderly because it can be described by rules and thus predicted. But where the lower and upper boundaries of this world fade into the subatomic and cosmic realms, one can neither experience nor test anything. As a result, we may be startled to find electrons described as mere energy blurs which extend everywhere they might possibly be. Creating even greater mental stress is the idea of an infinitely small point of something-or-other exploding to create the imsense universe we observe. (And presumably, it is still flying apart!)

This theoretical "groping-for-answers" would make up an almost endless list. It would include a world filled with space bubbles, and one that is a ball of yarn (string theory), a mere inch of which weighs billions of tons! Still further: a universe ruptured in various spots with black holes, worm holes, and space-tunnels. And at CERN, in France, deep holes are being dug in the earth. What are they looking for? Believe it or not, they are trying to find mass! I am reminded of a statement by Karl Pribram. [23] He said, in effect, that looking for the mind by digging into the brain is like looking for gravity by digging into the earth. And there they are, busy digging for it!

It is truly awesome to realize that some of these concepts may even turn out to be correct! One can only take comfort in the fact that they can't all be right. In any case, they provide something to chew on when my own speculations seem indigestible. In the meantime, many of them evoke large palpitating blobs of queasy questions. For example, using the indeterminate and chaotic model said to prevail at the subatomic level, how did the transition to the next higher level occur? Molecular and multimolecular matter at least, have an astonishing degree of orderliness and predictability. Question: whence came all this order and exactitude?

Along with everything else, there continues to remain the ancient mystery of organization itself. Terminology is particularly confusing -- possibly because of the variety of aspects and/or synonyms available. Orderliness, patterning, symmetry, "goodness of form," rhythm, harmony, and similar terms all seem to describe similar phenomena. At least, they have to be highly related. All appear to possess a coherence of parts as if purposefully fitted together, a belongingness of one feature with another.

Structures of this sort are extremely important to all aspects of life. They are readily recognized and people agree about them. But they are also quite intangible and currently beyond scientific definition or measurement. What is perhaps most surprising is the fact that these are exactly the same attributes ascribed to what we call *mind!*. It also is intangible, orderly, synchronized, and currently beyond scientific definition or analysis.

Now, here comes the real poser. It hinges on the seemingly wild conjecture that organization may actually *be* mind! Question: can organization or form, as we know it, exist independently and without some medium or stuff which is organized or formed? In other words, is it only an attribute of things, or the other way around? Perhaps the "thingness" is an attribute of organization!

Current theory says things exist, but that organization does not. Relations between things, as well as those between their so-called parts, are said to be products of the mind -- imaginary. They say this even though it can be proved that we see them! Can it be that they have all this in reverse? Perhaps our perceived reality consists solely of these intangible, but nonetheless perceptible relations, and what we call things are only figure-ground effects provided by our visual system. It is true that vision is very faithful. But it is only one of our senses, and all must be coordinated or kept in register. Inconsistencies among the senses often alert us to check things out. And when we do we sometimes discover that the things we saw actually were not there! [24]

Things seem to exist. Can organization or form also exist independently, in and of itself? Certainly it exists (persists) independently in our memories. This was recognized by Meinong a hundred years ago. It is demonstrated by the facts of transposition described earlier. Memories are molecular matter. And if it exists independently in mnemonic matter, why not in other matter? We have no qualms whatever about attributing independence and objectivity to the complexes of relations we call physical objects. And these are almost wholly Urstoff!

When considering whether organization might *be* mind, don't picture some company personnel chart, distribution of tools in the garage, or other simple instances of orderly arrangement. Instead, think of the symmetrical occurrence of our body muscles, the cathedral of Chartres, the intricate compositions of Chopin, or some of the classical art of ancient Greece. Such structures often require great amounts of time and effort in their development. Does it not seem feasible that they might retain some residual of that time and effort? Given enough complexity, could not some of this creativity become transformed into the structures so created? If we noticed something of this sort in a desert, would we not immediately recognize that mind had been operative? And if so, is not mind still there to be recognized? If not, then what is it we are identifying?

To create something is to give form to thought -- to add substance to certain features of the mind, thus enabling them to be recognized by the senses. "Things" themselves are merely personal creations used to classify and organize the inner world. People agree about them simply because the basic processes of different brains are alike. All evidence and logic point to the fact that outside the mind there is nothing except differences in the density and distribution of the surrounding energy goo. It is invalid to argue that organization doesn't exist because it is intangible. People equate existence (being) with material (mass). Everything gets weighed in with a scale. If it has zero weight, it is either hallucinatory or some otherworldly "spirit." Indeed, the very word "immaterial" means worthless or of no consequence.

Materialism of this brand devalues the most important features of our lives. The whole of our mental existence, our ideals, goals, and emotions are all insubstantial. The same is true of our sensory links with the outer world -- the images seen, the sounds heard, or the smells that make us hungry. None have any weight or identifiable density. The mind itself is largely "immaterial." Even some of the highly-touted particles found by physicists have no mass. And in last analysis, those large tangible objects we handle are equally devoid of substance. So organization doesn't have to be a material entity. Like everything else worthwhile, it is *meta-material.*

One might take a moment to consider still other nebulous thoughts. Suppose we admit that organization and form *can* exist separate and apart from the physical objects with which they are identified. One then wonders whether the mind (being organization) might not be able to exist without the brain structures in which it is housed. And if you are still able to follow this far-out train of thought, the same logic assumes that any given mind, yours or mine, might be simply part of some still larger complex. After all, life is organized into just such multiple tiers of complexity. In this latter case, we encounter the ancient concept of an "overmind."

To carry it still further (if such speculation is legitimate), it is also conceivable that death involves only our bodily awareness, but not the remainder of the mind. [25] It might be what physicists call a "change of state." Changes of state are matters of organization. Fantasies like these (and they *are* fantasies), would be quite appealing to the many who profess some sort of religious belief..

The foregoing mental gymnastics are admittedly abstruse and poorly illuminated. They flit perilously in and out of the twilight zone of religion and are almost as far-fetched as the Big Bang. They are prompted in part by some well established facts of psychology. The most important of these has to do with how we relate to outer reality. The truth is *the outside world becomes known to us solely by way of its organization!* The environment *must* be organized to some degree for the mind even to deal with it! We can neither recognize nor learn disorderly data unless they are extremely simple (7 items or less). Whenever we are faced with some sheer jumble of things, no matter what they are, we must always first rearrange them in "order" to make "sense" out of the chaos.

In brief, the existence of organization is a prerequisite for all our mental functioning! The philosopher Spinoza (1632-1677) was well aware of this. He even defined organization in these terms. He said that when items are so arranged that they are easily imagined and remembered, we call them orderly. But when not, we call them disorganized or confused.[26] It would have been more to the point had he said, "When we encounter orderly arrangements, we call them *mindful.* And by the same token, when they are chaotic, they are *mindless.*"

Orderly behavior and orderly surrounds obviously make for a simpler life. Predictability is greater. One doesn't have to search for things. If everything is properly arranged nothing is misplaced or lost, and little is misunderstood. Recognizing such facts, Lindsay proposed what he called the "thermodynamic imperative." This states that one should so live his life that, in every act, he leaves the world more orderly than he found it -- thereby making life simpler for those who follow. This persuasive ethic was subsequently extended by Seifert. [27] In other words, cleanliness may be next to Godliness, but orderliness *is* Godliness!

Whenever we encounter an orderly situation we immediately recognize that intelligence has been at work. A classic example was the sighting of the so-called "canals" on mars. But it is easily demonstrated to be a general truth. Take five piles of sticks. All are stacked randomly except one. And this one is arranged in neatly parallel fashion. Is there any question which pile was purposefully stacked by someone? Now, look at the other four piles. Except for size and location, one cannot be distinguished from another. All look alike. Wherever intelligence operates, the results are orderly. As E. G. Boring put it, "That organisms organize is psychology's great tautology." [28]

We speak of the insane as being mentally "deranged." Disorder is alien, even offensive to us. Do you like noise? It is only a disorderly tone. Or how about filth? Clutter? They are simply dirt or things in the wrong place. Such observations could hardly be valid were there not some kind of bond (identity?) between organic mind and organization. The very words suggest as much. One might quote the late K. S. Lashley, one of our most eminent physiologists of the mind: "Mind is a complex organization, held together by interaction of processes and by the time scales of memory, centered about the body image. It has no distinguishing features other than its organization." [29]

The possibility that mind may actually *be* organization is not without logic. Analysis discloses that both body and brain are made up of matter. There is nothing unique about this matter except for its atomic and molecular arrangements, i.e., its organization. Thus, unless we postulate some kind of non-material spirit, soul, or similar entity, the only way we could account for mind would be to assume that it is somehow integral with matter itself. The simplest hypothesis would be that it involves some kind of energy patterning or organization in the brain. Since the brain is a colloid or gel-like structure, the only reasonable candidate would be the inter-molecular energies known to exist in colloids. And it just so happens that these are exclusively energies of *attraction!*

Any such hypothesis would require that mind be identified with the organizing effects, as an emergent phenomenon, and not with the energies per se. (1) The same energies in other colloids do not necessarily produce organization. And (2) some living things, e.g., viruses, are not colloidal. To put it differently, the only common denominator of matter, life, and mind is not any type of energy, vital or otherwise. It is organization -- how the elements are arranged. Material elements themselves are virtually immutable. Only the organization can vary.

However, such speculation is reserved for later treatment and currently takes us out of context. So let's return to those evasive relations responsible for the organization, the coherence seen to exist in so many things. They bind our visual data together and literally create the forms we see. They are the "stuff" of perceived things. They make for thing-quality, and this thing-quality is what provides temporary fixation and relative permanence to remembered portions of the sensory input. Data are packaged by figure-ground effects, organizing and interrelating it so that it can be identified and classified by the mind for later recognition or recall.

Thingness is not an attribute of outer events. At least half a dozen notable scientists have made this observation. Why should it be surprising? Artists and camouflage experts have known it for centuries. Two conditions are necessary for the senses to create things. (1) The complex of sensory relations must comply with the Gestalt law of proximity. That is to say, the related items must be close enough together to be recognized as portions of some whole, one part belonging with the other. And (2) they must differ or contrast with their surrounds. Though not absolutely necessary, the process is greatly facilitated if the external configuration is also recognizable, that is, if it is similar to some structure in the memory of the viewer.

Occasionally we are aware of these relations which organize and create what we see. But for the most part we are not. Our concern is with the final product -- the 'thing' as seen. To realize how extensive and effective they may be, however, consider profile drawings and silhouettes. These demonstrate the primacy of form or patterning. They are processed by the mind with only the barest minimum of information present. They consist almost wholly of blank space and have no internal details at all. Nevertheless, they are recognized almost as accurately as photographs. Only the outer contours are needed to set up the necessary interacting relationships bonding one feature with another. And please note that they extend over considerable distances within the silhouette -- areas presumably unstimulated. Information, says Attneave, is concentrated at contours. [30] This is where the contrast differences are, and these differences are what get related. They make the figure-ground effect possible.

Some time ago when discussing information, it was explained that configural information (patterns) is what the mind feeds on. And it was said that any given pattern is actually a chunk of information. But patterns differ, and *amount* of information relates to pattern *complexity*. As explained by Sir Allen Cottrell, [31] structural simplicity coincides with conceptual simplicity. Something quite simple and very orderly (like a checkerboard) can be described in only a few words, possibly even a single sentence. But something whose organization is complex contains a wealth of information. It is therefore difficult to describe and requires a detailed listing of particulars. This is true for the silhouette of a face. It may be easy to recognize, but describing it accurately is another matter.

Percepts often become memories, of course, faithfully structuring the otherwise transient input into molecular patterns. Thus, one way of conceiving the mind is to look upon it as a molecular pattern-making device, a sort of personal god of unformed matter. And much as in the case of antibodies, this pattern-making can be quite precise.

Chapter 9

Getting Complexified -- in and out of the Mind

(The skeletal geometry of perceived organization, and the biological law of complexification.)

"This subject is becoming pretty foggy, even downright spooky," one of the students protested. "You lost me some time ago. I have a question."

I paused, then said, "Let's see if we can find an answer -- maybe it will clear out some of the fog."

"Awhile back where I got lost, you said that we can see both orderly and disorderly conditions. That is, we can tell whether things are organized (mindful), or chaotic (mindless) even though we aren't able to fully define or measure what we mean by these terms. Is that correct?"

"Right on the nose so far," I replied. "What we see is a direct representation of the structural features outside, and this outer world has various degrees of organization."

"Well, if we can see both these opposite conditions, and both are made up of the same kind of relations, what is the difference between the relations in the two cases?"

I smiled and remarked, "That's an excellent question. You weren't lost after all! I anticipated somebody would ask that. So I came prepared. I brought along some slides. They are taken from an article I published about fifty years ago. [32] And they illustrate these differences quite graphic-ally. Now, if someone will douse the lights, I'll show you.

Take a look at Figure 7 *(below)*. As you can see, this figure consists of five small spheres. Please note that the pattern they make is very irregular or disorderly. The dotted lines are added only to indicate that the relations between them all have different directions and distances. Of course, not all the relations have been dotted in this way. In reality, there are $N(N-1)/2$, or 10 of them present in any five-point pattern of this sort.

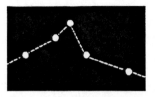

FIGURE 7. A disorderly group of five dots.

Do you follow me? O.K. I am now going to use this disorderly pattern to construct an even larger and more disorderly mess of dots. *(See Figure 8).*

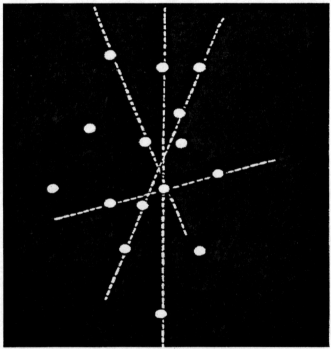

FIGURE 8. A disorderly total made up of three figure 7 patterns

Figure 8 is what we get when the preceding pattern is repeated three times. In other words, this larger jumble of 15 dots is made up of exactly three of the earlier 5 dot patterns. There is no overlap. All are separate one from another. Each is about the same distance from the next, and has the same orientation in the plane. Nevertheless, the result is very messy. In fact, it is so disorderly people have to study it just to divide it up into three equal parts. To use our earlier terminology, it is mindless -- utterly without organization. This state of affairs is due to the new mutual relations created when the patterns were combined. Like the disorderly piles of sticks I mentioned, these relations are a hodgepodge which provide no identity or 'thing-quality.' The pattern so created has no 'togetherness.'

Since this larger figure now has 15 points, the number of relations would be 105. They couldn't all be represented. So I have only dotted in the spaces where three or more of the points fall on a straight line, i.e., where their relations would be collinear. Please note that of the 15 points and 105 relations present, only four such lines can be drawn. No one of these has the same direction as another. And neither are there any parallels or perpendiculars in the lot."

"So what?" It was the same student who had interrupted earlier. "After all, when you begin with disorderly data you can expect to get a disorderly composite of them, can't you?"

"Not necessarily," I responded. "For example, it is also possible to produce an opposite effect -- show that order can arise spontaneously out of chaos. In short, we can create mindfulness! If you doubt this, take a look at our next slide. *(See Figure 9)*

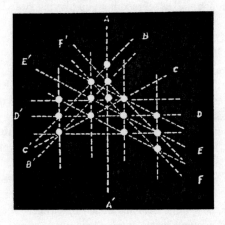

FIGURE 9. An orderly whole made of the same patterns.

This figure consists of the same three disorderly patterns used before. Again, all have the same orientation in the same plane with no overlap. In other words, the same rules of construction were used. But what a difference! When dotted lines are now drawn through all relations where three or more points are collinear, 16 such lines are found! Half of them lie in only two of the six directions given. And most importantly, these two directions are those of the vertico-horizontal system of body symmetry and the position of the eyes. Moreover, all points but two are intersected by lines mutually perpendicular.

When this latter (figure 9) is compared with the disorderly arrangement shown earlier, it is hard to believe that both were constructed of the same number of the same patterns following the same rules! The heightened organization which we now see can only be due to the new alignment of internal relations. All other variables have been held constant.

Such effects are not peculiar to these dot patterns. It is easily demonstrated that the same geometric properties are present in any array of items judged to be orderly. Their significance for the mind can also be demonstrated. No one would question which of the two figures possesses more 'thing-quality,' would be more readily seen against a background of similar dots, or would be easier to identify and remember."

"This hocus-pokus with dot patterns is interesting, all right. I'll admit that. But have you been able to measure such differences?" It was the same student again. He seemed bent on playing straight-man for the lecturer.

I stared at him for a moment. "As a matter of fact, I have," I retorted. "Back long before Berkeley became 'Berserkly,' my doctoral dissertation was based on precisely this problem. The psychological importance of order was recognized for all aspects of life. Its significance for the mind was not only verified, but several useful equations were evolved. [33] Unfortunately, doctoral dissertations don't get published too often, and the equations themselves are too complicated to be presented here. However, if you choose, I can take a moment to explain what was done.

In the Berkeley project patterns of 13 dots were used rather than the 15 dot ones used here. Otherwise, materials were much the same. There were 40 patterns, 20 symmetrical and 20 asymmetrical. They represented a graded series ranging from total chaos to maximal order -- and furthermore, there was a measured index for the orderliness of each. Experimental results showed that this index predicted how well people were able to judge the orderliness of the patterns, and in addition it also revealed that their ability to remember them was equally predictable.

After I left Berkeley, and quite apart from my own efforts, some of the faculty (Norman Livson and David Krech) demonstrated that the index actually correlated with a person's I.Q. [34] That is to say, the more intelligent subjects did a better job of discriminating the patterns. Apparently, they were capable of more extensive perceptual structuring. This raised some theoretical hackles at the time. But it was separately confirmed by a number of others. [35] Along these same lines it is interesting to note that perception of rhythm, the temporal counterpart of spatial order or organization, has been similarly related to intelligence measured by I.Q. [36]

Thus, it happens that equating organization with mind is not just another vacuous bit of theorizing. It is supported to some extent by experimental evidence. One wonders why it should have been considered worthy of argument. Anything which is organized is interrelated -- this almost by definition. At the same time, please note that intelligence (mind) obviously depends upon the ability to interrelate data of various sorts. Spearman, one of the first to define intelligence, regarded it as the capacity to perceive and deduce relationships. [37] Even in the vernacular of the street, the unintelligent are often described as being unable to put two and two together. And the term 'incoherence' is literally 'lack of relatedness' -- not being 'with it.'

But let's get on with the discussion. We commonly use the terms 'order' and 'organization' interchangeably. They refer to assemblies of independent items like the dots in these patterns, the distribution of furniture in a room, or other complexes of separate things. By contrast, the terms 'form' and 'shape' are also used interchangeably to describe entities rather than assemblies. Such entities have contours or boundaries. They are enclosed. Despite these differences, the same relational factors apply in both cases -- whether compounded as a group or unified into a form. For example, some of you may have noticed that our last slide (Figure 9) looks suspiciously like the diagram of a molecular space-lattice -- the kind of inner structure a crystal might have. And it may well be so. Here, I'll show you. *(See Figure 10)*

In this slide I have taken the grouping last seen and rotated it 90 degrees counter-clockwise. This way, the direction labeled AA' is horizontal. Then, the relations which would coincide with contours were filled in with solid lines. Those not representing contours were omitted. The objective was to make a form out of it. And voila! There was the crystal! At least it was something that looked like a crystal.

Speaking of crystals, I should like to digress a moment to say a few words about them. After all, they are used as components in our so-called 'thinking' machines. Crystals start out as seeds just like you, me, or the tree outside. And their development can be properly described as growth. Though they don't reproduce like kind, they do sometimes undergo 'twinning.' This is a kind of budding process similar to what occurs in plants and certain lesser aquatic creatures.

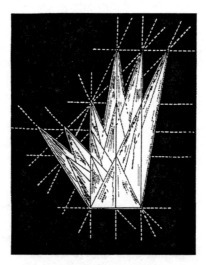

FIGURE 10. A crystal-like reconstruction of Figure 9.

I have heard it argued that unlike organic growth, crystal growth is a mere accretion of atoms. But this is no more valid than describing human growth as a mere accretion of cells. In both cases, the orientation of the new atom or cell is determined by the existing organization. It is not random. Neither crystal nor human end up as an amorphous mass. What I am trying to say I guess, is that something orderly tends to extend its basic pattern. If at all possible, it enlarges itself or *grows*. Thus, whether crystals are alive or not is a moot issue.

The tendency toward directed growth means that the crystal is characterized by structural consistency. This is what maintains its symmetrical shape. Now, 'consistency' is another of those many words having some of the same meaning as organization. So it should come as no surprise to find that consistency is also considered a major property of the *mind*. Indeed, numerous psychologists have designated it as the most prominent attribute of the human personality. [38] The thesis is logical. Were the mind not consistent, behavior would be random and irrational.

If I were to describe the typical mineral crystal I would say, Look! Here is a spot where mind (organization) has started to develop using inorganic matter! It had nothing to work with except identical molecular building blocks. All had the same size, shape, and composition. But it grew as best it could. The result was this crystal. However, suppose it happened to have access to some extraneous matter, perhaps minor traces of grease such as occur on a frosty kitchen window pane. Crystallization might then have taken on the form of ferns or other plant life. The chief reason we are not rigid like the crystal is that we consist of proteins. These are highly varied asymmetrical building blocks. They don't fit together so neatly. Thus, the human is flexible and grows for many years. He does not 'crystallize out' quite so readily. But he does tend to grow more stiff (and finally rigid) -- as any elderly citizen will testify.

'Life is older than organisms,' Ehrensvärd said. [39] It may even be older than the primordial soup with its amino acids and proteins. The sources of organization could have begun with the complexities of matter itself. For instance, liquid crystals will swarm and undergo twinning. And a variety of wholly inorganic materials can give rise to amazingly life-like forms which grow and behave in a rhythmic, pulsing fashion virtually indistinguishable from primitive living things. These are called 'Liesegang rings' and have been known for many years. [40]

If simple enough, living things can be found as crystals. Notable among these is the justly famous tobacco mosaic virus. It has been crystallized as a white powder. But when returned to the tobacco leaf, it again lives, reproduces, and is active.

As one proceeds up the time scale of evolution, living matter appears to become ever more intricately organized. At that point where we reach the living cell it is already enormously complex. In short, the evolutionary process begins to look more like a *growth* process! [41] At no time in all the aeons of geological history has any species evolved to become simpler. They can and do become extinct. But they cannot simplify! This fact of ongoing and increasingly complex organization is inescapable -- almost synonymous with life itself.

It was precisely this observation, and not the needlessly belabored 'inheritance of acquired characteristics,' which was the central argument of J. B. Lamarck's *Zoological Philosophy* in 1809. [42] The idea was not

picked up until more than a century later. At that time his fellow country-
man, the Jesuit priest Teilhard de Chardin, rephrased the concept and
couched it in somewhat mystical language. In his *Phenomenon of Man*,
Père Teilhard called it as the great 'biological law of complexification.' [43]

In his opinion, as well as that of Lamarck, this ever-increasing complexity of organization represented the evolution or growth of *mind*. He
even defined consciousness as simply 'the specific effect of organized
complexity.' It is evidenced in the evolution of life in general, the
embryonic development of the baby in particular, and is now becoming
ever more obvious in the growth of human culture. If this law is true, and
I think it is, then development of larger and more complex brains would
not require any special creation or fluke of nature to explain. They would
be expected!

During development of a baby the increase in brain size is not only
obvious, it is startling. When considering brain enlargement during evolution, however, the picture is not so clear. Even among different species
of living animals, total brain size has always been poorly related to their
assumed intelligence. Much of this disparity is doubtlessly due to the fact
that different sizes of old brains result from the need to regulate different
kinds of bodies. On the other hand, intellectual capacity is almost exclusively dependent upon the new brain or cortex.

These and related factors were carefully considered by Harry Jerison,
an authority on brain history. [44] Jerison then devised a new and more
effective method of estimating 'braininess' from over-all brain features.
He called it the encephalization quotient, or E.Q. The argument was that
it allowed for a more realistic appraisal of potential intelligence. This included extinct creatures as well. Casts were made of the cranial cavities of
numerous extinct fossil animals. And after much labor and measurement,
it was found that *relative* brain size had indeed increased during the course
of evolution. What had developed, therefore, was not necessarily a
superior body -- something which might otherwise have been inferred --
but a superior *intellect*."

The class had not interrupted once! Apparently the topic was of
considerable interest. I was just about to continue when I noticed a
student on my left. He looked as if he were lost in thought. Turning to
him I asked, "This make sense to you?"

He was startled. "Yes, perfect sense," he replied. "But I guess I
must have missed something." He then asked that the dot patterns be
shown again. And after studying them for a moment, he commented, "I
can understand the biological need for direct perception of relations and

form. And identifying mind with organization also seems logical. What baffles me, I guess, is your analysis of order. The crucial difference between the orderly and disorderly patterns appears to be the presence of parallelism and perpendicularity of relations. Why parallelism and perpendicularity?"

It was now my turn to show surprise. I pondered the situation for awhile, then announced, "We'll have to back-track a bit. I must have been going too fast. As a result, I skipped over some important points in the argument. These have to do with the fact that parallelism and perpendicularity constitute the skeletal geometry of most everyday equilibrium states. Now before everyone starts objecting, I'll admit that the term 'equilibrium' has become such a buzz word it doesn't denote much any more. So, it is better that I demonstrate what I mean."

Walking over to the blackboard I noticed a yardstick lying in the chalk-trough. Luckily, it was straight. (Most are warped!) I picked it up, blew away the dust, and with some difficulty balanced it upright on the floor. "As you can see," I said, "this yardstick is perpendicular to the floor. It is parallel with the direction of gravity. But it is an unstable equilibrium."

Much as if cued, the stick toppled over flat on the floor. I grinned and added, "It is now in a more stable equilibrium parallel with the earth's surface and perpendicular to gravity. If I took it outside and tossed it in the river, it would either become parallel with the current or reorient itself to become perpendicular -- deviating with changes in the current. It could even be placed on a pivot and used as a weathervane. If it were, it would move in the wind with the same geometric results.

When waves act perpendicularly against the beach, they produce parallel markings in the sand. When a tree grows, the trunk displays two growth vectors perpendicular to each other -- resulting in concentric parallel growth rings. Even the leaves of the tree will orient themselves either parallel or perpendicular to the sun's rays so as to minimize or maximize their effects.

But we began with perception, so let's go back to that subject. Any examination of the experimental literature will turn up numerous examples in which these geometric attributes become obvious. After all, the eyes are arranged in a plane perpendicular to the main axis of body symmetry. So it might be expected that visual acuity would be superior in vertical and horizontal dimensions -- and so it is. [45] But regardless of body orientation, image contours from the two eyes will fuse when parallel, and give maximum rivalry when perpendicular. In the windowframe-and-cross drawing shown earlier (Figure 4), parallel lines were seen to attract each other, whereas those lying perpendicular to them had no influence. They also acted together separately. And it might be added that electromagnetic fields behave in exactly the same fashion.

Such observations could be continued until the subject became tiresome. But I am sure you have already guessed the conclusion to which they lead. I shall try to state it as plainly as I can. In our relationship with the external world, the great outstanding mystery has always been this: How do we acquire such extremely precise representation of external things and events? Stop and think about it. Consider the heterogeneous neural structures of the brain and optic systems. It seems almost impossible that they could provide any exactitude whatever. Nonetheless, we use this jumbled hodgepodge to perceive exactly straight lines, squares, circles, or whatever. And we do so with an accuracy (vernier acuity) far surpassing the structural resolution of the retina itself!

The answer to this ancient riddle is believed to be straightforward and unambiguous. And hard as it may be to understand, it is the only answer possible. The energy used by the brain, no matter what it may be, is in an organized state called the mind. It is little influenced by the heterogeneity of cortical tissue. Instead, it acts according to the same basic principles as the energies of the outside world.

The mind is not the brain, nor is it the energy per se. It is most likely the *organization* which prevails. But whatever it is, it can be demonstrated that it operates the same as that which creates organization in the outer world. In one of his university lectures, Max Wertheimer is said to have expressed it this way: 'The material of sensation is indeed different from the material of the physical world, but the *structure* is the same.' [46]

Thus, our perception of something results in what is best described as a miniaturized replication of its external form. If there is a square-like distribution outside, there is a smaller square energy pattern inside. If external events are orderly they have some degree of equilibrium. The geometry of the equilibrium state is replicated in the optic system. We see them as organized. That which is orderly is differentiated from the disorderly. It creates a figure-ground effect and we see a 'thing.' But if there is no stability or organization, the sensory input is literally incoherent. There is no tell-tale geometry, and we cannot distinguish one set of events from another. Events then become like the disorderly piles of sticks described earlier. They have no identity. All look the same.

Everyone admits that an aroma, the particular hue of a color, or a feeling cannot be expressed in words, codes, or anything else transmissible. It is a private experience obtained directly from the input. Indeed, *all* sensory experience is personal. Data making up the perceived world have to be immediately representative. Were they not acquired directly, perception would necessitate a prohibitive amount of detail processing by the brain. Such processing might be possible for the human. I don't know. But it would be manifestly impossible for simple creatures like insects.

Insects have little neural equipment with which to classify, modify, and interpret what their senses tell them. They must accept it 'on faith.' Though many of them can be shown to have accurate vision, they lack the neural 'hardware' with which to do any extensive processing. Consider the 4000 species of jumping spiders. Most are quite small, no larger than a BB shot. Individual brains are even smaller, about the size of one of their eight eyes. But it is easily demonstrated that they have excellent depth perception. In addition, they recognize mates, mating rituals, prey, enemies, and a variety of environmental features. Or how about the chicken? One can remove its entire cortex without disturbing its pattern vision! [47]

According to popular neural network theories, a volley of impulses presumably gives rise to the perception of something, say a square. But from what we know of neural impulses, no such volley could possibly retain its shape and be transmitted as a 'square' in the tissues. So we hide our embarrassment by rationalizing. We say that the perceived square must be a 'code,' and that the code is learned. Physically, however, codes rarely bear any resemblance to the objects they stand for. They can only be denotative, not connotative. They are surrogate symbols, seldom representative and never real. For example, the code for a square could only be some formless cloud-like spray of ionic blips seldom the same a second time. Whereas, the experienced image of a square would be meticulously exact and always the same every time.

It is the old semantics fallacy all over again. The name is not the thing, and the map is not the territory. To illustrate, suppose a child identifies someone as 'Mary.' At some prior time she had to have acquired a mental *image* of Mary -- either from seeing her or her photograph. Having seen a 'code' would not have helped. Matching codes in memory (presupposing they had signal fidelity) still would not provide an image. If one can only perceive codes rather than images, what is the source of all the imagery which the codes presumably evoke? In other words, the logic is faulty. The problem remains right where it was when Aristotle puzzled over it.

The immediate perception of form, qua form, is inescapable. There is no way of bridging the gap between symbol and reality. Codes would require an intracranial homunculus to do the translating. He's the fellow whom one should really talk to! It might be argued that I only 'think' I see a square. But try convincing a spider that she only 'thinks' she sees a fly!"

Minding the Overmind

Chapter 10

Organic Relatedness of Man and his Culture

(Long-range relations in the physical world compared with those in the organic realm. Vertical relatedness: the cell is to the human as the human is to his social being.)

I wound up my eleven o'clock class and called it quits for the day. As I sauntered across campus I noticed the grass was greening and the trees beginning to bud. Spring had sneaked in unannounced. The better halves were meandering about hand in hand with lesser halves, indicating that the nest quest is not strictly for the birds. The thought made me feel good. Biology! It's like spring itself. It can't be legislated, militarized, or dogmatized. It just is. One can depend upon it.

I yanked myself out of the revery by opening the door to the outer office. And there was my teaching assistant. He was sitting with one leg propped up on an open desk drawer, busy grading exam papers. He looked up, blinked his eyes in the sudden sunshine, and asked, "Say, have you ever heard of Bell?"

"Crazy question," I responded, "of course. He invented that nuisance called a telephone."

"Not that one. This was a Scottish physicist who worked at CERN."[1]

"Doesn't ring a bell," I punned. "What did he do?"

"He more or less demonstrated mathematically that everything was related to everything else, at least subatomically," Greg responded.

"That would be interesting. I have a suggestion. Why don't you ease up on the scoring for awhile, get on that device by the other Bell, and order us a pizza -- medium size with pastrami. Then, while we're lunching you can fill me in on what happened." I grabbed a handful of papers to help grade and retreated into my office. But I didn't get much done, perhaps half an hour's worth, when the pizza arrived.

"That was pretty fast for a noon order," I remarked.

"It's the usual pepperoni, not pastrami," Greg apologized. "Most likely they had it ready to go."

"No matter. Here, take half." I pushed the papers aside and relaxed lengthwise in the chair. "Now, tell me about this Bell thing."

"O.K. What made me think of it were those dot patterns you showed the class awhile back. They had no physical connections between them. But anyone could see that the dots were related somehow. Then, just this morning I noticed something very like them. It was a flock of birds. They all moved at the same time, wheeling every which way like a school of fish I once watched. They acted just as if they were connected somehow. This reminded me of the Bell studies. He dealt with something similar that happens between subatomic particles. So I thought you might be interested"

"I am. What did he do?"

"Actually, he wrote a very profound mathematical theorem. The prof. didn't explain it fully, so I'm not sure I really understand it. Anyhow, it has been verified several times experimentally. [2] What struck me about it was the implication that the world we commonly know is illusory -- phony. You used a word for it. I believe you called it 'maya.'"

"Phony in what way?" I asked.

"Well, as I recall, Bell's math implies that the universe is mostly made up of relations instead of things. Every part is pretty well connected to every other part, particularly at the subatomic level. Furthermore, the relations themselves are rather weird. They would have to be action at a distance. They don't involve any mediating energies, at least none that can be identified. In this way they are like the relations in those dot patterns. And the interesting outcome of it all seems to be the organization that results. Another British physicist named Bohm referred to it as an 'implicate' order which pervades everything. [3] All in all, it sounded very much like what you were describing as 'mind.'"

"I'll be darned," I chuckled, pulling some pepperoni slices out of the stringy cheese. "If I am reading you rightly, you are saying that the physicists have been busy confirming the original thinking of us Gestalt folks. If that's true it will be the irony of the century -- considering the treatment we received from the ruling clique of psychologists. Guess I'll have to bone up on developments in quantum physics. Did your instructor say how Bell and the others got off on this track? Were they dabbling in oriental philosophy?"

"As a matter of fact," he laughed, "some of them were. [4] But Bell was primarily trying to find a way to test one of Einstein's thought experiments. Einstein and a couple of others felt that quantum theory didn't tell the whole story. It was incomplete. So they conjured up this paradox. [5] If the theory were correct, then subatomic particles had to be related synchronously over long distances, say galaxy to galaxy, with no responsible energy between them. And as Einstein saw it, this was impossible."

"No one should try to second-guess Einstein," I commented. "He's been proved right on a lot of weird things." I uncoiled myself from the chair and shoved the papers back toward him. "Here, finish these up and give me a ring at home. I'll help you force-fit the grades to a normal curve. That will make them abnormal. But it will comply with the screwy thinking of the education people, and most importantly, it will keep the dean happy."

During my walk home I got to mulling over what Greg had said. There have been numerous arguments that our outside world is all interrelated in some unknown fashion. The relations themselves are said to extend far beyond what we recognize as the immediate contacts and causes of daily events. They are not only action at a distance, but *long* distances, or so the argument goes. It is felt that the universe is simply too well organized and synchronized for it not to have some sort of superstructure to account for it all. The claim is that this hidden framework occasionally makes itself known between happenings which are otherwise completely unrelated or even alien to each other.

When incidents like these occur, everyone is dumbfounded. They are usually pointed out as evidence of unknown, perhaps exotic influences at work. If not the hand of God, then either the universal gaming wheel becomes loaded periodically, or some mysterious world-wide network has to provide the connectivity. This latter is often described as a universal infrastructure completely beyond our measurements and detectable only through its effects. [6] There are no rules of evidence as to what constitutes effects. They include almost anything we commonly consider coincidents: dreams of impending tragedy followed by the tragedy itself, occasional high correlations in ESP experiments, prolonged winning or losing streaks when gambling -- in fact, everything that seems extremely improbable.

All the hard-nosed scientists with whom I had discussed the matter were invariably against such speculation. They contended that it is largely based on wishful thinking, gut-feelings rather than logic. What little experimental evidence exists comes from cookbook statistics. These usually ignore their underlying assumptions because the assumptions can't be investigated. My own opinion on all this has been ambivalent. My guess is the jury will be out a long, long time -- possibly forever.

Theorization about such issues, I told myself, is a form of mental recreation. It is harmless, even healthy if it isn't taken too seriously. Just so long as it does not become fanaticized, or evangelical, I am all for it. On the other hand, cookbook statistics belong in a medicine cabinet with a large red label warning: Use with Extreme Caution! May be hallucinatory! Keep out of the hands of children!

Having made up my mind on the "iffy" status of Bell's theorem -- which I really didn't know anything about -- I went into the kitchen for a cool drink. I was just pouring myself a lemonade when I noticed Greg swinging in through the back gate. The large manila envelope under his arm obviously contained the exam papers.

"I rang, but nobody answered," he said.

"Must have been on the front porch," I explained. "Here, have some lemonade. Put the papers on top the fridge. I'll get to them later. In the meantime, it's been a warm day. Let's go out on the front porch, pretend we're a two man think-tank, and brainstorm this Bell thing."

The porch swing complained with its usual high-pitched tone of voice, but we settled down anyhow, and I lit up my pipe. "For starters," I suggested, "let's consider those long, drawn-out relations between particles of matter -- presupposing there are such things as particles. If I remember rightly, you said they are not represented by any energy. That correct?"

"That's the way I understood it," he replied. "The interactions are instantaneous. So any energy would have to exceed the speed of light."

"How about the statement that everything that happens in the outside world, if it is known, also happens in the brain -- else it would not be known? And in the brain it is represented by energy. In fact, I think I know what the energy is."

He grinned. "Good try, but it won't play. Nobody has seen these relations. They are mathematical deductions and don't exist as perceptual constructs in the brain."

"Touché! One point for you! So we just let Newton and Einstein both roll over in their graves. We'll admit that it is action at a distance. There is no mediating energy. Of course, there's always the possibility that it's something totally unknown which doesn't follow the same rules as other energies. But in any case, there would still have to be some reason why the relations were said to exist, whether mathematical or otherwise. They have to have a *raison d'etre*. So, what do they do?"

Greg popped a stick of gum in his mouth and said matter-of-factly, "when one particle changes, the other one also changes -- so they carry information."[7]

"They WHAT?!" I almost came out of the swing.

"Carry information," he repeated. "They are communication links between particles."

I settled down again. "If they're between particles, they're between everything," I observed. "I am unfamiliar with the subject -- just learned of it -- but from what you have told me, I would guess it to be quite a can of worms.

Suppose it turns out that these quantum people are right. The implications could be awesome. Let me think aloud for a moment. First, we have connecting links between particles. These links are neither material nor any kind of energy. But they nonetheless carry information. Now all information is patterning or organization by definition. And in my opinion at least, organization is *mind!* You know what this sounds like? It sounds like they may have very well discovered the long sought mind-stuff out of which the universe is made according to Eddington, Jeans, Schrödinger and others. Has anyone come up with this suggestion?"

"Not to my knowledge," he replied, "at least not in those terms."

I sat and quietly ruminated the idea for a minute or two. "Tell me something," I finally said. "Do these relations interact with each other, extend themselves, change somehow, or have any influence on anything except the two particles at their ends?"

"Not that I have heard of. They just are. As described to me, they are merely connectors between two points."

"Then they can't be mind-stuff," I replied, "because they are much too sterile."

"Sterile? Why sterile?" He looked puzzled.

"I'll explain," I answered. "Mind is the motive force of life. And all living things have something in common. Whether cells, plants, animals, or evolution in general, all exhibit a process known as *growth*. They use and frequently create the energy necessary to extend themselves, and the extension is always consistent or organized. Organization is the hallmark of life.

In last analysis the reason behind this orderliness of growth is that consistency of structure channels free energy into consistent paths. As you are aware, all energies flow in paths of least resistance. In structured things like organisms, the directions of least resistance are always predetermined by existing structure. Look at the movement of electricity for example. When lightning strikes through amorphous atmosphere, its path is extremely irregular. But when electricity moves through a crystal, the path it takes is dictated by details of the crystal structure. Makers of computer components depend on this fact. To sum it up, growth maintains and promotes organization. Stated otherwise, living things grow in directions consistent with their Bauplan. And in like manner, their behavior follows the same rules. That is why organisms organize.

What identifies growth processes is their continuous *directed* changes. They are progressive. For instance, the mind relates all its content in a sequential forward and consistent fashion. As a result, our memories expand cumulatively and consistently with an internal order of their own. The development of a plant or an animal occurs in much the same fashion. Its growth is cumulative, consistent, and always in the same direction. Nothing ever grows younger, smaller, or simpler. It can only become older, larger and more complex. The same appears true of evolution in general. It is progressive and has grown ever more complex. Some species like the horseshoe crab or roach may lapse into stasis, and numerous others may become extinct. But so far as I know, none of them regress or simplify."

"I think I see what you mean," Greg answered. "Relations like those described by Bell and Bohm would be too inert and invariant."

"Right. Presupposing they really exist, it is conceivable they might be part of some unknown universal infrastructure. I wouldn't want to guess. But in any case, they don't appear to have the properties of mind-stuff."

Greg pondered this for several minutes, then remarked, "There is one point I might mention where you and the quantum people tend to agree."

"What's that?" I asked.

"You both describe the universe as being made up of relations rather than things. I think I know what they mean by the word relations, but just how do you define the term?"

I couldn't help grinning. "It's a slippery word, all right. But let's see if I can get a grip on it. Basically, a relation is something which occurs between two points, objects, or organisms. It can be either transient or relatively permanent. Nothing's really permanent. Most are occupied by energy of some sort. Many physicists would say they are all occupied by energy or they don't exist. I am not so sure about that. Einstein's gravity relates everything. But it's not energy. It's thought to be a condition of space itself. For the time being, let's keep it simple and just say that some relations are vector paths taken by energy, whereas others are not.

For some reason, we usually think of relations as extending outwardly on every side from the Here and Now -- much as if the present were somehow flattened into a plane perpendicular to the flow of time. But it is easy to realize that they must also extend vertically, as it were. Everything has a history, and all causes recede into the past. So they are best visualized as a sort of three-dimensional web, or a volume.

The most important, as well as the most intricately detailed relations exist in the brain. These go to make up the mind. All are represented by an energy of attraction which acts somewhat like gravity. But whether in the mind or the world outside, all relations are attractional by definition. It is a contradiction in terms to speak of negative or repellent relations. They couldn't form a bond. They would not relate."

"How about a beam of light?"

"In and of itself, light does not relate anything. It is free moving energy. If the light enables us to see something, say a star, it is *we* who relate what is seen in the optic system. We do not relate to the light itself."

"Do these relations have any width or thickness?"

"Never thought of them in that sense," I replied. "Everything that has one dimension has all three. Things having only one or two dimensions are intellectual fabrications. Anyhow, when a vector is extensive enough to be measured in more than one direction, a different term is used. It is called a 'field' -- magnetic fields for example."

"I have another question," he added. "What is their significance? What do they do?"

"That's a class-A super-question," I laughed. "Actually, they constitute the entire universe. I hope you don't want the answer in a single sentence."

He grinned. "Since everything that exists is in the mind anyhow -- else you say we wouldn't know about it -- why not start with these?"

"Better yet," I offered, "I'll demonstrate." Digging into my pocket I came up with seven coins, mostly pennies. I leaned forward in the swing and quickly spread them in a small group on the porch. Turning to Greg, I asked, "How many are there?"

"Seven," was the prompt response.

"How do you know? You didn't have time to count them."

"It's obvious there are seven. I don't have to count them." Then he realized what I was driving at. He looked at me and exclaimed, "You're right! Those coins got related into a group automatically! There are even smaller groups in the larger one, just like in star constellations."

"Exactly," I said. "In former years there was considerable interest in such relatedness, particularly in Germany. It was found to occur in all our senses. And the better organized the array, the more of it was apprehended simultaneously. Husserl came up with the phrase 'figural resultants' to describe the seemingly invisible relations holding the group together. [8] It was an apt phrase because they interact to produce resultants much as do other energies."

"What about social groups?" Greg interposed. "People are separate entities, and they collect in various groupings just like the coins."

"The difficulty there," I answered, "is largely that common bugaboo about action at a distance. Obviously, the mind is what organizes the coins. So the relating activity can be ascribed to local energy interchanges of some unknown sort occurring in the optic system. However, social groupings are another matter. At least they are considered so. They are mobile and extend over appreciable distances. This makes it difficult to recognize whatever it is that organizes people into groups. As a result, the idea of a social organism has always been regarded as fantasy. Personally, I believe this outlook to be narrow and unjustified. For example, our culture exhibits exactly the same growth curve that characterizes other living things. And if there is growth, something has to be *growing!*

Wherever there is relating activity there is organization of some degree -- this by definition. And when one considers all the many types of relating linkages existing in the material world, he will find none so varied, useful, or effective as communications. These carry information patterns over interminable distances with so little energy cost they may as well be called action at a distance. They are extremely efficient. Whether between insects or humans, every nodal point in the net is a transceiver. Just about anything can serve as a signal carrier -- ranging from chemicals to laser beams.

Furthermore, communication links are amazingly versatile. As chemical transmissions they hold the cells together in a society called the human. In fact, they are the *sine qua non* of all organic social assemblies. And every living thing is a social assembly, including the cell itself. Socialization is a major imperative of life."

I didn't want this to be a monologue. So I paused and looked across the swing at Greg to see if he had anything to add. But he simply grinned and said, "No, please carry on. I'm interested in what you are leading up to."

"Social organisms," I answered. "I'll get some more lemonade. Then we can take it from there."

I returned shortly with two glasses, handed one to Greg, then resettled myself in the complaining swing. "Now, where was I?"

"Relations as communication linkages, the sine-something-or-other of social groups."

"I remember now, thanks. You know, our dogmatic classifications of the living world are little more than assumptions resulting from man's painfully bloated ego. He finds it difficult to visualize anything except himself as a justifiable individual, often including other humans. Comparing himself with a cell would overtax him in the extreme. But regardless how the public may feel about it, cells are nevertheless small self-contained creatures which can live and prosper quite well outside the body provided their basic needs are met. The human himself can do little better.

Nearly all the vital processes of life pertain equally well to both the cellular citizens and their human societies. Cells even have their own careers and their own life spans. They are born individually, pass through periods of youth, maturity and old age, then die individually. There is cellular replacement in the human, and human replacement in the society. And despite the death of their society, not all cells die at the same time. Gruesome though it may sound, brain wave activity (the EEG) has been detected as much as six days following a person's 'official' demise. [9]

But let's skip over this side of the picture for a moment and consider man as a component part of a much larger social organism. When we go from societies of cells (man as organism) to societies of humans (man as cell), comprehension becomes still more difficult. Nonetheless, it seems quite logical to suggest that cultures may be living organisms also. Of course, it is almost certain that this could never be proved one way or the other. But it should be studied very seriously. Even if only analogy, the concept could have enormous pay-off. Were the analogy close enough, it might give rise to a system of diagnostics enabling us to analyze some of the social ailments which afflict today's world. And perhaps, just perhaps, it might further suggest remedies. Surely if we wait for the economists to agree, the social body will be taken to the morgue.

I'll take a moment to explain why discussion of the organic nature of human society restricts one to the use of analogy -- regardless of the evidence. This has to do with Gödel's theorem. Expressed metaphorically, this theorem says that the tree can never fully know about the forest of which it is a part. And for the same reason, the human is unable to fully understand his own society. [10]

Unfortunately, analogy is often held in ill repute. But there is nothing really wrong with it so long as one bears in mind that it *is* analogy. Were it possible to map it onto reality in one-to-one fashion, then it would cease to be analogy. It would become identity. But this latter is extremely dubious for social organisms of any sort. They are growing, shifting, and have no particular shape or boundaries -- that is, no skin.

The most basic self-contained biological entity is the cell. And though it is the building block for all higher life forms, it too has proved to be a primitive society. The human, in turn, is a complex society of cells.

And since larger groupings of humans obviously exist, why should we rankle at the idea of social organisms? Man has changed the earth to such extent with dams, buildings, bridges and other masonry, there can be little question about society having a skeleton. Indeed, he unearths the skeletons of buried cultures with the same fervor he digs up those of his own ancestors.

Also self-evident is the specialization or division of labor which occurs when our body cells become consolidated into organs. For example, the digestive system of the body has parallel facilities in the social body. Both are devoted to processing and storage of foods and elimination of wastes. Glands, pancreas and liver are equally comparable to certain chemical installations in the larger organism.

In general, body organs may be viewed as families of cells much like the guilds of earlier times. Workers are related, have the same trade specialty, grow up in that trade, and die in it. The role of the vascular system is also straight-forward. Food and other supplies are transported into and out of population centers by rail and roadway networks. And in the social body, highways are even called 'arterial.'

The principle communication carriers of the social organism are telephone wires. These elongated structures even have shapes similar to nerves. They form nets and branch out into all areas. More general to-whom-it-may-concern information is disseminated by newspapers, radio, and TV in broadcast fashion -- a feature which suggests hormones, those widespread chemical messengers of the body's cellular society.

Still other close analogies lie in the body's immune system. This compares favorably with society's minions of law and order. Sometimes these forces fail, as with wild cells called cancer, and radical surgery becomes necessary in both cases. In general, however, social stability (homeostasis) is maintained by numerous feedback loops to smaller decentralized control centers. And it is significant that this feedback technique is found nowhere else except in living organisms like man and the structures he has created.

For whatever it is worth, one could carry such comparisons to rather minute detail. Fights become wars, habits become customs, sores become slums, and depressions are simply called depressions. People talk themselves into depressions individually. And by consensus they achieve the same general malaise for the social body.

Analogies of this sort make for interesting mental gymnastics. But for most people there are stumbling blocks. It seems that the single largest of these is the fact that societies simply don't look like organisms. They have no enclosing membrane, no skin, and they are not shaped like us. But the same lack of consistent over-all patterning is also found in many primitive colonial life forms. Besides, why should our societies look any more like us than we look like our cells, or the termitaries look like termites?

Another common objection, equally superficial, is the argument that relationships between cells are much closer than those between people in a society. Not so. Both are closely packed in some areas and loosely packed in others. It would even seem that the physical differences between cells (units of the body) are of approximately the same magnitude as the differences between people (units of the social body). And many of the same rules apply. Those of like kind are packed together.

Many are quick to point out that cells act en masse, and that their behavior exhibits no individuality. Against this it may be argued that humans also act en masse, and not just during war. Should some alien observer view us from the same perspective we use to examine cells, he would be at a total loss to explain the huge crowds at sports events, the simultaneous migrations into and out of public buildings, or our assembly into cities. Most cells have less mobility than people, true. But cells are city dwellers who have no need to travel. Given a reason, as in the case of blood cells, they are constantly on the move.

What appears to be a major disparity surfaces with that ultimate criterion of life, namely, the reproduction of like kind. All youthful animals tend to reproduce, to create new and similar cellular societies. Emissaries (sperm) are sent out to locate a neighboring representative (ovum), and through joint action, found a new society -- the baby.

In the case of social organisms, reproduction leads immediately to the thought of colonization, a simple analogue of cellular fission or budding. But I should like to suggest that sex may pertain to the social organism as fully as it does to the individual -- and possibly more so. There is ample evidence that the family is a natural (probably crucial) unit necessary for society. And the family does not originate solely to further the cellular DNA as argued by some sociobiologists.

With regard to this point, it should be observed that the cell already has its own reproductive technique called mitosis, or fission. This maintains the complete integrity and individuality of its DNA. The DNA, or genes, gain little or nothing from sex at the human level. In the genetic shuffle producing the child, it loses virtually all individuality. It gets drowned as it were, in the so-called 'gene pool.' Thus, neither the cell nor the human is perpetuated by sex. The only thing perpetuated is the social organism.

Seen from where I sit, sex is exactly what it appears to be, namely, an instinctive (inbuilt) method for reproducing humans much as mitosis replicates cells. As such, it is the primary growth mechanism of the social body. Reproduction is necessary for the survival of both the cellular and the human societies, and the family is an equally necessary step in their social development. For the social organism, the family provides the womb and nurses the embryo. Its dissolution may well spell death for the culture.

Suppose that the social organism doesn't exist. In such case, what is the advantage of sex? -- amusement? The patent answer that it advances the 'species' is really no answer. Other than social bodies of one sort or another, the human animal does not congregate into groups. And most assuredly he does not gather together harmoniously as a species! Among humans at least, being a single species does not make for any naturally occurring group. A species is not an entity. Most likely, it is simply a generalization like 'all trees' or 'all automobiles' -- an ideological system designation allowing for convenient classification. [11]

Inability to breed productively (produce fertile offspring) is one of the most prominent criteria used to demarcate species. However, this also occurs *within* species. So it could be nothing more than accidental genetic incompatibility and could arise for almost any reason. Should such genetic disparities appear and somehow become perpetuated, reproduction would become restricted to this sub-set of the species. The individuality of that particular group would then be assured. But because the great majority of the infertile produce no offspring, their genes are automatically weeded out. So genetic incompatibility could hardly be used to explain species origin.

Most evolution theories carry the unstated assumption that all creatures would interbreed indiscriminately if at all possible. This is obviously nonsense. Membership in a social group is what promotes selective breeding, and it occurs among members. It leads to 'inbreeding' and would tend to fixate distinctive features of the group. Thus, socialization *has* to precede speciation because it fosters breeding patterns -- not vice versa! The social organism has priority. For instance, there is precious little sexual promiscuity occurring between Eskimos and Hottentots. They are isolated from one another. Given that this isolation continues for a sufficient period, it seems possible they might become unable to interbreed productively. In any case, to say that they share a common 'gene pool' is not even good science fiction."

Chapter 11

Social body, Social Mind -- Social Thinking?!

(Does a social body presuppose a social mind, or is it mindless? And if such a mind exists, what is it? Also other vague questions about the substantive nature of conceptual data, including the possibility of mental evolution!)

The following morning Greg and I alphabetized the exam papers, recorded scores, and posted grades on the bulletin-board outside the office. Then we sat back and waited for the miscellany of phone calls that always follow an exam. During a quiet period between calls Greg remarked, "I've been told that successful graduate students first study their professors, and after understanding them, they study the subject matter. So I'd like to see if I have your position straight, may I?"

"Fire away," I replied.

"As I understand it, you believe that everything is made up of a network of relations. The observed differences between things are largely due to whether the network mesh is fine or coarse, and particularly how it is organized. The relational processes composing the net may be divided into two general categories. First, there are the submicroscopic ones that make up inorganic matter. These are sterile in the sense that the linkages carry little or no information. They simply hold things together.

Then, secondly, there are the relations that occur within and between living things. These are largely information-laden links. When used as communications, they act like a kind of adhesive which holds social groups together. This applies to bacteria, cells, fish, people, or whatever. The reason groups hold together is seen as some sort of mysterious attraction between things of like kind. And links carry information because they connect living organisms sensitive to the patterning being transmitted. Living things can receive, transmit, and profit from information. All such entities, including cells, are therefore said to be intelligent to some degree. This is implied by their ability to use the information. All are highly organized."

He paused and looked at me questioningly. So I assured him, "You are certainly doing O.K. so far."

"What have I missed?"

"Nothing much except some highlights and conclusions."

"Such as?"

"Well, for one thing it should always be emphasized that relations are matters of attraction. They are emergent and they increase exponentially. The resulting process is what we call growth. There is even a simple equation for emergent relations. It was mentioned when we discussed the dot patterns earlier. But the prime feature for all social organisms is the fact that like kind obviously attract each other, whatever the reason. Thus, members of a well organized social body tend to become ever more closely integrated and similar to each other. The *dis*similar is the *dis*like.

The gist of the whole concept lies in the fact that things do not exist by reason of what they *are*, as commonly assumed, but by how they are *organized*. The startling difference between graphite and diamonds has been cited as an example. Both are pure carbon. But there are also countless hydrocarbons made up of the same components, some differing only as mirror images of each other called isomers. Despite this virtual identity in what they 'are,' they may differ markedly because of their organization.

I dislike repeating myself, but the whole is always more than the sum of its parts -- else it is not a whole. It is parts *plus* organization. And that 'plus' is more important than the parts! Think about it this way, a person can build a vast variety of different buildings using exactly the same number of the same bricks. What makes the buildings different, and what provides their identity, is not the materials used. It is how they are organized. A brick is a brick is a brick. But a building is manifestly a product of the mind.

The trouble, I feel, is that people are unwilling to accept the generality of this Gestalt principle. They agree that it operates at the physical and chemical levels. But when it comes to living systems (also physico-chemical), they protest wildly. It seems to threaten the mystique with which their assumptions, beliefs, and even their formal training have surrounded living matter. When applied to psychological structures, needless to say, it is simply dismissed out of hand. This makes it difficult for them to even think about the relationship between organization and mind."

The ringing was the phone again. When Greg answered I heard him explain that no, she didn't necessarily flunk because she missed the exam. There was a make-up test scheduled for 7 pm. tomorrow evening. If she also missed that for reasons other than hospitalization, she flunked. When he returned I suggested that the whole issue might become clearer if we considered the critical nature of the role played by communications in the social body. He agreed, so I continued.

"The minimum requirement for a society is the existence of cooperative and reciprocal communication which mediates behavior among the members. Just as the word organism implies organization, so community implies communication. Further, a communication is not the signal itself. Nor is it the response. Both can occur without communication. It is the *relationship* which results between the participating individuals. And relationships are the intangible essence of organization. They provide belongingness, commonality of thought, and understanding. Inside the brain they also account for the 'associations' which occur during learning and thinking, the stuff that holds the mind together." [12]

"Before you go any further," Greg interposed, "just how would you define a social organism? What are the criteria?"

"Defining a social organism is not easy," I admitted, "and I am not sure it can be done very meaningfully. In part, the difficulty arises from its complexity and ever-changing structure. But more significantly, it depends upon the degree of belongingness or cohesiveness in the total -- the extent to which individual members identify themselves with the society.

Vague as this may sound, it nonetheless provides us with at least one major criterion. I would say that any social body or nation, for which the member organisms will fight virtually to the death, is one which transcends the individual, as seen by that individual. It is one to which he feels he belongs, and with which he identifies. Certainly this is true for all social insects, members of most human families and their extensions into clans and tribes, and most nations when they are subject to attack. It is also obviously true for our cellular societies or bodies -- as witnessed by our highly developed immune system. [13]

It is much easier to simply describe a social organism because of the many similarities it bears to other life forms. For example, almost all organic bodies develop and are governed in hierarchial fashion. There is, as it were, a cephalocaudal gradient of authority extending from the 'head' of state downward. In simple form, this is seen in the pecking order of chicken flocks. But the human baby also develops along a cephalocaudal gradient.

The birth of a new society, like that of the baby, is often a violent episode for the parental organism. In most cases it progresses through something very similar to a vulnerable childhood, an adolescence of rapid expansion, a more stable and reproductive mature period, then aging and death. Many thinkers, particularly Spengler, have been quite impressed by these developmental analogies between the human and his societies. [14]

As people age there is an ongoing bonding of the collagen molecules in the body with consequent tightening of the cellular organization. Outward symptoms include changes in the skin, loss of flexibility, stiffening of the joints, and a sort of behavioral rigidity, i.e., we become 'set in our ways.' This may be compared with what happens in an aging social body.

In social organisms, natural and healthy bonds attending growth are variously called customs, mores and traditions. But the analogous collagen bonds are communication rigidities called laws. As in the cellular society, they have only one purpose -- restriction of behavior. Legislators work overtime generating them. Individual differences become ironed out for the so-called 'common good.' And though the lives of people often become homogenized, routinized and sterile, the process continues inexorably. This is *not* an indictment of all laws. Some are necessary just as collagen bonds are necessary in the organism. But excess is pathological in either case. [15]

Like all other organisms, our body cells have a limited lifespan. As they grow older they undergo mitosis less frequently and with greater error. This includes the immune system. Thus, the ultimate reason people age is that their cellular citizens age. The same has been suggested of human societies. Older societies usually contain a higher proportion of older citizens. Bearing offspring is for the young. They can be companions for their children and act as role models. For all the prattle of education theorists, teaching and preaching do little to mold child behavior. The child is a primate, and primates learn by imitation. Monkey see, monkey do.

When plotted, the growth curves of social bodies have the same sigmoidal shape as human growth curves. And it is interesting to note that just as in the case of humans, growth of the governmental 'head' is much more rapid than the rest of the social body. Anyone familiar with bureaucracies is well aware that governments tend to grow out of all proportion to the citizenry governed.

Aging is the terminal portion of the growth curve. It begins when the zest for life diminishes and growth becomes internalized, i.e., limited to sheer maintenance and elaboration of microstructure. But it never stops till the organism 'crystallizes out' and total rigor is attained. In both Greece and Rome there was last-gasp legislation to increase the birth rate and loosen the grip of government. But legislation is restrictive by nature, and *biology cannot be legislated!"*

There was a knock at the door. Greg was visibly irritated by having to shift mental gears. But I was pleased to note that his dealings with the students were nonetheless gracious and helpful. Errors in exam answers were carefully explained and the students left seemingly satisfied. Upon returning he made himself comfortable in the chair and remarked, "You have really sold me on the idea that societies are organisms. But since they are, they should have some sort of brain, shouldn't they?"

I nodded and said, "The government itself is often cited as the brain of the social body. But if this were solely the case, the body would surely have to be that of an idiot. No, the government is what we call the *old* brain, or sometimes the 'reptilian' brain. In the human this is a very basic and ancient neural section devoted largely to regulating body processes -- a sort of janitorial staff. As for its counterpart in the social body (the government), it goes without saying that janitorial or regulatory work is simplified by increased legislation. In both cases it keeps the plant working and maintains the integrity of the system. However, this old brain plays little or no role in psychological processes such as thinking. The average legislator is a lawyer and doesn't know diddly-squat about science. Whether human body or social body, all such matters are functions of the new brain, or cortex.

You are right in noting that if a social organism exists, then the analogue of a cortex probably also exists, and with it a *mind*. If a society of cells such as the human can develop a mind by continuously increasing its complexity, there is no apparent reason why a society of humans could not develop an equivalent social mind by the same process. But since the social body is tenuous, or loosely and irregularly structured like colonial organisms, it seems doubtful that its mind would be centralized like ours.[16]

As you are no doubt aware, speculation of this sort leads directly into that narcotic realm variously known as the Überseele, Volkgeist, overmind, social mind -- call it what you wish. Primitive peoples attributed their dreams to it. Others turned it into a god. But today's cognoscenti usually picture it as a sort of free-floating intelligence which infuses its constituent life forms, whether these are societal, biospheric, or universal in scope. Whatever the case, the roster of serious scientists who have espoused these or related concepts, reads like a list of Nobel prize winners. One even has misgivings addressing their arguments.[17]

I should like to preface my remarks on the subject with two bits of skepticism. First, it seems extremely improbable whether the existence of an overmind could ever be proved or disproved. Because of this, some would consider it a waste of time even to discuss the issue. Secondly, if it does exist, there is little likelihood we could ever communicate with it. Communication would only be in one direction -- from it to us. This means that any interaction with it would be severely limited at best."

'Why one-way?"

"That's an easy one. Our own minds are almost exclusively one-way. Our senses provide information about the outside world. But the old brain takes such good care of the body that we don't even know what's happening inside. The information flow is: Sensory input ⇨ Mental processing ⇨ Orders to the body. And the flow is restricted to information-bearing patterns. No energies from the outside world enter or leave the CNS. Senses and muscles are only triggered into action, *not* energized by stimuli.

Remember, we are assuming that any social mind would have to be an emergent structure having the same relationship to the social body that our minds have to us. If it were some independent and preexistent entity, then it would belong to the realm of theology, and nothing said here would apply. Otherwise, it appears that Gödel's theorem is applicable. This was mentioned earlier. It says that if something is to be understood fully, one must be detached from it, situated outside. And the mind is so self-contained there is no way it can acquire complete information about itself as an entity. Of course, there are some who have doubts about the general applicability of Gödel's theorem, including an old friend of mine named Köhler. [18]

No control systems engineer could ever devise anything so isolated as the mind. If he did, he could never know what was transpiring inside. It should be obvious that systems of this sort can only grow from *within* like the seed of a plant. They can't be constructed from the outside. The same is true for *all* living things. They evolve outward, upward and onward -- but always from an internal nucleus. The process is from seed to plant, from fertilized egg to human, and from one-celled creatures to man. And here we are -- asking whether man himself could be such a nucleus! Admittedly, the concept is almost incomprehensible. But it is nonetheless logical.

However we may feel about a social mind, the CNS definitely is *not* an 'open system' as so many biologists like to describe it. And the mind (yours or mine) is even less so. I am alone, and you are alone. Of myself, my decisions to act, my thoughts, feelings and perceptions, I have the most intimate knowledge. This is awareness entirely different from any structures or processes I can identify in either body or brain. It is so completely my own, and so isolated from equivalent minds of others, that I can communicate with them only by artificial symbols such as words and gestures. Even though we join bloodstreams for a common circulation of our brains, we cannot feel or think the same!

I believe it was Chuang Tzû of 4th Century BC, China, who noted that one never hears what is said. Nor does he ever read what is written. The best he can do is sit in the private theater of his own mind, watching the play brought about by the words. The words are not reality. They are merely cue-cards used by our own actors on our own stage. [19]

Let us pause and think about Chuang Tzû's stage for a moment. It comes equipped with props, backdrop, and personal lighting. It provides a kind of context or 'setting' for whatever enters. The meaning of anything depends upon context -- no context, no meaning. Such effects typify all mental operations. They constitute a backdrop of related mental structures which are not in awareness when we attend to something. But they are nonetheless always present. Something which is meaningful can only be defined as that which satisfies our immediate needs or fits into our psychological belief systems. In doing so it acquires context. This is why it makes 'sense' to us. It may not make sense to anyone else.

Communication between minds depends exclusively upon the similarity of their contents. This has obvious disadvantages. But it helps explain why organisms of like kind attract each other, and why members of closely-knit social groups grow increasingly alike. As Chuang Tzû implies, two minds maximally alike will communicate with maximal efficiency -- whereas, those totally unlike will be unable to communicate at all!

The foregoing is borne out by a variety of evidence. (1) Identical twins have brains which are essentially clones of each other, and accordingly, they seem able to communicate almost without use of words. (2) Social insects are better described as large families. In most of them, e.g., bees or ants, the degree of relatedness is 75%. Therefore, communication between separate members is superior to that of any other insects. (3) Sociobiologists have provided a miscellany of evidence establishing that social grouping, communication, and altruism are direct functions of relatedness. (4) Many creatures, including the human infant, have an instinctive fear and/or dislike of the strange and different. Being strange means it doesn't 'fit in.' And finally, (5) there is the logical proposition that no communication is possible when separate data banks contain no common elements.

Sorry about this lengthy digression. Let's get back to that theoretical emergence called a social mind. Among others, Julian Huxley [20] felt that evolution, as commonly conceived, screeched to a dead stop sometime in the dim geological past millions of years ago. It was replaced by a psychosocial over-mind. This was not genetic, individual, or mind-in-society, but a wholly different phenomenon which he called a 'noosystem.' He described it as being closely akin, if not identical , with what we know as *language!* In its broader aspects it represents a culture. Favoring this view is the observation that language does seem to have a life of its own. It appears to grow, and it falls into genus and species categories. We do not control it. We merely partake of it.

However, identifying overmind with language seems somewhat misleading. We end up playing footsie with that semantics fallacy again. Language is only an arbitrary set of symbols that code for activity of the mind. What Huxley probably intended was the mental content symbolized by the language: ideas, concepts, percepts, and such. We do *not* think in words, as some early psychologists assumed. We think in the *meanings* of words, and sometimes in meanings that have no words! [21]

As for Huxley's assumption that evolution came to a halt millions of years ago, I have very strong reservations. He may have been right, but I see no evidence whatever that evolution has ceased. In fact, the whole idea seems basically illogical. It appears much more reasonable simply to assume that evolution became mental evolution when the brain enlarged. After all, the brain could still be undergoing growth which was no longer attended by visible changes in the body. The evolving factors were more likely molecular changes in the cortex -- and you can't see molecules.

We must remember that an organism can build almost any kind or shape of molecule it needs, and that it often has to do so in the form of antibodies. The number of possible proteins is essentially infinite, having been estimated as high as 10^{2700}! So there is plenty of potential variance of structure with which the brain can deal.

.When and if biochemists finally prove that acquired memory is molecular (and this is now well underway), it will be easier to visualize evolution as continuing on an invisible sub-microscopic level. And just why couldn't the brain/mind system be undergoing further development separate and apart from the body? Certainly its growth and maintenance are almost wholly independent of the body. Moreover, molecular adaptations *do* occur. The influenza virus, with even smaller dimensions than any assumed mental structures, has undergone several evolutionary changes within recent times. And the medical profession is constantly fighting bacteria which adapt to new drugs.

I have always been amused by the amount of loose thinking which prevails whenever this subject is brought up. For example, theorists tend to ignore the fact that anything which becomes transmissible by heredity automatically contributes to evolution. This is what the word 'evolution' means. Now, it is well established that both longevity and intelligence are largely inherited, possibly even related. The longevity question doesn't disturb them. But the very idea that some people are born smarter than others, though patently obvious, grates against their idealistic dogma. It seems unjust. So they ignore it -- pretend it doesn't exist.

Perhaps I should mention that I am not alone in suspecting that mental evolution may be continuing. One of our most prominent biologists, viz., E. 0. Wilson of Harvard, also 'sees no reason to assume the cessation of evolution in either mental capacity or social behavior.' [22] Moreover, this is stated from a standpoint accepting current mutation theory!

However, I have drifted off the subject again. What I really wanted to discuss was the thesis of a social mind, and to identify it with the proliferation of thought processes and their products in today's external world. All individual animals carry information in both their genetic and central nervous systems. But when we look at the information free-floating about us, the data in the outer world, it becomes obvious that possibly one species alone (man) possesses much more information *outside* his body than inside! It is to be found everywhere: in books, computers, films, tapes, newspapers, and whatnot. It exceeds what is available in all other mammals combined. It is many times as much as any given individual possesses, including what is in his DNA!

Such huge amounts of outside information could only belong to a social soma. And to some extent it could even be called species specific. Portions pertain solely to particular cultures. Its acquisition and transmission have long since out-raced the capabilities of any separate individual. And its on-going internal organization provides a rather cogent explanation of how a social mind could evolve. Only a larger social organism could encompass such massive quantities of information. For a minor parallel, look at the beehive or termitary. The individual bee or

termite is extremely limited in neural equipment. But consider the behavior of their social bodies! This presupposes an intelligence second only to that of the human!

As one looks out upon today's world, there are compelling reasons to believe that something is growing out there -- something living, something developing with ever increasing speed. Among others, Toffler contends that cultural growth has already exceeded the rate at which we can adapt to it. [23] Thus, we are now witnessing a disorder aptly called 'information stress.'

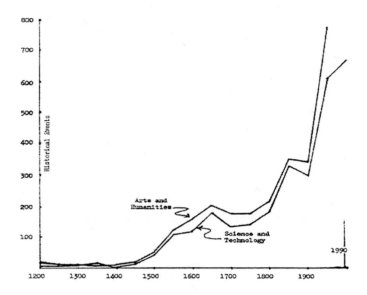

FIGURE 11. Growth of culture from 1200 AD to 1990. Tabulated from Grun, B., *The Time Tables of History, 3rd. Ed.,* N.Y.: Simon & Schuster, 1991. Comparable data for important inventions and discoveries from 1000 AD to 1900 reveal the same acceleration though compiled from other sources. See: Lenski, G., *Human Societies: A Macrolevel Introduction to Sociology.* N. Y.: McGraw Hill Book Co., 1970.

(*NOTE:* The above curve for Arts and Humanities is necessarily made up of value judgments, and opinions differ. Many feel that the arts, especially since 1900, have become increasingly incoherent, and largely reflect the same conflict and disintegration observable in public morality and character. Thus, it should be interpreted only in terms output *volume.* The Science and Technology curve, on the other hand, is much less subject to opinion, and would therefore seem to be valid.). .

And please note that this cultural proliferation is a *growth phenomenon.* It is not merely another aspect of the population explosion. [24] It is proceeding from the simple to the complex, branching out and differentiating. This is precisely the program used by developing life forms. It is found nowhere else except in certain processes of crystallization. Just how it all got started is anybody's guess. The mind of man appeared late in the course of evolution, and societies of one sort or another appeared with it. Perhaps it was triggered by some subtle molecular change in the brain. Then again, it may be that all biological organisms tend to transcend themselves. Upon reaching a critical level they contribute as units to a still greater organization. Who knows?"

I paused to extract a pipe from the rack on my desk. As I stoked it with burley, the phone rang again. I glanced at the clock. This would be the last call. Office hours were nearly over and everyone was well aware that the phone went unanswered except during office hours. This was not arrogance. It was necessity. Privacy for most teachers is a rare commodity, has a high cost, and is usually obtainable only by fiat. When Greg returned I had him post the make-up test schedule on the bulletin board. The door latch was then slipped shut, and we settled down to continue the bull session.

"What kind of stuff would this social mind consist of?" he asked. "It is certainly not the same molecular energies responsible for the relatedness in individual minds, is it?"

"No, and I'm not quite sure what it is," I confessed. "Asking 'what stuff' may not even be meaningful. It looks suspiciously like patterning divorced from any substance or mass. I know this sounds nonsensical. So let's examine some minor feature of the culture -- say poems or melodies. I don't mean what they are printed on, but the poems and melodies themselves. Do they really exist? The Copyright Office apparently thinks so. They are clearly identifiable, listed as property, sometimes have cash value, and are even stolen!

Moreover, they have contours of a sort: beginning and end, as well as internal structure. On the other hand, there is nothing physical connecting their 'parts.' Nor are they constructed out of anything physical. So they have no mass. They can be seen, heard, and recorded both physically and mentally. But they can't be smelled or touched. They can be grasped mentally but not physically. In short, they seem to be something intermediate -- some kind of mind-stuff which we recognize as patterning.

Let's carry the question further. Can poems, melodies or ideas exist *without* the paper upon which they are written? I would have to say yes. They may be far more substantial than any paper. Longfellow and Cole Porter have long since disintegrated. But the constructs they created are still with us. The same is true for Plato. His ideas are also present. In fact, ideas and concepts are so thing-like they can be classified and named! Otherwise we could never index a book. If something occupies space, we readily admit that it exists. So if some recognizable item lasts for long periods of time, why can't it also be said to exist? Duration in time would seem to be just as valid a criterion as extension in space. [25]

What accounts for such extreme durability? The items themselves have no mass, so they can't be matter. And they are much too fixed and invariant to be called 'spirit.' Thus, one is almost forced to conclude that they are a separate type of existence. We speak of them as patterning or organization -- what the Greeks called 'form.' The popular term today is information. It must be the stuff which goes to make up the mind

Meinong, whom I mentioned earlier, showed that such stuff can exist without the matter in which it usually manifests itself. But contrariwise, matter can't exist without it! (Remember atomic explosions!) Form and organization are therefore more fundamental than matter itself. And if it can have being and be recognized independently of matter, one can't help wondering whether the mind could not also exist independently of the tissues upon which it is printed. People die for mentalisms (ideals, religious convictions, etc.) much more readily than they do for material goods.

Just take a moment to consider that paragon of substantiality called matter. Think particularly of that so-called 'particle' known as an electron. Its status in spacetime appears very 'iffy,' being more an event in time than a structure in space. One might even say it has a lot of *wherever* -- the *where* being much less identifiable than the *ever*. Like a well-known song which keeps recurring in one's head, our awareness of it lies more in its recurrence than questions of what or where it is. Perhaps it also is a mentalism!

We ascribe thing-quality, materiality, tangibility, and value to what we *per*ceive even though physics proves it to be no more substantive than what we *con*ceive. And to make the matter more confusing, every *per*ception is a *con*ception. Sensory input has to interact automatically with some memory structure in order to acquire meaning.

Thus, it is illogical to say that when several people see a dog the dog is real, whereas if they all see the same idea the idea doesn't have any reality. They argue this even though the idea obviously had to be there for anyone to grasp. Else what entity is it they recognize? Don't they 'real'ize the idea as fully as they do the dog? One would think that if enough different people recognize a given concept, the concept should have as much validity as the Statue of Liberty. It might not weigh as much, but if it exists independently of the individual, and persists over time, then somehow it has to be real! All that is left of ancient Greece are the *ideas*. The remainder is only a scatterment of the cultural skeleton -- buildings.

Ask yourself, just what *is* the true existence of the New York Stock Exchange or the Vatican at Rome? Does it lie in their meanings or the physical buildings? Note that the buildings could be destroyed and rebuilt, but this would not be possible for the meanings. Consider the importance attached to titles, idols, crucifixes and cash. These are symbols to which people dedicate their entire lives. Why bother working for a promotion if the new position has no reality? Does all formalization have to be represented in wood beams or steel bars?

When carefully analyzed, it is always the intangible relatedness that people cherish. It has value for the only world they know -- the inner one. Crucifixes and cash have only mass, and titles and bank accounts don't even have that! Look at it this way, if ideas have no substantiality our mental life arises out of nothing, consists of nothing, and vanishes into the same void. Everything of which we are proud, our accomplishments, goals, and ideals are shadows on moving water -- and we can't even be sure of the water! In such case, mind becomes only a figure of speech."

At this point Greg stood up, turned his hands outward, and said, "I hate to tell you this, but you are losing me."

"Sorry," I replied. "Let's approach it from a different angle. Suppose we consider the fact that each mind has its own set of ideas, concepts, and so forth. This constitutes a highly elaborate communications net between brain cells. It is never fully identical with that of others. But partially integrated into this personal network, there obviously also exists a body of common mental constructs held by the thinking public. This latter is *independent* of individual minds because it continues even though separate participants die. Therefore, it necessarily exists outside. There it constitutes a communications net of enormous extent and complexity.

Now, consider the argument that each of our personal minds is enduring and substantive only to the extent indicated by personal memory. By the same token, then, this common body of exactly the same sort of memories must also have some degree of substantiality. If communication nets of cells in the brain can give rise to an individual mind as the sum (whole!) of their emergent relations, why shouldn't the same logic apply to the sum (whole) of emergent relations socially?"

"But wouldn't this more general stuff be purely subjective?"

"No. If studied fully, it is seen that the subjective-versus-objective distinction is illusory -- only a play on words. Everything must be subjective in order to be known. The only criterion we have for the so-called objective is that it is the same for you, me, or anyone else who recognizes it. For example, the mental counterpart of a baseball is roughly the same for everyone who knows of baseball. The perception of a baseball is therefore said to be objective. But there are many other counterparts of events, objects and relations which endure and are common to all who know of them. And these are recognized with equal fidelity. Thus, the size, model, or condition of an automobile does not prevent us from immediately knowing it is an automobile. We sense a supposedly non-existent concept, viz.,'all automobiles,' no less than we sense anything else. To summarize, the theory says that we are nodal points in a webbery of mind, transceivers in a vast communications grid. And some aspects of this grid are now even being materialized, supplanted by wire, as in personal computer nets."

"Has anyone else dealt with this hypothetical social mind in these terms?"

"Quite a few. In fact, more than one might anticipate. [26] For the most part, however, they have been concerned with defining a 'genetics' for the culture. They use the term 'meme' to designate ideas, concepts, beliefs and the like. This 'meme' is described as an enduring unit of cultural transmission. It is said to play the same role in the culture that the gene plays for the individual. I presume they would have a 'meme pool' possibly resembling the so-called gene pool. But I don't see how it could be called a social mind, or anything similar to Huxley's 'noosphere.' It would lack internal organization .This is the hallmark of all mind.

All such theorizing would seem to imply an equivalent social 'body.' But so far as I know, they have not bothered with such biological questions, much less the related thought that a social body might possess a social mind. Perhaps their suggestion that the culture could be propagated by mental 'genes' is feasible. I don't know. But I would be more inclined to view their memes as portions of our memories (ideas, concepts, etc.), the constructs utilized during thinking. Unfortunately, their memes would have to mutate -- a happenstance alien to normal growth. Mine would grow. There is a profound difference. Unless fully armed, I wouldn't trust anything around me that 'mutates.' It would be too unpredictable!

Mental growth, as well as the independence of the mind, is demonstrated by the fact that ideas come to us when *they* want to come, and not necessarily when we want them to come. We cannot always call them up at will, nor can we arbitrarily exorcise them when they are unpleasant. Those who suffer from insomnia always testify that they can't sleep because they can't control their flow of thought, much less turn it off completely. This flow of thought frequently has its direction altered by inputs from the out-side world. But even the deviations themselves usually relate to inconsistencies or other difficulties arising within current memory structures.

My point is simply this: *you* can't decide what you are going to think about. The decision itself is thinking! Thought processes are guided by the over-all system organization. Mental meanderings have to be consistent with the assumptions, beliefs, and other content of the mind. Even when redirected by new inputs, it is the ongoing organization, the *growth* and needs of the mind which dictate the manner in which new data are handled.

Thinking is a kind of creative energy patterning which occurs in the brain. This is what it seems to be, and this is about all it could be. At present we may not be able to positively identify the energy. But it can be demonstrated that conceptual systems tend to expand, organize themselves into ever more consistent structures, perpetuate themselves, and quite often end up as fixed beliefs.

It cannot be emphasized enough. The mind is self-organizing. It *grows!* Thinking can be identified with this growing organization. Thus, one way of looking upon mental phenomena is to regard them as simply a further and more variable extension of what occurs during all biological growth. In other words, psychological functions may have arisen from the need for a more rapid and modifiable organizational process, one which dealt in the structuring of energy rather than protoplasm

Ideas are offspring of the mind, as it were. They develop from mere seeds much as do other organic entities. Given that our theorizing is correct, they can also become part of a burgeoning social mind. If this occurs, they may replicate themselves like bacteria, skipping from mind to mind. Many, like the God concept, could even be considered infectious. They frequently employ 'carriers' called missionaries. And if they spread throughout the entire social body, eliminating all variability, they could sap its vitality -- as in that lengthy mental sickness known as the 'dark ages.'

The German philosopher, Von Ditfurth, came up with an unusual argument recently. His book has the interesting title, *Der Geist fiel nicht vom Himmel: Die Evolution unseres Bewusstseins* (The Mind did not fall from the Sky: The Evolution of our Consciousness.) In it he contends that the very existence of mind and consciousness presupposes an overmind!

Specialization of various body parts such as limbs and organs, are noted to be evolutionary adaptations to corresponding features of the internal or external environment. For example, feet, fins, and wings were developed for locomotion. Their very nature indicates that they are adapted for use on land, in water, and through air respectively. The fact that they exist pre-supposes that these terrestrial features also exist. In other words, they are acceptable evidence for them. Similarly, the eyes could not have arisen without the presence of light. The fact that we possess eyes is therefore proof that light exists. Needless to say, the argument is extrapolated to include consciousness and the mind. The sheer existence of these, in and of itself, is said to be evidence for the existence of an overmind as a feature of the external world!" [27]

Greg adjusted himself nervously in his chair and asked, "Does the individual mind interact with this proposed overmind as the eyes do with light?

"Who knows?" I replied. "But I assume that if it does, then it would do so in the same fashion as the eyes. That is to say, the action would be in one direction only. The light influences the eyes. But the eyes have no effect on the light. Given such an overmind, we could receive information, but it would do us little good to ask for information. It would be largely a one-way street much like the authority of our own minds over our body cells."

"Maybe it's just as well," he laughed. "I'd hate to think of the chaos and disaster if some God answered all the prayers!"

"Of course, there are still different arguments," I pointed out. "The one that most impressed Hermann Weyl, Eddington, Jeans, as well as other scientists, has to do with mathematics. This subject is exclusively a product of the human mind just as is language. [28] For the most part it developed prior to, and independently of the major discoveries of physics. Unlike verbal languages it is used worldwide. Most significantly, however, it is based on certain axioms of order or *organization*. For example, all ones are the same whether added, subtracted, multiplied or divided. And its rules of grammar are much more rigorous. Nevertheless, it is a man-made structure.

The truly amazing thing about mathematics is that it coincides with processes of the external world so precisely that the latter is incomprehensible without it. It permits extensive predictions and leads to discovery of events which otherwise would be totally beyond investigation. Indeed, mathematics and the physical sciences have almost a one-to-one correspondence. As someone once put it, if there is a God, then He thinks mathematically!

Precise correspondence of this degree could scarcely be called coincidence. When one can be mapped onto the other in such exact fashion, they begin to approach identity. Two possible explanations present themselves. (1) The universe either is, or else is infused with an overmind which was involved in the formulation of mathematics. Or (2) the energies constituting the human mind follow exactly the same rules, and have the same organizational features as the energies of the outer world. And I might add that this would indeed be the case if our mental energies were colloidal forces of attraction. These would make for a sort of gravity for the mind, and gravity is the attraction which organizes the outer world

Numerous scientists, including the above, have preferred the former explanation. And while not discounting this view, I am more inclined toward the latter. My reason: the things I see and hear are not mathematics. Nonetheless, they also correspond exactly with the external world. And in my opinion at least, this is what underlies the correspondence of the mathematics. Sensory processes are just as accurate as the math. Indeed, they couldn't be otherwise. And they occur despite the devious and disorderly structures of the nervous system. Furthermore, it can't be explained away by any naive concept of 'sensory coding.' I have no homunculus in my head to do the decoding, much less one with a Ph.D. in mathematics."

Greg looked thoughtful for a moment, then remarked, "I don't know whether that makes sense to me, or not. Both outer space and the brain certainly appear disorderly. You say that the organization which occurs in them is due to the similarity in how the different energies behave. Both the inside and the outside worlds use energies of attraction. I don't know enough about thermodynamics to form an opinion. But I have always been told that the outer world tends toward disorder -- so I don't see how organization could possible arise in it."

"Don't feel badly about it," I replied. "Much of physics is equally confused. It is due to the single greatest *faux pas* in the history of the subject. The outer world tends toward increased entropy, and entropy was identified with disorder. What they really meant was *randomness* -- and randomness is *not* disorder. Besides, the calculations don't apply to structured systems like organisms. I won't bother getting into the subject because it can become quite abstruse. But look at it this way. If the same physical principles (thermodynamics) apply equally well to all energies, then the energies have to be operating in the same fashion -- no matter what they are!"

Chapter 12

Sacred Tortillas and Bugs that Think!

(Popular beliefs about an overmind: summary of the arguments and evidence. Do social insects employ a chemical language to create an overmind for themselves? Can it be they are capable of social thinking?)

Proponents of an overmind, one type or another, include many illustrious scientists. The foregoing are but a few. Arguments vary with the individual. The general public, however, seems most impressed by what might be called coincidents. For example, great leaders are said to appear when the need demands. They match their times. But one wonders whether this "matching" involves anything unique about the individuals. Perhaps others could have done as well, or even better. It seems possible that those "selected" just happened to be on hand when problems arose in public awareness. That is to say, they simply plugged a hole which had become obvious. They were in the right place at the right time!

One has this suspicion because a great man *must* match his times -- else why should he be considered great? No matter how eager the potential leader, how significant the issue, or how important the invention may be, all effort is wasted unless it is acceptable within the context existing for the period. The history of science is one long sad saga of great ideas and inventions which have been rejected or ignored, then rediscovered, often repeatedly.

As noted earlier, if a social mind exists it grows. And unless it has developed to where it contains a niche for a particular item or action, any sales pitch does not communicate, much less get accepted. Nobody knows how many geniuses die in poverty, worn out from seeking recognition, and all too painfully aware how much more frustrating it is to be ahead of the times than simply behind the times.

Also commonly mentioned are those periods in history (e.g., Periclean Athens or renaissance Italy) when innovative thinkers and

artists emerged like flowers in the Spring. There have even been instances
where impressive discoveries have been made about the same time by
separate and independent thinkers, much as if produced by the Zeitgeist
itself! Notable examples include Darwin and Wallace (evolution), and
Leibnitz and Newton (calculus). Events suggest that the time must have
been ripe for them. But what could it mean to say that the time was ripe
unless something were "ripening?"

All such blossoming of genius, whether simultaneous or sequential,
is visible only in retrospect. And when so viewed it becomes obvious that
recognition depended upon the condition of the garden in which they
blossomed. No one can build without available materials, and not even the
wisest of us can think beyond the data contained in his data banks. This
is precisely why all generically new discoveries are made serendipitously.
They are lucky accidents. Otherwise, they could not have been discovered
at the time. [29] The classical story of radium and the Curies is a case in
point. Summarized in different terms, successful events are those which
contribute to the growth pattern. Given a different pattern or a different
phase of growth, most of man's benefactors might have been labeled
eccentric, possibly even insane, but certainly not geniuses.

There are still other popular arguments for an overmind. Some derive
from those many instances where groups of organisms behave as a single
body without any apparent reason. They act like lemmings. The
implication is that unknown influences have taken command of them. And
under certain conditions perhaps this might be true. However, all living
things are cooperative to some degree, and primates are notoriously
imitative. Moreover, concerted action and synchrony of behavior are not
unusual as popularly thought. They are quite common at all levels.

Consider body cells. These typically synchronize their activity and
behave in unison. It is particularly observable with the simultaneous
contraction of large muscles. But the synchrony of neural structures is
more interesting. The electrical brain rhythm, discussed earlier, is best
known. And since it is tied in so intimately with the phenomena of
attention, the similar synchronization of social behavior would seem to
suggest compar-able attributes for any social mind. For example, it might
be reasonable to describe fads as social attention to first one thing then
another.

Our perspective is necessarily always ego-centric. As a result, we tend
to focus on the mass actions of cells because they produce our behavior.
We are their societies. But we have an opposite orientation when it comes
to human societies. Here we tend to emphasize the individual rather than
any group behavior. Nonetheless, it is a commonplace that given such

assemblies as gangs or mobs, something seems to come over people. They are readily swayed to almost any kind of bizarre behavior by gang leaders, witch doctors, evangelists, politicians, or others whom they would disregard when alone. Mass hypnotic effects, lynchings, murders, hysteria, and hallucinations have all been reported. If synchronous rhythm is added as in chanting, war dances, or the repetitive intonations of certain preachers, all manner of pathological phenomena are easily induced: glossolalia, unconsciousness, and even mass suicide. The compulsion to believe (hunger of the mind) temporarily overrides any logic. First they buy it. Then (usually much later), they check to see if it fits into their belief systems.

Possibly the most baffling and spectacular of these group effects are the psychologically-induced illnesses or demonic " possession" cases which are standard fodder for the tabloids. To illustrate, suppose we go to an American owned semiconductor factory in Malay. Hundreds of local women are employed. One day a young woman looking through her microscope sees the face of a wrinkled and hideous old hag peering back at her. She emits loud screams and topples to the floor where she remains, eyes rolling and arms flailing about. Grotesque though the behavior may be, it sets up a chain reaction. According to reports, dozens of others soon become "possessed" and fall over shrieking.

Newspapers are filled with accounts of crowds who all see the same apparition (usually a sacred image) on rain streaked walls, mountain profiles, and even tortillas! In short, we see what we expect to see! Under certain conditions, the sensory input becomes modified during the recognition process -- much as it does when interpreting Rorschach blots.

Phenomena of this sort are not peculiar to Malay or Latin America. Local factories are also plagued by similar episodes. Someone smells a foul odor. Others smell it. And soon the factory is emptied. Schools would seem to be a favorite location for mass effects of this nature. The young are "impressionable." They have high curiosity and suggestibility. Reported symptoms include nausea, vomiting, abdominal pain, itching, and fainting. Inability to determine any physical cause or biological etiology has led them to be classified as EPI -- short for "epidemic psychogenic illness." [30]

Needless to say, arguments for a social mind are not too impressive when dependent upon pathological events, questionable history, or coincidence. Events themselves are either judged *ex post facto*, or are otherwise beyond investigation. Explanations involving EPI, mob psychology, or related concepts, are equally questionable because they usually reduce to matters of rapport with some demagogic figure like a hypnotist or preacher.

In general, it appears that the psychological activity and/or behavior of human groups rarely evinces anything the participants could not have brought about individually. Effects of a social mind, if one exists, are certainly not obvious under such conditions. Any valid argument would require some sort of group where mutual interaction of minds could be shown to create *more* than the most capable member could have achieved by himself. So far as I can determine, this has occurred rarely, if ever.

Committees are notorious failures when it comes to creative thinking or problem solving. Too often they turn into little more than sounding boards for some particular ego. And when this happens the whole degenerates to even less than the sum of the participants. Hence the statement that a camel is only a horse designed by a committee. The efforts of think-tanks employing brain storming sessions, group-think meetings, in-depth discussion panels, idea encounter groups, or the Delphi technique developed by Rand Corp. are slightly more productive. But after years of close association with such efforts, I have yet to see anything spectacular emerge. [31]

All of us have heard the constant calls for "teamwork." It has been drummed into us because it is essential for joint activities of a physical nature. Four men can pick up a weight four times as heavy as one man can handle by himself. Beyond the physical, however, teamwork translates only as cooperation. Apparently there can be no teamwork of the minds -- the reason being that individual minds are completely isolated from each other.

Group behavior among people seems to be much like that among social insects. This is something we should expect. Aside from humans, these tiny creatures possess the world's most highly organized societies. And as described earlier, when a "committee" of social insects is isolated from the parent organization, their behavior is essentially random unless some physical task is introduced. Given a goal, teamwork emerges spontaneously.

The ancient stoic philosophers emphasized that under conditions of disaster such as war, the pain of all the people could be no greater than the pain of one man. Pain can only be experienced individually, not collectively. Feelings are not additive like labor. But suppose we were to apply the same rule to intelligence. Suppose we were to declare that the intelligence of all men can be no greater than that of one man. Considering the scope of our present-day culture, such a statement would sound ludicrous. And the fact that it does seem ludicrous speaks for the existence of an overmind.

Why this difference between feelings and intelligence? The answer is that the raw material of emotions are chemical (hormonal) reactions, where-as the raw material of intelligence is information, patterning or organization. No one can transmit or record feelings. But information is transmissible and can be stored on everything from stone tablets to microfilm. Feelings belong to the person. But thoughts are not necessarily the property of just one individual, unique to that individual. Many are social by nature. They get passed around like beer at a summer picnic. What I am trying to point out is: *information has features conducive to the formation of an overmind!*

It is this transmissibility of thought to which we refer when we speak of communication. Efficiency of transmission is believed to be roughly proportional to similarity of minds. Members of bee and ant families are 75% related genetically. And though human families are not so close, understanding is still better among family members. By contrast, most committee members are essentially strangers to each other.

Whether social insects or humans, individuals removed from their normal context are displaced entities. When grouped they do not represent any naturally-occurring bodies, nor are they products of growth like bee hives, families, and tribes. They are artificial assemblies serving only nominal needs. They could scarcely be expected to show any life-like properties as a unit. There is obviously little belongingness, one member with another, and therefore little similarity between minds.

Given that there is no mutual mind of significance among members of heterogeneous groups, and dismissing popular arguments based on historical events and mob psychology, what is left of the contention of an overmind? Surprisingly enough, when all evidence is assembled, it makes a rather compelling list. Let me summarize the different arguments briefly.

(1) *The argument from logic.* If we go back to Figure 2 and attendant discussion, it will be recognized that self-awareness can emerge among otherwise separate entities by means of feedback. Though self-awareness is not synonymous with mind, it is a necessary condition for it. The neurons illustrated in Figure 2 are individual beings sensitive only to their surrounds. But when connected into a net carrying complete information among members, self-awareness can (and probably does) arise within in-dividual members and the net as a whole. Only nerve cells can organize into such nets, so the same effects would not be anticipated among other cells. Its occurrence among neural cells, however, provides insight into the ancient mystery about how our own minds got started.

The argument from logic states that the cell is to the organism as the organism is to the social body. Individuals are seen as units in a socializing sequence beginning with the cell. It is an assumption based on the observable fact that cells have an inbuilt tendency to socialize to the maximum whenever possible. Multicellular creatures are thought to be expressions of this tendency, and they are believed to carry it further in creating their own social groups. In all cases, the limiting factor is communication. Current animal societies (e.g., wolf packs) are limited in their social development because of the short range of their communication systems. Despite minor implementation, they are still essentially chemical.

Humans have largely overcome this barrier by developing a symbolic verbal language. This enables the social sequence to continue and expand. Thus, to the degree that members of a human society achieve mutual communication, to that degree the society will develop self-awareness as a social body. Members will evolve similar aims and outlook, come to depend on one another, take on specialized role behaviors, and produce a culture consisting of unique customs, folklore, mores, and traditions. These are thought to be the rudiments of a social mind, overmind, Volkgeist, or call it what you wish. Since language (communication) plays the critical role in this "meeting of the minds," it is understandable that Huxley and others would identify it with the overmind itself.

(2) *The physical analogy.* This parallels the foregoing and deals with the homologies of structure involved. The analogy is that between the cellular society (human) and the human society (social soma). It should be emphasized that this latter is not necessarily the same as a nation. Possibly the best word for it is *culture*. Its physical parameters are therefore ill-defined and loosely structured -- the closest living analogues being certain colonial marine organisms.

The similarities between comparable features of the body and society have already been covered in some detail and will only be listed here. Both are said to possess: skeleton, old brain (government), organs having similar chemical functions, food and waste treatment facilities, peace-keeping forces, as well as supply and communication nets. They even go through the same phases of growth and therefore exhibit the same growth curves. Distribution of authority is laid out in the same fashion, being represented as a cephalocaudal gradient.

Most significantly, both the human and his society depend upon a hierarchy of feedback mechanisms making for homeostasis, or system maintenance. Like growth itself, homeostasis is a major criterion of life. The societies of humans, like those of social insects, are therefore said to possess the basic attributes of living things. The argument states that if all major components and their functions are alike, it is justifiable to look upon the one (social soma) as a natural extension of the other (human). When so defined, this would mean that social organisms would have to possess a mind. It would be necessary to identify, process and record information from the past. Without this mnemonic history, nothing could operate or continue to grow in a consistent fashion.

(3) *The presence of transcorporeal information.* It is well established that human minds (indeed all minds) depend on the reception, processing and storage of information. No matter how it is analyzed, this information ultimately must be defined as differences of patterning or organization. Different books are printed from the same stockpile of words, but the words are *organized* differently and therefore carry different information. Spoken words are trans*form*ations in sound patterns, and pictures convey information by reorganizing light distributions. The presence of information presupposes communication, and communication requires the existence of mind -- or something which communicates. None of it is *sui generis*. It is all related and does not arise nor exist in and of itself. Mind is required.

The argument rests on an obvious fact. There is a huge, ever-growing, and well organized quantity of information in the external world. Humans and possibly social insects are the only known creatures possessing more information *outside* their bodies than inside! The information itself is independent of any given individual or group of individuals. So it exists in its own right. And if it exists outside the body, it suggests that there is mind outside the body. Whether one refers to this as an overmind, the vital aspect of a culture, or simply a growing body of self-organizing information, is merely a matter of choosing names. The facts remain the same.

(4) *The argument from mathematics.* Mathematics is a language -- a carrier or medium for transporting information. However, it is so different from verbal languages it must be considered separately. It consists largely of rules or regulations based on axioms of order (organization) , and serves largely as a guide for structuring information. It has little substance or content of its own. Rather, it is a framework for reliable construction in the mental world. Logic is a part of mathematics. Anything that is illogical or mathematically false is irrational by definition. In short, there is a very close relationship between mathematics and the rational functioning of the mind.

This should not be construed as meaning that mathematics *is* mind, or that those with mathematical skills are necessarily more intelligent. There are idiot-savants who are whizz-kids in math, but a total loss in everything else. What it says is that math is the grammar of organization. On the other hand, mind is most likely organization itself! It has been said that infants as young as 5 months can be shown to use a sort of "rudimentary mathematical reasoning." [32]

All this would be little more than esoteric philosophy were it not for an equally significant fact. It would seem that mathematics also holds somewhat the same relationship with processes of the external world. Indeed, the physical world cannot be comprehended without it! So, if math maps onto mind, and also maps onto outer reality, there has to be a very close relationship between the mind and outer reality. After all, two things equal to the same thing are equal to each other. This strongly suggests that mind is at least a part of the outer world --possibly overmind of some sort.

(5) *The critical nature of organization.* In the physical world organization permeates all matter. Without it matter cannot exist. It is always present to some degree depending on temperature and other factors. Thus, it is interesting to note that differences of organization are said to be the only clearcut distinction between the living and the non-living. Living things simply have much greater complexity. Indeed, life might be described as an ongoing process of complexification. As a result, progressive elaboration of structure is perhaps the most outstanding feature of both the individual mind and that of the culture (social mind). Such facts make it rather obvious why axioms of order underlie mathematics, and why orderliness is also necessary for human understanding. That which is simple is easy to comprehend, and in like manner is easy to express mathematically. In every case, increased complexity increases the difficulty proportionately.

Though largely ignored since the disappearance of Gestalt psychology, organization should be studied because organisms organize. The mind cannot deal with the disorderly. It is distasteful. Irregular sound waves are heard as noise, and disorderly visual arrays are seen as clutter. Disorderly thinking is even deemed pathological. Whether physical structure, system events, or sensory inputs, organization means predictability. It allows for understanding. Thus, it is a necessary precondition for the mind to deal with anything.

All the foregoing arguments are obviously related, and all favor the thesis of an overmind. But what about the opposition, those who disagree with the concept? The most commonly encountered statement is that it can't be proved. This is quite true. But it is also true of almost everything else, including a goodly portion of physics. Aside from immediate sensory examination of objects and events, there are no reliable criteria for what constitutes proof. And when it comes to testing theories, the absence of such criteria becomes quite noticeable. Even if they existed, one wonders whether they would be used.

One hard-nosed colleague of mine, a biologist, put it this way, "An overmind is possible. Anything is possible. But I don't believe it because there's nothing I can see, feel, or smell that is recognizable as an overmind." Such statements assume that anything which really exists has to be a material, perceptible object. It eliminates all possibility of a personal mind as well as the existence of life itself.

As I pointed out to him, nothing can be seen to leave the body when it dies. Yet the dead body is admittedly different. And the same might be said of a mindless person. What we are dealing with is not a thing, but a change of state. A change of state is a difference in organization brought about by a major alteration or cessation of the natural energies involved. The term natural is used to differentiate them from concepts like vital force or spirit. But the distinction is somewhat meaningless, labels being of little consequence. What counts is identification.

Let us assume that organization is indeed what we otherwise know as life, mind, overmind and the like. If so, it would be imperceptible except through its effects on material things. Now it just so happens that these material things we *do* see are themselves no more than the effects of exactly such *unseen* determinants. These are the complexes of relations variously called organization, order, rhythm, harmony and so on. They were mentioned earlier when discussing Figure 6.

To refresh the memory with an example, suppose one considers a photo of his friend. It is flat, paper and inert. Whereas the friend is solid, flesh and alive. Nonetheless, one can be recognized interchangeably from the other. What is actually seen, therefore, are the relationships (proportions or ratios) *between* salient features of the respective images. These are relationships, not replicas, because the picture is smaller than the person. Though invisible as such, these relationships or ratios can be proved to exist on the images. They are not only real, they are the *only* reality present in the snapshot! Everything else about it can be altered so long as this complex of relations remains unchanged, i.e., proportional. The image will be recognized though reduced, enlarged, printed in color, matte finished, projected in light, or represented only as a silhouette.

The point is straight-forward. All we can perceive, know or deal with are organized distributions of relations. And from what we can tell from physics, these are precisely what is present in the outside world. Nobel physicist Werner Heisenberg is notable among others who have described this outer world as consisting exclusively of relations. He called them connections. It is a picture quite opposite to the traditional one in which everything was made up of discrete entities. He noted that all we can discriminate are these "connections." As he saw it, outer reality is "a complicated tissue of events" woven out of relations which overlap, interlock, and otherwise combine to make up the world we recognize. [33]

For the inner world (all that we know), such relations (or connections) are recognized only as patterned clumps called shapes, forms, orderliness, harmony, tonality, and so forth. They need not represent any equivalent outside energy or substance, and they certainly are not "things." It is we who make things out of them. The organizing procedures of the mind require such imagery for classification and identification. Otherwise it could not be used during recognition and recall. It constitutes memory.

It follows that if our hypothetical social mind has the same nature as our personal minds, it also is comprised of patterned relationships variously organized. As such, it would not be discernable as a material entity. Worse yet, it would necessitate action at a distance. This may be disturbing to some, but I have no trouble with the idea. Indeed, it seems likely that all action is action at a distance. If there are particles, and they interact, then they interact across empty space. No space between, no separate particles! How can one have action of any sort unless space is traversed, however briefly? Space is what keeps everything from being the same thing. As for the imperceptibility of mind, who has seen gravity or electromagnetic fields? These are not material things, and they do exist.

Central to any discussion of the mind are the relations known as communication links. When communications are virtually perfect as between identical twins, understanding seems possible almost without words. The rest of us are not so fortunate. Among most humans failure to properly and fully interpret messages of others is the rule rather than the exception. Moreover, it appears to be a shortcoming largely peculiar to humans. Man's extensive use of words and other symbols allows for a complete cleavage between what is meant-and-sent, and what is read by the recipient of the message.

For the most part, chemical communications do not engender such problems. Because the shape of molecules is unique, they carry unique meanings free of ambiguity and potential error. Thus, when we witness chemical communications being used, as among ants, it appears to us that they elicit obligatory responses. And we immediately dismiss the behavior as being instinctive -- whatever that term means. However, these chemical transmissions are the forerunners of *all* later communication links, and they are still the most essential as well as the most widespread. They serve not only to interrelate our body cells, but they are the preferred means of exchanging information between all animals except humans.

Most likely our inability to communicate with, and fully understand the other animals is due to our own inadequacies, not theirs. It is man and his ambiguous abstractions which are abnormal. From the standpoint of sensory ability, we are cripples in the animal kingdom. We are blind in a major sense modality -- in fact, the most important of all sense modalities! The chemical signals are still there. They flood the atmosphere and are everywhere around us, but we cannot read them. Our olfactory system has atrophied to almost nothing. And in our brains the olfactory lobes themselves have been largely usurped to develop a cortex dominated mostly by vision and hearing. In effect, we are isolated from all the chit-chat going on. And since the cortex comes replete with its own capacities for deceit, arrogance, worry, and immorality, one wonders whether anything was profited by the trade-off.

When one examines the skull of a deer or a dog he quickly realizes that those multiply folded bones in the nasal cavity once led to extensive areas of olfactory epithelium. All we have left are two small patches, each the size of a penny or less. We can see and hear. But they can do as well. And in addition, they can *smell*. It was *they* who developed along the normal channels of evolution. This emphasized chemicals because that's what organisms are. Where visual and auditory communications could be used, most animals developed them. But they did not come to depend upon them almost exclusively as did the human.

Contrasted with our world, theirs is one that is rich, vibrant and alive, filled with the basic smell-stuff of life. It makes for immediate relatedness. Animals are moral. There is no way they could hide deceit. Appearances are not necessary to identify each other, nor can appearances be masked. The enemy, or even the mood of a stranger is obvious. In fact, they can recognize what passed by yesterday and where it went. You can't tell what is around the corner. But they can. And were it possible to transmit feelings, they could do it. They have the necessary equipment for it. [34]

People have difficulty recognizing the fundamental sentience of all life because they are largely isolated from it. Verbiage and symbolic abstractions remove one from the Here and Now -- the living IS. Nonetheless, this basic sentience is an attribute of the cells themselves. Plants are made up of cells. But reports that plants respond to music (vibratory patterns?), or that trees communicate with one another, have always been matters of amusement. (How far out can you get?) Despite the bemused skepticism, however, there is ample evidence that such is the case.

For example, a variety of trees have been shown to defend themselves against assault by caterpillars by changing the chemistry of their leaves. They make the leaves less tasty to the caterpillar. Within about 60 meters other trees then react similarly. This has been traced to some unidentified chemical warning which is air-borne. Question: did the trees think to do this? It is a complicated ploy. And why the concern (if any) for other trees?

Perhaps the most surprising of such phenomena involves the neem tree of India *(Azadirachta indica)*. Recent findings disclose that it defends itself against insects with an assortment of about 20 chemicals called limonoids. Instead of killing the insects outright, these chemicals mimic the bugs' hormones. One of them *(azadirachtin)* approximates the hormone which induces molting. When eaten by the caterpillar, normal brain secretions are inhibited. The caterpillar fails to undergo metamorphosis and dies. It were as if the tree had somehow learned the chemical language of the insect! [35]

Still further studies suggest that plants may well have a memory of sorts. In at least one instance, sensitivity to touch has been found related to changes in cellular RNA, and RNA is one of the more likely candidates for acquired human memory! Such findings lead one to speculate whether plants, lacking a nervous system, depend more heavily upon the suggested intelligence of the cells themselves. [36]

Whatever the case with plants, there can be no question but what chemical communications predominate in the animal kingdom. The nature of this chemical language, as well as its importance, is difficult for us to grasp. This is because we use words, and these are only a code. For example, the phrase "build a house" bears no resemblance to any house or construction project. And unless the listener knows both English and carpentry it is only noise. Few words carry any meaning in and of themselves. No matter how lucid the description, if spoken in Urdu it is just so much gibberish. The meaning has to be awakened in the brain of the listener. It belongs to him. The trouble arises from the fact that his brain is never identical with that of the speaker. His meanings are not the same.

Chemical language does not involve such difficulties. It is vastly different from the verbal. For one thing, it is far more efficient. It is not a code. It is a *direct representation*. The meaning is carried by the word itself, whether this word (molecule) is hormone, pheromone, neurotransmitter, or whatever. There can be no misunderstanding, no deceit, no play on words. The call for the ovaries to ovulate is neither an instruction nor an order. It is a key which triggers action directly. No one has to interpret anything, and no one has to describe anything in chemical language. The word *is* the action to be taken or the thing described. Its stereochemical shape is an exact full-scale pictograph. *All shapes are unique*! So the vocabulary is essentially infinite. The resulting communication is totally free of potential error. And the process itself is so simple it can be employed by one-celled organisms. [37]

Chemical language is widely used for social communications, and the most versatile linguists are insects. Long before some nimble primate climbed a tree to escape a hungry lizard, there was a great buzzing of small creatures like bees, ants and dragonflies. Even today, at least 90% of all living things on earth are insects. E. 0. Wilson estimates that for ants alone there are two hundred thousand for every man, woman and child alive. [38] They even outweigh the humans! How did they become so dominant? There are several reasons, but the most important is probably their broad and varied use of chemical communications.

Socialization is almost synonymous with the exchange of information, and social insects became particularly adept conversationalists. Humans use words, but think in terms of meanings. Social insects use chemical language, and for them the meaning is transmitted *directly*. The full impact of this observation comes home to us when we realize the beehive or termitary must be literally alive with free-floating meanings! They are in the air, on the surfaces, everywhere. These are the makings of thought. They are mind stuff. The fact that they are molecular reduces them to manageable proportions, and being raw meanings eliminates any need for interpretation. In a sense, therefore, the hive or termitary possesses a memory independent of any of its inhabitants. It might even be called an *overmind!* This, I would suggest, is what enables them to create such complex societies. [39]

Behaviorists say that to be objective and scientific one must draw all his conclusions from behavior. And when judged by their behavior, some of the social insects have extremely elaborate cultures. Certain tropical termites erect veritable cities which, in proportion to their size, are more impressive than anything constructed by man. They far surpass those built by surrounding peoples. Moreover, the complexity of their social systems is commensurate with that of their architecture. Because of this complexity of organization it has often been proposed that the insect itself, whether ant, bee or termite, is only a mobile cell in a larger organism. It is the hive or termitary, they say, which should be looked upon as a living organism. [40]

The social insects with the greatest variety of culture and life styles are probably ants. When one considers the amount of information required to accomplish all this, it seems almost mandatory that something beyond the individual must be involved. There appears no conceivable way in which so huge a bulk of information could be encoded within the individual -- even at a molecular level! By human standards their neural structures are quite meager, and the usual practice is to attribute everything to neural action. However, please note that the glands, say those of an ant, are more massive than the neural tissue. And ants are *not* mindless little robots as so often depicted. They can be tamed, and they learn. [41]

Students of social insects are usually loathe to attribute conscious thinking or other higher attributes to them because of rote activities they sometimes exhibit. When interrupted, these habitual behaviors will be repeated time and again in a closed loop analogous to a stuck phonograph record. They have been called *Erbkoordinationen*, or simply inherent reflexive sequences. For example, one species of wasp has a fixed series of activities preparatory to laying her eggs. If the sequence is interrupted at some point she will repeat parts of the behavior pattern even though the repetition is wholly unnecessary.

Personally, I see nothing particularly enigmatic about this. Humans with well established habits frequently do the same thing. Memories are doubtlessly molecular hydrocarbons, and such structures readily combine to form long sequences. So there is a feasible mechanism. But more importantly, pre-packaging of relatively invariant behavior patterns is an efficient mode of operation. It eliminates useless decision-making. After all, insects are small beings crammed into hard shells. They are in need of inner space.

There are increasing numbers of investigators who do not find it so humiliating to believe that lesser creatures can think. [42] Indeed, numerous instances occur where this conclusion seems almost unavoidable. Consider the underwater nymph of the dragonfly. It possesses a hinged lower lip which is unfolded outwardly. Two sharp claws at the end are used to clasp prey. It then retracts the lip to enjoy its meal. In 1939 an entomologist wondered what would happen if this underlip were lost. So he removed it from a nymph kept in an aquarium and watched. Lacking its usual mechanism, the young dragonfly slowly worked out an entirely new strategy. It stalked its victim until close enough to leap upon it. Then it used its jaws directly. This, I submit, looks suspiciously like problem solution requiring thinking. [43]

Another instance involves females of the firefly *Photurus versicolor*. These prey on males of other firefly species by mimicking the flash sequence made by females of that particular species. *P. versicolor* adjusts her own flash rate until it is the same as that used by honest females of the intended prey. The familiar signal then lures the unsuspecting stranger in for dinner rather than sex. And it is reported that she uses quite a repertoire of false flash patterns for this treacherous type of hanky panky![44]

But what about our initial thesis, the concept of an overmind? If an overmind exists, then social insects are assuredly prime candidates for it. They more than meet the criterion mentioned earlier, viz., that the group possess abilities and reveal behavior well beyond the capabilities of any given individual. Social insects not only demonstrate that their society is greater than the sum of its participants, but they do so without any identifiable body of recorded data such as available to the human.

That all this is somehow wired into each member appears physically impossible by reason of its size and equipment. Moreover, closer observation discloses that not all siblings in the hive or formicary behave as if they were identically programmed. They definitely cannot be mere social atoms performing in a rote fashion. Whatever their buildings, whether hive, termitary, or formicary, each differs in detail and reveals adaptations to terrain and other features.

Unlike inorganic entities, all living things exhibit homeostasis. One of the reasons for considering them individual selves is that they engage in self-preservation. As applied to a beehive, the individual bees have no body temperature control. They are cold-blooded. The hive, however, does have! Thermal regulation is quite precise. It is normally kept between 34.5 and 35.5 Centigrade. In the coldest weather it rarely gets below 30C. This is accomplished by amazingly synchronous team work which is "tuned" to the temperature outside. In brief, this is a case where the hive engages in self- preservation, whereas the individual bee is unable to do so.

Social insects are often described as being *"eusocial."* It is a life style also observed in naked mole rats and at least one species of snapping shrimp. Living in a eusocial body means that the individual is completely subordinate to the social organism as a whole. The bee doesn't matter. It is the hive that counts! Members have little freedom or individuality apart from what contributes to the "common good." Since this common good shifts with environmental conditions (and is an undefinable abstraction), the result is total control of the individual. Extreme cooperative and altruistic behavior of this sort most likely developed from simple like-kind related-ness, the belongingness one individual had for another -- as seen in present day coral reefs. These are composites of individuals not otherwise eusocial.

Suppose we compare this with the socialization of cells. The latter came about during the Cambrian period and allowed for multicellular life in general. Here the significant feature was the appearance of *role spec-*

ialization. Though this emphasized cellular individuality, it enabled development of true multicellular organisms each having an identity of its own. It was an identity distinctly apart from (and transcending) that of their component cells. In all cases, however, and whether cells, bees, or ants, the degree of socialization was a function of cooperative/altruistic behavior among individual beings. Basically, *we are all eusocial phenomena,* though higher species are much more complicated than the bee hive.

According to Hegel, living things constantly try to transcend themselves. We epitomize this transcendence beyond the cellular level. But at our own social level, as shown by our societies, things did not go as smoothly as with the social insects. Human societies have always been torn apart by the obvious contradiction between individual freedom and eusocialism — rugged individualism vs. "big brother" tyranny for the so-called common good. Man is both a predator and a social animal. He is one of few species afflicted with this biological dilemma. Most predators, e.g.,the cats, are "loners" -- the lion being possibly the most sociable of these. He at least hunts in packs. The human, however, extends this inbuilt relatedness from family into clan or tribe. Any further extension into cultures is not required biologically, and is therefore mental rather than genetic. This does not make it any the less real of course, because his entire inner world is also mental.

If some extremely large and utterly alien intelligence were to observe human behavior as we observe that of insects, unquestionably much of it would be attributed to instinct. And there would be arguments as to whether we could think. Sleeping, eating, and working habits would likely be identified as circadian rhythms. And to some degree they are. It would also be observed that when music occurs and both sexes are present in appreciable numbers, they pair off together and go through a sequence of stereotyped motions. This would mean that such dance rituals and courtship displays were an instinctive prelude to mating -- which much of it is.

Humans certainly are not aware of any mass mind to which they belong, and into which many hope to get absorbed again following death. Moreover, such issues are like the Big Bang. They are totally beyond verification. They are unanswerable. So, if all our intellects actually do go to make up a common intelligence (which is possible), any thinking it did would be literally over our heads and completely unthinkable. It may be that social insects have much the same problem.

Biosphere, Gaia -- and What Else?

Chapter 13

It is Hughmongous!! — But is it Alive?

(All living things have many features in common. This is said to indicate a common origin. But doesn't it also indicate a common course of growth -- a living entity? And how about a common intelligence?)

I was sitting in the cafeteria, Student Union Building, contemplating some corned beef hash. It was topped with an egg whose single eye stared back at me. On every side the usual drone of voices was garbled by the shuffling of feet, dish clatter and giggles. In short, it was lunch hour. I glanced up as the chair opposite me was drawn back. It was a member of the anthropology department.

"Mind if I join you?"

"Of course not," I replied, "good to see you again."

The plate and coffee were deposited. "I've been hoping to run into you," he explained. "I've been puzzled ever since that confab we had with a guest speaker several months back -- and I'm still confused."

I was polite. "About what?"

"The human brain," he answered, "why it enlarged so rapidly during evolution. As you recall, it was attributed to the utterly defenseless character of the human. It was said to have forced him to use his wits. I can see how such conditions might have acted selectively and caused the brain to continue growing. But I don't see how it could possibly have started the process Was it a matter of mutation?"

"Could have been," I replied, turning the egg over on my hash. "Who knows? As I see it, though, brain growth really didn't get anywhere until the early human took his nose off the ground."

He stared at me from under those bushy brows for a moment. "You're handing me a line, aren't you? Look, I'm serious!"

"So am I," was the response. "When the proto-human started to stand erect, the nose became largely a distance receptor. Eyes and ears are much better at that sort of thing, so they took precedence. Also, with the head up-right, anatomical changes could take place in the throat area allowing for development of primitive speech. The new sensory emphasis, plus this rudimentary language, are most likely what promoted abstract thinking. [1] And this was the tool needed to outwit his fellow animals. Abstract thinking involves foresight and permits deceptive ploys as well as trickery."

He nodded. "I guess you were serious after all. Sounds reasonable. It certainly was a lucky shift in his habits."

"I suppose so. But he paid through the nose for it -- and quite literally. When the proto-human lifted his nose from the ground and stopped depending upon it so heavily, the entire olfactory system began to atrophy. He gained a forebrain, but he lost most of his intimate contact with the environment."

He swallowed a mouthful of hash, then leaned back and asked, "Why should that follow?"

"Well, for one thing, that's what abstract thinking *means!* It removes a person from the Here and Now. But more importantly, when the human traded off his conscious use of the chemical language for artificial verbalisms, it made an alien of him. It divorced him from all the rest of life. He no longer communicated. He didn't belong. Except for pets, other animals now shunned him like the plague. In fact, he even went so far as to invent phony stinks called perfumes to mask his own identity, sex, and moods. To 'smell' became insulting, socially taboo."

"About this chemical language which enables animals to commun- icate among themselves, I presume you are referring to pheromones. Are they really used that extensively?"

"In my opinion, yes. We have only recently begun to examine the various ways in which organic chemicals are employed to carry information between animals. We know a good bit about animal social habits and rituals. These are much more obvious and easily investigated They constitute a sort of inbuilt culture. However, even this instinctive culture must be transmitted genetically -- which means it becomes brain chemicals. After all, it is inherent. So whatever gives rise to it must belong to the same general class as those used for other chemical communications. When employed internally, they are called hormones. But when extended outside the body for social purposes, they are called pheromones.

As I visualize it, the chemical language might be looked upon as a sort of 'basic English' common to all members of the biosphere. The vocabulary is potentially infinite. Separate species and social groups have their own dialects, phrases and idioms based on somewhat different molecular structures. The further removed animals become in genetic terms, the less chance they have of understanding each other. Naturally, there are exceptions. For example, ants make pets of certain beetles. And recent evidence indicates that the beetles have somehow learned the chemical language used by the ants. [2] Pardon me for a moment while I get rid of this crockery."

I picked up the dinnerware and weeded my way through the now thinning ranks of students placing dirty dishes on the conveyor belt. Upon returning I noted he had fired up his pipe and made himself comfortable. Apparently he had no afternoon class to meet, and neither did I.

"I find your ideas refreshingly different," he commented with a smile. "For instance, I always looked upon the biosphere as little more than a catalogue of different species, usually antagonistic toward each other."

"So do most biologists," I told him. "It's largely a hangover from Thomas Huxley's interpretation of Darwin. He was obsessed with the competitive aspect of natural selection -- you know, the 'red of tooth and claw' outlook with everything fighting everything else."

"But surely you admit that there is competition for survival."

"Certainly I do. There is competition for survival in our own society, and with much greater ferocity, I might add. Wild animals don't kill for the fun of it like 'sportsmen' do when collecting trophies. With very few exceptions predators kill only for food. And they do so as swiftly and mercifully as possible. Behavior which can be interpreted as cruelty is extremely rare, and torture is unknown. Competition for authority, sex, territory or food seldom results in the death of the loser. With humans it is a commonplace. By and large, wild animals get along together appreciably better than most people. They even show consideration for species other than themselves."

"Let's see if I understand your earlier statement about the biosphere." He stroked his beard for a moment, then said, "Correct me if I'm wrong, but I gather that you consider the biosphere as something more than just individual plants and animals which we have classified into species and such. Beyond their families, clans, ecosystems and other groupings, there is some kind of organization to life as a whole. If this is a fair statement, I have a question. What is the logic behind it? In other words, what reasons have we for thinking the biosphere is an organized entity in its own right?"

I pulled a pipe from my jacket pocket and borrowed some of his burley. As I tamped it in the bowl the thought occurred to me that few people, at least to my knowledge, had asked this particular question before. Biologists are usually so busy trying to classify the differences between creatures, they seldom have time to consider what they might have in common.

"I have never really examined the thinking behind the concept," I conceded. "It simply seemed obvious that all life is so intimately related it had to constitute a single organic entity, or at least a very close family. So I can't give a definitive answer to your question -- not right off the top of my head at this moment. About the best I can do is provide a few of the reasons which appear significant to me."

I parked my feet on an adjacent chair, relaxed, and thought over the question for awhile. "To begin," I said, "there must be about one and a half million species of animals and maybe some half a million species of plants. Nonetheless, they all seem to follow the same Bauplan. That is to say, they involve the same structural principles. They are neither fluids nor solids. All are mesoforms or colloids. So they are necessarily membranous.

Membranes are not simply inert partitions or walls as commonly presumed. The organic ones are almost always found at naturally occurring interfaces where they exchange energy and chemicals between different entities or materials. The cell and its internal bodies are encased in such active membranes. Organs and muscles are packaged in membranes. The skin is a membrane, and the brain is simply one that has thickened and been crumpled up inside the skull. In fact, organisms are essentially made up of membranes because this is where all their many vital processes take place.

To get some idea of their actual extent, suppose we begin with a cube only 1 cm. on the edge and subdivide it into smaller cubes of 5 millimicrons per edge We would end up with almost an acre of free surface. So you can imagine how much area must be involved in the many trillions of cells making up our bodies. When all membranes are considered, it would probably have to be measured in square miles.

Life is thought to have begun in the tidal waters at the interfaces of sea, earth and atmosphere. And locations of this sort would have been ideally suited to the formation of membranes. These would have been sensitive by nature, and may well have preceded the appearance of life itself. [3] In fact, some have even suggested that before any life could have arisen, the early oceans must have floated with a membranous oil-slick of hydrocarbons.

In addition, the fossil record reveals that the earliest known socializing of cells was to create membranes. The small multicellular organisms found just prior to the Cambrian period are merely elaborate variations on this membrane theme. They had little or no body, nothing to enclose, and therefore did not adapt too well. None have survived." [4]

"These are certainly interesting observations," he commented. "But just what do they have to do with the biosphere?"

"Tsk! Tsk!" I chided. "You are missing the over-all picture. I'll explain. The biosphere *itself* can be considered a huge membrane -- an extension of the same principle. It is about 20 miles thick. From where we sit we can go up 10 miles, or we can go down 10 miles, and beyond these limits life disappears. It is a living envelope enclosing the earth. And considering the diameter of the earth, it is extremely thin despite its enormous complexity. Like other living membranes it mediates energy transactions at an interface, this time between earth and outer space.

Because it is self-enclosing (spherical) and maintains a relatively constant environment conducive to life, the biosphere is what physicists would describe as a 'self-regulating steady-state.' This enables the internal growth processes of life to proliferate undisturbed. And one might further point out that the existence of a steady-state usually indicates something alive. Analogous conditions pertain for the human brain. It also is a self regulating membrane kept at a constant temperature and isolated from outside influences. This allows the mind to continue growing long after the body has matured and lapsed into a maintenance program. Indeed, the closest analogue to the biosphere could well be the brain."

"Never thought of it in that light," he admitted. "But I still don't see how such features would necessarily relate all living things into a single gigantic organism. Trees, people and bacteria are pretty diverse."

"Of course they are," I responded. "They have much different lifestyles. And they seem even more diverse because we judge them from the middle of the membrane. Superficially at least, our own body cells appear quite different. Those from the brain don't look like those from the liver, muscles or skin. When we put them under a microscope, however, they are seen to be constructed in the same fashion and therefore closely related."

He studied this for a moment, then asked, "What common denom-inator relates all the cells of different species?"

"Well, let's consider the nucleus of the cell. Here the most significant structure is the DNA. Whether from plants, people, or bacteria, DNA is surprisingly alike. It is composed of the same nucleotide units assembled in the same way, fulfills much the same role in all species, and even twists in the same direction! In fact, genetic engineers splice pieces of DNA from one species into another quite freely. Genes for making some body chemical may be isolated and inserted into the DNA of a bacterium, say *E. coli*, and the little bugger will accept this alien stuff and go right ahead making the chemical for us. So far as I am concerned, this is rather compelling evidence for the relatedness of all living things. If anything were fundamentally different from the human, it would have to be a bacterium."

"Bacterium?"

"Precisely -- and from the colon too. One shouldn't look down his nose at bacteria just because they receive a bad press. They could live without us, but we couldn't possibly live without them -- and neither could anything else."

"But most of them are disease entities, aren't they?"

"Far from it," I replied. "A small percentage are parasitic in this sense. But the percentage is no greater than that for humans or other animals. The overwhelming majority are breaking their little backs trying to help. Microbes are the oldest inhabitants of the earth. There are literally hundreds of thousands of species, possibly millions. Their ancestors formed the atmosphere we breathe, and they are still helping to maintain it.

Long before plants or animals existed, some of them (chloroplasts) arranged symbiotic relationships with cells later to become plants. Still others (mitochondria) formed similar liaisons with cells destined to become animals. Today, both plants and animals still depend on these small creatures for their continued existence. They generate all the energies of living things. [5] Life is not some special vital force of unknown dimensions donated from another world. It is an energy conversion process, a sort of slow, controlled burn. They provide the necessary fuel."

"So they are necessary," he remarked. "But why all the concern? Surely, bacteria are about the bottom rung on the ladder of life."

".More than that," I answered. "They are the original essentials -- the basis upon which the ladder rests. They have been around five times as long as multicellular creatures like you and me. And in those billions of years they have probably devised about all the molecules of life. They could not possibly make use of them because of their limited physiology. But the molecules themselves are most likely still floating about in the oceans as a vast library of the chemical language. Bacteria have access to this library, and they shuttle DNA around among themselves indiscriminately. If there is such a thing as a 'gene pool,' then certainly it is the bacteria who carry the swimming permits."

"Since they possess such tremendously large quantities of available biological data, why haven't they evolved further?"

"I used to wonder about that myself," I replied, "until one day I suddenly realized that, indeed, they *had* evolved! All living things are their descendants. The geniuses of the family are probably the cells carrying our own DNA. Moreover, evolution could still be continuing on most fronts. It is a growth process, and the very term 'process' means change. Total cessation of growth is death.

As I see it, evolution is to the biosphere what embryogenesis is to the human The latter would seem to be simply a speeded up (fast forward) replay of the successful mutations (*decisions!*) of the evolutionary past. And much as in our own memories, unhappy events have been glossed over. Recapitulation, meaning that ontogeny follows phylogeny, suggests that all animal life is caught up in much the same program All proceed from single cells outward and upward to greater complexity, and all follow much the same steps. They unfold from within. And this places the origins of intelligence at the cellular level. Such concepts may not bed down comfortably with certain belief systems, but this does not alter the facts."

He stared at me from under those bushy brows again. Apparently I had said something discordant with his own belief system. "I simply cannot buy the idea that cells are intelligent," he finally announced.

"And why not?" I inquired. "You began as a single cell. And this proliferated into what you now are. Unless you think that some other-worldly item was injected into you en route, your current intelligence had to be due to that original cell. It has already been established that intelligence is largely inherited. Of course, your first cell and its immediate offspring were primarily concerned with forming you and keeping you operating. But that in itself required intelligence of a sort -- even purposive intelligence. One couldn't expect it to be the abstract variety we are now engaged in. Cells don't have time for such recreational nonsense. They can't relax after lunch like us. They put in a twenty-four hour work day."

"Doesn't the environment play any role at all in this developmental process?" he asked incredulously.

"Certainly it does," I replied. "It plays the same role as in evolution. I use the following analogy in my class. It begins with two exposed photographic films. Each is technically perfect. One is a French nude, the other a scenic landscape. They are carefully removed from the camera and taken to the drugstore to be developed.

In this analogy the drugstore is equivalent to the environment. During the developmental process all manner of things can happen The photos can be finished in gloss, matte, sepia tones, enlarged, or even ruined entirely. Development can radically influence or even destroy the quality of the final pictures. But there are certain things it *can't* do. It can't change the nude to a landscape or anything else. And it can't add anything to either picture. It can only maximize what is already present, or diminish it and possibly ruin the whole film."

"I see," he said. "Heredity sets all the parameters and natural selection has to work within these. But let's get back to those microbes that juggle the DNA around. Isn't that sort of humiliating?"

I grinned. "We could use a little humility. It's in very short supply. Throughout history man has always stood in awe of the magnitude of his own sublimity. I guess it must be part of the push that put him where he is. Thus, his eyes are focused outward and upward. His aspirations are toward the stars. This is the heaven where he seeks his gods because this is the direction in which he grows. But the push has to come from somewhere, and it has to be from somewhere *inside* himself.

The billions of people, myriad trees, and the still greater numbers of insects all drop back to a single cell every generation. Whether person, plant, or bug, they can't even transmit their own complexity! This requires the cell. And for the formative period at least, it means the cell is in command. Living things can only grow. They unfold from within like a blossoming plant. They are organized from the inside outwardly, not vice versa. They are not assembled whole-cloth from some outside source. So if man looks for his gods, he had best look within himself. And if he seeks the source of his intelligence, that also is within.

Aside from what little information a person acquires during his lifetime, everything else about him has its point source in that first cell. It does not carry any miniature image of the person to be. But neither does it carry any code. The sequence DNA ⇨ RNA ⇨ Protein does not represent the translation of any code. Codes are symbols requiring decoding, and there is nothing to do the decoding! The term 'code' is a misnomer -- verbal putty to patch another hole in their cog, gear and machine thinking. What the cell actually carries is a *mind*! It is not the mind of an Einstein, true. But it is intelligence 'sufficient unto the need thereof.' And the need has to do with the juggling of molecules.

We marvel at the computers and aerospace equipment we build, and rightfully so. But we regard our own insides with disdain. Ugh! Messy! Nonetheless, the smallest part of its organization far surpasses the complexity of anything yet conceived by man. Our best chemical engineer could not possibly manage a kidney. I can picture him at a desk cluttered with phones. One rings. 'A salt overage, you say? That's serious! Check the osmotic pressure. Tighten up on the flow and notify the thirst receptors!' A different phone sounds. 'Metals Department? Yes, save the potassium. We don't want the muscles complaining again! Also save the magnesium and zinc. But first check the supply levels, then discard the overages. Wait a minute! Hold everything! We have a runaway emergency! Some fool dumped diuretics into the main input channel!'"

He broke into laughter. When the tears were wiped away and his pipe refueled, he parked his own feet on a nearby chair and remarked, "Yours is a strange world, my friend."

"How so?" I asked.

"Well, instead of looking onward and upward toward the future, you ask that we look inwardly toward the ever smaller."

"That certainly wasn't intended," I replied. "Apparently my rambling discourse was not too clear. Let's see if I can state it a little better. When dealing with the Here and Now, as well as the future, I say onward and upward. This is the direction of growth. It is healthy . But when seeking what is responsible for living phenomena like mind, man, or evolution, one has to reverse this perspective The true roots of the biological world still lie in the DNA, starting with that ancient biospheric blanket of bacteria. I say this because life still unfolds from within. All the answers are there if we know what to look for and can recognize them once they are found.

Because our natural orientation is onward and upward, it is almost impossible for us to visualize events at the infinitely small range. When we try, everything seems to come to a point with subatomic particles. This is irrational. Surely the universe is not an inverted cone! Our difficulty, I would guess, arises from the microscopic nature of our mental world.

For example, all the stuff in our heads, whether memories, ideas or whatever, is of molecular dimensions. Our visual images of houses, horses, and such, appear quite large to us. But on the retina they are very minute. In actual extent of retina covered, our visual resolution (acuity) becomes microscopic The same is true of what we hear. Think of the actual size of those tiny bones of the inner ear, then try to imagine how extremely small their vibrations must be!

What I am saying is that we look at the external world through the wrong end of a microscope. And we are also looking the wrong direction! For the sources of mind and life we must search our molecular inner world. Along with this, we should carry with us a morality based on self responsibility, not guidance from any dogma above. No facts will visit us from the future, and no laws will be handed down from outer space. We must look within ourselves and on our own. This is where our real world lies. So much for the sermon," I quipped. "I'll stay away from the subject hereafter."

He grinned. "By no means! I think it should be required reading, especially your remarks on self responsibility. But just how do you relate this outlook to the biosphere? After all, it is large, upward and outward."

The biosphere is Here and Now," I explained. "Were one to define it in simple terms, it would be described as the single largest living thing produced by the on-going process of growth. All its constituent 'parts' are closely related. In fact, they are largely symbiotic."

"A living organism in and of itself?"

"It's possibly a matter of viewpoint, I suppose, but I believe it could be considered so."

"Another question -- does it have a mind of its own?"

"There would be no way of knowing," I replied. "Communicating with it would be just as unlikely as our cells communicating with us. But from what circumstantial evidence is available, one would tend to favor the idea. After all, we are not apart *from* the biosphere. We are a part *of* it. We are not man-made. We grew. We are Nature-made. And since we grow, amass knowledge and think, there is nothing basically illogical about attributing mental features to the rest of the biosphere -- at least to some extent. Indeed, it would appear egotistical not to. Increasing numbers of us are convinced that animals think And not too long ago one of our most prominent molecular biologists even brought up the question whether bacteria can think!" [6]

Man's assumed isolation and superiority to the rest of the biosphere is his most unique hallucination. It borders on paranoia and derives, no doubt, from that vastly inflated ego which is part of his elaborate mind. The truth is he is no more divorced from the organic matrix where he was born than is any other animal. And he can't subsist any better without it. Should he continue his present destructive course he may learn this the hard way.

Man is fruit of Nature's creativity, not some other-worldly artifact. Nature does not manufacture things and piece them together. It conceives and grows them. This even includes what we normally consider products of our own minds. They also grow. Art works or inventions are conceived in the mind as ideas. Following a normal gestation period, they are born as art, playthings, gizmos and machines. And though they may expand and complexify later, they are usually viable upon delivery. This is not true of cultures or societies, however. Extremely few cities are pre-planned this way. Social entities are immediate products of growth like ourselves."

"Just how would you interpret the term 'mind' in this more universal sense?" he asked.

"That is a truly ponderous question and very difficult to answer in any simple fashion," I replied. "But perhaps I can 'talk around' it sufficiently to make some sense. Let me think out loud for a moment. To begin, the body is a being. The mind is more of a process, a *becoming*. [7] As such, the mind can imagine activities well beyond anything the body could possibly accomplish. As a being, the body stops growing early. But the mind continues growing until death. Properly visualized, it is not a 'thing.' It is largely devoid of mass, contours, and similar physical features.

Under most conditions of the external world, mind is thought to exist as a diffuse state of relatedness. However, there is something mutually attractional about things which are related. This is implied by the very term 'related.' As a result, conditions frequently arise where this relatedness tends to condense, to become more intense, more closely assembled. When this happens, it gives rise to recognizable patterning which makes the materials visible. Astronomers describe something similar as an on-going process in outer space. Events become 'things' in the sense that they evolve into measurable bodies.

What makes the brain uniquely adaptable for the appearance of mind is its colloidal structure. It is a mesoform -- a gel containing more water than the blood itself. This fact, plus the electrically charged asymmetries of both hydrocarbon and water molecules, actually promotes molecular movement and allows for ever-shifting conditions of internal structure. Perhaps its closest physical analogue is paracrystallinity, or liquid crystals. But mind cannot be identified with brain matter itself. Instead, it is the systematic activity within the brain matter. Little is known about how it operates in the DNA where, logically, it must also exist.

You are no doubt familiar with what physicists call a 'change of state.' It refers to what happens when something condenses itself from a gas to a fluid, and then from fluid to crystalline solid. The worm changes to a butterfly, so to speak. Well, the appearance of mind is a change of state. Or better yet, it is a condition of state -- a complex condition of intense interrelatedness. In the crystalline phase of inorganic matter such heightened organization results in stability and rigidity. But living things consist of more flexible and irregular molecules. These temporarily forestall the onset of rigidity and allow for growth. The human mentality lies at the upper end of this continuum of organization because of its extreme complexity.

I don't know whether such verbal meandering helps, or whether it just further confuses the situation. I'm sorry that any so-called 'explanation' must be so vague, esoteric and abstruse. It makes me think of Herbert Spencer. In his famous *'First Principles,'* Spencer tried to explain the same type of changes -- this was back in 1862 -- and he was forced to use the same sort of inexact and wooly language. He recognized it as something fundamental which was happening in all areas, whether physical, biological, or social. And for want of a better term, he identified it with evolution. Perhaps the word was well taken.

Spencer's 'evolution' was defined as an 'integrative' process in which 'matter passes from an indefinite, incoherent homogeneity to a definite, coherent heterogeneity.' In brief, it was simply another way of describing the ever-present on-going change of state called *organization.* Some would claim it is the 'neg-entropy' necessary to counterbalance the equally continuous process of disintegration, the other side of the coin as it were. Possibly -- I don't know.

What I find truly startling is the realization just how much of our presumed outer world actually does not exist materially. It is not a world made up of 'things.' Some features -- houses for example -- might be called things. They are held together with nails. But what about a basket-ball team, the USA, the English language, our family, or our church? Nothing holds them together except a sort of mental glue. It is this glue which makes them more than mere collages of other non-things. Fortunately, there is this counter-force which I call *mind.* It integrates everything by a process we know as organization. Call it 'neg-entropy' if you prefer."

"You mean you would identify mind with what we call organization?" he asked with a look of bewilderment.

"Yes, I would. Mind is active organization, or better yet -- the organizing itself. Both terms (mind and organization) refer to intangible conditions which no one has been able to define, much less analyze. And in my opinion, they are the same conditions. The really clinching piece of evidence is the fact that one seems to be necessary for the other. Wherever we find organization we know mind has been at work, and mind always works by organizing.

Now I recognize that matter/energy and mind/spirit are the only two categories of basic stuffs available in today's catalogue. Thus, the idea of mind/organization would not be acceptable to either scientists or theologians. If it were accepted as a new and updated entry, then mind/spirit would have to be dropped from the inventory.

Reasons for calling it a 'new' entry are straight-forward Though necessary for matter to exist, organization is *not* a property of matter. It is a necessary precondition for material existence. And it can be shown to *determine* the properties of matter. So it has to be something separate and different. Whether it is wholly independent of matter is not known, and possibly may be unknowable. On the other hand, it is not completely free and unpredictable as implied by the term 'spirit.' It is subject to context.

As I picture the concept, it is somewhat similar to what was formerly called 'natural law' -- the essential difference being it is active rather than passive. It is the embodiment of logic/math coupled with an innate tendency to become more integrated -- to grow, proliferate, and complexify. I have been told that this simply passes the buck upstairs, that something has to 'enact' the laws. Mebbe so, I dunno."

"Man! That's really dense stuff! I think I follow you, but it sure grinds the mental gears! What has been puzzling me, I guess, is how your mind *qua* organization could possibly be present in such heterogeneous assemblies as societies or the biosphere."

"Let's hope I can be a little clearer on that subject," I replied. "In some earlier publications I demonstrated that whenever we see things as organized, there are always certain imperceptible relations present. [8] For over a century, Gestalt psychologists had been aware that this happened. But for some reason, everyone overlooked the fact that relating activity of this sort necessarily required attraction between the items related. If a bond exists, then something has to do the bonding!

Now, if we accept the thesis of a mind, its major function is exactly this relating activity. It operates by means of mutual attraction almost like that between magnets. [9] The point I should like to make here is that these observations apply to *any* type of organization, including the social variety. Things which are organized are seen to cohere, no matter what they are. As a result, they require less effort to perceive, understand and remember. They hang together. They 'belong' to one another. In fact, the very word 'coherent' means mindful -- sane or understandable.

There is a great variety of relatedness because mind/organization is everywhere. At the submicroscopic level, material things have to be related else they can't exist as such. At more extensive levels, like the social relations among organisms, it is a commonplace that like-kind attract each other. Fish of the same species school together. Birds of a feather flock together. And between people possessing a likeness of DNA, they are genetically related. They belong together as family or tribe. But even those who merely think alike or have like interests are attracted to each other. In all cases there is some degree of mutual belongingness or coherence. The newborn infant craves it. He rejects the strange and different and does so quite emotionally. To him, the unfamiliar is disorderly and incoherent by definition -- this for the simple reason that it doesn't 'fit in.'

Given these observations, suppose we go to your question concerning how mind/organization exists in societies or the biosphere. If we look at a social group having common language, mores, customs, folklore, and the sort, it would appear that these common features act almost like a kind of glue holding the members together. Because they enhance predictability of behavior, they make for feelings of heightened security. They obviously increase communication, and the very word 'communication' implies community -- just as organisms imply organization. The group tends to become an entity in its own right. To the extent that minds are alike, there is a common mind -- call it what you will. It can be demonstrated by the decisions the group makes, for they will be almost unanimous. Members feel they belong together and are uncomfortable if separated. And it can only be the mind that provides all this vital coherence.

As to the biosphere, the assumption that it is a 'heterogeneous assembly' merely reflects our unfamiliarity with the full spectrum of life. Throughout the animate world, there is an underlying commonality of DNA. Metabolic principles are the same. All are similarly constructed with membranes and comparable modes of internal activity. And to top it all off, there is an unbelievable degree of interdependence and cooperation among species. Consider plants. Most of our toxins and medicines come from them. Yet plants and humans are kingdoms apart. All such features bear testimony to a common origin. Multicellular life could only have arisen through symbiotic cooperation, and it can only prosper to the extent that this 'activity for the common good' continues.

Wherever it is found, mind/organization exerts an integrative influence upon events. It produces a mutual attraction which, at the social level, appears as an affiliative tendency among living things. It explains why like-kind attract each other, and why the family is the basic unit of any culture, human or otherwise. When one considers its wide-spread importance for all life, it is understandable that this basic urge for 'togetherness' and 'belongingness' would become identified with *love*."

He stared at me for a moment. "Of course you recognize that these are pretty far-reaching statements. They are vague, and they border on religion. Do you have any scientific way of explaining them so they don't have to be accepted on faith, or mere say-so?"

"They are only conclusions," I admitted. "But the underlying logic is sound. It begins with the fact that everything we are aware of, no matter what it may be, has to be reflected in the human mind and involve brain tissue If not, it can't be perceived, much less known. To understand outer events, therefore, one must take the responsible mechanism into consideration. Otherwise, the 'outer' and 'inner' become confused. If it is outside, and we are aware of it, then its mental counterpart is *inside!*. And this latter is all we can possibly deal with.

Now, it should be obvious that the mechanism of mind cannot be explained over some lunch in a cafeteria -- regardless how well the words are chosen. So about the best I can do is state my conviction that the cortical energy is identifiable. It is a molecular energy of mutual attraction. And this is precisely what would be needed for all the relating activity. For . . . ."

He interrupted me rather brusquely. "You are over my head! Anyhow, I have a Dean's council to attend. See you later."

And with this, he left. I gathered he was a bit miffed -- obviously it had been something I had said! But what? The range of subjects over which we had rambled was quite broad. Later I discovered he was on the board of a local church. I wish I had known!

I am not against religions. In fact, I sympathize with them -- so long as they do not attempt to force their views on others. Man is predominantly a believing animal. He has to be. The mind must have answers in order to grow. The resulting belief systems are what he lives by. Science itself is often evangelistic and takes on the trappings of religion. Demonstrable facts are pitifully few and sometimes hard to discern. About the most one can say is this or that "seems to be in the ball-park." What counts, therefore, is not what one really believes. It is his *behavior* -- how he acts upon his beliefs.

Chapter 14

Anatomy of a Hypothetical Superorganism

(The idea that the earth is alive -- the Gaia hypothesis, and some of the accompanying arguments pro and con.)

It was the young lady in leotards again -- possibly my most dedicated student! But she was not lolling on the back seats this time. She was up front and center. Her hand was already in the air as I stashed my brief case behind the podium.

"Yes?" I asked, fumbling some notes from a jacket pocket.

"I overheard your discussion yesterday at the cafeteria," she commented. "I couldn't help it. I was sitting directly behind you."

"Odd, I should have recognized you."

"I was wearing street clothes. I am not always in gym suits."

"Well, you should stay in them!" I informed her. "They're very becoming." The class guffawed. "Just out of curiosity," I broke in, "what about the conversation?"

"I thought you made a good case for the biosphere," she replied. "And I've been reading Lovelock. It's an option on our reading list. What's the difference between the biosphere as you see it, and his idea of the earth as a living organism called Gaia?" [10]

"Not much," I conceded. "And you are right. He does insist that the total earth is a living organism -- not simply a planet with life on it. However, the distinction may be largely a matter of semantics. For example, as I view the biosphere it cannot possibly consist of any mere catalogue of unrelated living things. It has to include all the inorganic materials with which they interact. These form a matrix permitting their continued existence. Neither organisms nor anything else can exist or be understood in isolation from the background in which they are embedded.

Thus, one must look upon the atmosphere, oceans, soil, and sedimentary rocks as part of the biosphere. Living things interact with, and make use of virtually all surface components of the planet. There are few features that would be exceptions -- some of the rare elements, the deeper tectonic plates, and the molten interior. Even these might be included with the argument that they support the rest of the system."

A hand went up in the back of the room. "I thought Lovelock's idea of Gaia was largely discredited by the biologists." [11]

"Far from it," I countered. "They might object to his implications, and indeed, some of them do. But implications are like beauty. They are in the mind of the beholder. So far as I know, Lovelock's scientific observations are not a matter of dispute. No one questions his data. And in any case, there are always objections to new ideas. They rock the boat."

"What were the implications they objected to?"

"Well, for one thing, some sensitive souls felt that calling the earth a living being was much the same as calling it a god. So he was charged with stirring up a hornet's nest of vague religion. This charge, I should add, was unfounded. He recognized the threat and took considerable pains to avoid it. However, subsequent writers like Sahtouris were much less concerned with potential criticism. [12] She bluntly describes Mother Earth as a goddess -- a Greek goddess yet! And moreover, the concept is said to be much more defensible and meaningful than the current mystical and often vicious father-gods imported from the Middle East!

Though I can't go along with any of these god/goddess vagaries, I can see how belief in an earth deity might even have advantages. For example, it might awaken people to the fact that man currently filthies the bed in which he sleeps. And there is also the possibility it could lead him to weigh ecological consequences against his all-consuming greed. This whole hassle about religious implications would be pathetic were it not so amusing. Not too long ago there was an even more significant postulate that the entire universe is mind-stuff! [13] No one seems to have objected to that. Perhaps it meshed better with their own brand of mysticism. But more likely, they simply did not understand it.

For another thing, Lovelock gets accused of 'holism.' This is a loose epithet which was used earlier against Gestalt psychologists. Actually, it should be considered more of a compliment. What it really means is that he takes a modern *systems* approach. Orthodox reductionists pick things to pieces and expect to gain some kind of insight from the scatterment of pieces. By contrast, the systems engineer begins with the whole and studies its functions. Analysis then proceeds according to the observable functions, rather than any parts or pieces which are often arbitrarily defined. This is what Lovelock does. He examines the biosphere and observes that its variables are in a steady-state. His analysis discloses that this steady-state is maintained by the interaction of various life forms, both among themselves and with the matrix of the earth."

"What's a steady-state?" -- this from the young lady in leotards again.

"It's a phrase physicists use to describe objects or states of matter undergoing continuous change," I explained. "If they tend to maintain themselves and endure, i. e. , remain relatively steady, they are identified as steady-states. This means they have to he self-regulating. Corrective action must be taken against any serious deviations. Such correction usually occurs via feedback.

In biology we refer to this self-maintenance process as homeostasis. It is what keeps our body temperature, pH index, blood sugar level, and numerous other variables from getting out of bounds. Constancy of this sort is particularly exact for the brain. In the outer world the overwhelming majority of naturally occurring steady-states are organic. Lovelock recognized this, which explains why he concluded that the earth had to be a living organism. Its familiar surface conditions are obviously maintained at levels conducive to life."

"For example?"

"Well, let's begin with the atmosphere," I suggested. "Lovelock was an atmospheric scientist, and the paradoxical nature of the atmosphere fascinated him. This was what led him to consider the manner in which it is regulated. It is a mixture of gases which, if left to itself, would soon equilibrate to a different composition -- one that would be lethal to all living things. In other words, it must be constantly undergoing renewal or development if it is to provide a life-sustaining mix. And as he saw it, such homeostatic action appeared organic, almost purposeful!

When we look at the oxygen content of the air we breathe, we find that it stays at roughly 21 percent of the total. A trifle less and all oxygen breathers would suffocate. Going the other direction, a mere 5 percent more and even the wettest things would ignite and burn. The other major components (nitrogen and carbon dioxide) possess comparable limits which are critical. Obviously, such a highly 'contrived' state of affairs must be extremely well regulated. And the regulation itself could only be due to the interaction of plants, animals and bacteria. It couldn't be accomplished by the inorganic rocks.

As a matter of interest, there is now general agreement among theorists that the atmosphere was initially produced by bacterial organisms, and that its maintenance is still organic to large extent. Therefore, it has to be part of a living steady-state."

"Does Lovelock cover this issue in the books on our reading list?"

"Yes, he does, and in considerably greater detail than I can do justice to here. Since we are currently discussing his theory, suppose we change those reading list entries from 'optional' to 'required.' There will be exam questions on them in the final.

To get back to the steady-state nature of the biosphere or Gaia, I should like to touch upon a point which Lovelock does not emphasize. This has to do with a chemical principle known as the Van't Hoff-Arrhenius equation. It states that all chemical processes will speed up or slow down by a factor of about 2½ for every 10 degrees Centigrade. Now all life processes such as growth, are basically chemical. Delicate elaborations or 'fine tuning' of these would not be possible with any significant fluctuations of temperature.

Our own brains illustrate what is meant by this. All psychological processes are extremely sensitive to temperature. Even one degree of fever can be detected. And at five or six degrees of fever, the train of thought gets derailed into delirium. Thus, all higher order creatures have evolved some means of controlling body temperature. Those not possessing such thermostasis (warm-bloodedness), have had to modify their life styles very seriously. Living things have optimal temperature ranges. Those from the tropics can't survive in the arctic, and vice versa. In lower order creatures, lifespan itself may well be contingent upon seasonal temperature.

It follows that life on earth could only have evolved within relatively narrow ranges of earth temperature fluctuation. Other planets of the solar system are probably lifeless because of this fact. For example, current conditions on Venus are estimated at 459° C -- much too hot. Whereas mean surface temperature on Mars is thought to be -53 degrees C, which is too cold. The thermal range permitting life to flourish on earth fluctuates around an average of 13 degrees C. [14] A cooling of only 2°, if sustained, could produce another ice age. This protective greenhouse condition has existed for 3½ billion years. The oceans have neither frozen nor boiled off though outer space is not much above absolute zero, and heat from the sun is thought to have increased by at least 25% during the same period."

A hand went up toward the rear of the room. "Isn't this temperature constancy just another aspect of the original problem? I mean isn't this also due to the protective atmosphere?"

"For the most part, yes," I replied. "But it is much more complicated than simply explaining the maintenance of a constant atmospheric envelope. It involves the earth's oceans as well as reflections of sunlight from cloud formations The entire scenario appears to be a complex lacework of interrelated processes. Some are inorganic, but the greater majority are due to the activity of living things.

The oceans themselves give rise to still further steady-state puzzles. There is reason to believe that their salt concentration has been kept at relatively the same level throughout evolutionary time. It has been estimated that if all the salt washed from the land were retained during this period, they would now be a heavier brine than the Great Salt Lake. Life, as we know it, could not have evolved. Extremely few creatures can survive in brine concentrations much above 6% by weight. The present figure is about 3.4%. [15] So we have a question. How is it maintained at this level? What happens to all the salt? Still another issue just as crucial from the standpoint of physiological chemistry is the pH index, the acidity~alkalinity balance. Even less is known about how this is regulated."

The girl in the leotards spoke up again. "But suppose all these processes *are* constant like you say, and *are* necessary for life to exist. Why should this imply that the entire biosphere is something alive?"

"Because," I replied, "it indicates the extreme interdependence and relatedness of otherwise separate life forms. These are what maintain the constancy. The 'parts' of the biosphere have to be organized as a *whole* --with cooperative behavior aimed at the continued existence of this whole. Though they appear completely separate, they have to be interlocked into a single gigantic system which is invisible to us. The living things making up the biosphere are also individual organic systems of course, and they contribute to this larger system just as our cells do for our bodies The key to it all is the relatedness or systematization which prevails."

The result was a blank stare. Then it occurred to me that I had never taken the time to explain what the word "system" means. Neither had Lovelock. If he had, some of his critics might not have come up with medieval accusations such as "teleology." There is a very real sense in which all systems seem to behave purposefully. They appear alive. And except for those we manufacture, they *are* alive.

I paused in thought for a moment before stating, "I'm going to have to explain what a system is, I guess. So I may as well get on with it. To begin, a system is *not* any arbitrary collection of variables as frequently asserted. The very fact that processes are often found grouped together in nature, indicates that such organized grouping has mutual advantages. What is observed in these organized cases -- the events taking place -- have to have a sort of 'naturalness' about them, a rationale as it were. The processes seem to belong together. They possess a degree of inter-meshed regularity enabling the total to continue over time. Were they separate, and not dependent on one another, mutual interference would occur.

Other descriptive phrases include: process-covariation, counter-balancing of function, interdependence of action, mutual interregulation, and self-organizing. All are applicable only to system behavior. They cannot be applied to the processes taken individually, nor to any arbitrary assemblies of these. [16] Admittedly, phraseology of this sort is vague. Indeed, the very term 'organization' is itself vague and ill-defined.

From a materials standpoint, organic systems are neither solid nor fluid. They are something in between. They are called mesoforms -- flexible steady-states which can withstand the constant flux of environmental change. They are internally organized and externally 'tuned' to their environments. This enables them to correct for whatever tends to displace them. Like a candle flame, they bend with the breeze but return to their original shape. Their lesser internal processes may fluctuate, but over-all functioning remains relatively constant.

Self-regulation of this sort requires that they be much more complicated than any simple mechanical function like a swinging pendulum. Displacement of the pendulum is automatically corrected by an opposite action. It swings back and forth between fixed limits on either side of a midpoint or zero norm. The functions of organic systems also have the same kind of limits and norms, but are made up of many pendulum-like processes each of which depends upon the action of others.

In biology we speak of such self-correcting regulation as 'homeostasis.' The term was coined by Cannon [17] and refers to the methods biological systems use to preserve over-all constancy of operation. For example, when maintaining body temperature it would include all the different physiological and behavioral measures taken to correct for uncomfortable (and possibly hazardous) extremes, e. g., shivering, sweating, metabolic and respiratory changes, donning or doffing of clothing, exercising, and so on.

Homeostasis has a generality of application possessed by few other aspects of the life sciences. No other subject is so vital to understanding the nitty-gritty of how organisms manage to live. In fact, it carries over into many of the machines man has devised. Our homes have 'homeostatic' feedback systems with thermostats to keep the temperature constant. Our cars have regulator switches to keep the battery charged. Airplanes have autopilots. Even everyday tools and appliances have 'throw~out' switches, fuses and warning lights to notify us that unseen variables have reached unacceptable limits and require control.

Such devices have given rise to a whole new branch of engineering called 'control' engineering or sometimes 'cybernetics.' By use of feedback, computers can now simulate simple brain operations and robots can simulate equally simple functions of the body. With respect to biology, which is our prime concern, the systems approach is relatively new. Thus, it might be helpful to explain some of the differences of outlook brought about. This can be done merely by observing mechanical systems.

First, let us look at the labile nature of steady-state operations. They are not fixed and invariant. So they have the flexibility necessary for *adaptation.* [18]   To examine this, suppose we consider the servomechanism known as an autopilot. This controls the plane's orientation in the sky (called its attitude). It enables the plane to remain on course despite atmospheric forces tending to alter its bearing in one direction or another. Its behavior might be likened to that of a human walking to the store. He maintains his course and posture despite wind, curbs, and the need to detour puddles. In brief, he *adapts* to the immediate environment. Like the plane on autopilot, he may not take exactly the same route a second time.

The autopilot can guide the plane so *purposefully* passengers are not even aware that a human is no longer at the controls. The plane exhibits what animal psychologists call 'goal-seeking' behavior. However, some of the simplest mechanical steady-states, if examined closely, reveal traits formerly attributed only to living things. A spinning top will 'jump' from one step to another going down stairs. Not only will it follow the path of least resistance like most humans, but after each jump it will stagger, then right itself and move on.

Finally, I should like to point out that steady-states, whether organic or inorganic, tend toward regularity of behavior. This is an important point because regularity is really incipient *organization* -- the stuff of life as it were! Since systems of this sort begin as closely related processes kept within limits, it should be expected that they would tend to acquire attributes like periodicity, structural orderliness, and symmetry. This was noted as long ago as 1893 by Ernst Mach. [19] A very simple example would be a water fountain. It becomes beautifully symmetrical despite the irregular flow of its component water molecules. As for organisms, some of the most elaborate instances of radial symmetry occur among the simplest sea creatures such as diatoms and radiolarians."

I paused for awhile, then noted, "We are getting somewhat afield from our original focus on the biosphere. Autopilots, computers, and similar machinery do not occur naturally. They are man-made contrivances which use negative feedback to achieve constancy of operation They were mentioned because much of their behavior is quite life-like, often spectacularly so! Indeed, some computer enthusiasts working with artificial intelligence even claim that mind can be duplicated! This, I believe, is more enthusiasm than logic."

"Why do you consider it so unlikely?" This came from the youth who had spoken earlier.

"Because computers have no initiative," I replied. "They can only follow fixed program orders. They are constructed from the outside and are not self-correcting or self-organizing. They do not grow internally like the mind. It is the energizing nature of this growth that provides initiative, innovation, foresight and insight -- traits that computers cannot duplicate."

"I thought that both the mind and the computer were basically information processing systems. Isn't all information the same?"

"By no means," I assured him. "Computer information is merely a series of on/offs and extends in only one direction, bit after bit. It is coded linearly as a function of time. And it *is* a code -- symbolic, not representative. By way of contrast, the information which the mind processes is in patterns or forms which are directly representative. They occupy two or three dimensions simultaneously. This results in emergent relations which cannot be coded linearly."

"Whew!" he exclaimed. "I pass. What I was really trying to bring up was a communications question. Lovelock states that the most compelling argument against Gaia (or biosphere) is a matter of communications. [20] As I understand it, this says that if the biosphere were an organism kept alive by mutual interaction of its member beings, such action would necessitate communication between all the participating life forms. And though he didn't say as much, I'd think this would mean it had to have a mind. What does a person do with this argument?"

"Well, for starters," I replied, "the argument is a straw man Mutual and beneficial homeostasis in the biosphere would *not* presuppose that all the living participants communicate with each other. Not all the cells and centers in the human brain communicate with one another. All it would require is that there not be any significant interference among life-sustaining processes. And should this occur, the interfering processes almost certainly would be weeded out genetically. That is to say, they would not be selected during the natural selection process of evolution.

Among the vast majority of organisms, communication with each other is precluded for a variety of reasons. I don't see how a crabapple tree in West Virginia could either contribute or interfere with the chit-chat between magpies in Idaho, much less influence the salt concentration of the oceans. Conceivably, it might communicate with other nearby trees, but I doubt if it is even aware of marine organisms. In short, I think the argument must have arisen as a loose metaphor based on the presumed general understanding among people. And I *do* mean *presumed*. Few people in one location necessarily have any knowledge about problems in more remote areas. What passes for media news is filtered for sensationalism and presented without context.

But let me pursue the argument further. Even if interaction between different life forms *were* required to maintain the biospheric steady-state, I still would not find the problem totally insoluble. DNA is fundamentally alike for all species, and it becomes more so as species become increasingly similar. Now, DNA is probably far more than any simple linear file of templates for protein synthesis. Such concepts, currently in vogue, leave the entire problem of biological organization up in the air. We do not know at this time, of course, but it seems quite likely that it is capable of functioning in ways well beyond those required for routine protein synthesis.

Given the observation that commonality of DNA means a similar commonality of chemical functioning (which is admitted), and recognizing that virtually all creatures except man communicate chemically (also admitted), we have every reason to assume the existence of an underlying chemical language of life. Now, the most common interactor or liaison agent between living things is bacteria. The socializing of these is what gave rise to the variety of life in the first place. They pass DNA around among themselves quite indiscriminately. So it seems possible that the bacterium could be an unwitting carrier of messages. All we would need would be a link between this little fellow and the big multicellular fellows. And for all we know, links of this sort might be both varied and numerous."

I happened to glance at the girl in the gym suit again. In fact, she was hard to ignore. This time she appeared upset about something, so I paused.

"I can't go along with that!" she announced. "It's too far-fetched --

despite the world-wide blanket of bacteria which is supposed to relate everything! I'd like to get back to what started this far-out discussion. As I recall, it began with the question whether homeostasis presupposes the existence of mind. Doesn't this go considerably beyond Lovelock? I don't remember him even mentioning the word 'mind' anywhere!"

"You're right. He didn't." I conceded. "He foresaw the opposition it would arouse in the orthodox establishment. It's their duty to defend the faith, and the concept of mind is contrary to scripture. However, in his smaller volume, written before he was thought-policed, he clearly states that if Gaia exists as an organism it has to exist because of homeostasis. Then, later on, he further states that homeostasis requires at least some intelligence. [21]

Now, intelligence does not occur without a mind. There has to be something that is intelligent. A related argument applies to homeostasis. It seems to be found nowhere except in living systems and the machines devised to extend these systems. Given this observation, his conclusions look eminently logical. Moreover, the fact that homeostasis exists in the biosphere is not contestable."

"I can see how mind and intelligence could bring people together so that a social mind would evolve," she replied. "People are pretty much alike, their brains are similar, and great gobs of them even think alike. But to me at least, the biosphere is a totally different kettle of fish. Plants, animals and bacteria don't have much in common. They are not built alike, and they don't act or look alike."

"It's true that living things are enormously diverse at the macroscopic level," I replied. "And we are acutely aware of this diversity because we also live at this level. But when one examines life from a cellular perspective the inhabitants of the biosphere don't appear all that different -- the major distinction being that between plants and animals.

We tend to overlook the fact that all living things drop back to a single cell every generation. This means that it is largely the features of their multicellular design, the cell's social structures, which produce this miscellany of creatures. The cellular societies of different organisms have greater variety than those of the cells themselves simply because the responsible DNA has greater variety. Since the heterogeneity of the biosphere seems to prevent you from seeing it as an organism, let's compare its development with that of the human. Maybe this would help.

During prenatal growth of the human, cells of the body evolved through many successive generations. As a result of this growth and differentiation, they became more specialized. Certain members with exceptional skill at communicating were able to provide the body with a measure of intelligence. These are called neural cells, and most particularly brain cells.

Now, compare our presumed biospheric organism During evolutionary growth of the biosphere, life forms evolved through many successive generations. As a result of this growth and differentiation, they became more specialized. Certain members with exceptional skill at communicating were able to provide the biosphere with a measure of intelligence. These are called animals, and most particularly people."

She laughed. "Sounds like one of those TV commercials that go over and over the same line repeatedly. I have a question."

"Shoot."

"I presume this implies that more recently evolved organisms, especially humans, account for the intelligence of the biosphere. Is that right?"

"It's only an analogy," I protested. "Further, I think it is less a matter of individual beings than their *becoming*. Beings are transient phenomena. The process is the important feature. And don't forget the bacteria. They may well be at the bottom of all this."

"If the human is at the top, then why is this privileged 'biospherically intelligent' human making such a frightful mess of the planet?"

"You know, that puzzled me for quite some time. It seemed insane -- not just suicidal, but genocidal! Fortunately, other members of the biota behave rationally. Their behavior is in keeping with the interests of others as well as their environment. So the biosphere continues. But the human acts more like a spoiled brat, completely self-centered, arrogant, and even contrary to his own welfare. So, after much thought, I concluded that Sahtouris had the only feasible answer."

"Sahtouris?"

"Yes, Elisabet Sahtouris. [22] She recognized the same paradox and suggested that the human species is adolescent. Offhand, it sounds utterly ludicrous. But the more one thinks about it, the more logical it becomes. The human is the new kid on the block, a very recent species that is undergoing rapid growth much like other adolescents. His behavior is primarily emotional rather than rational. He suffers from 'know-it-all' egotism and is hopelessly idealistic.

For example, entire nations exhibit Messiah complexes and go to war over communism, democracy, religion and what not! In our own country the current 'in' thing is an effort to legislate biology, to do what the genes can't do -- make everybody equal. Emphasis is on civil, gay, ethnic, sexual, and even criminal 'rights.' ! The greatest single problem, however, is still the teenage sex drive. He is overpopulating the planet."

The class thought this hilarious. But when the laughter subsided, I pointed out that overpopulation was far from funny. It either underlaid or contributed heavily to all the other problems of society -- particularly environmental deterioration and the cultural and ethical dissolution we observe. Zoo keepers, I noted, have long been aware of the abnormal behavior which accompanies over-crowding of any animal species. [23]

"What's the bottom line on all this?" I was asked.

"I am optimistic," I replied. "Present day social fads are largely temporary and will go out of style when more pressing crusades arise. The important thing is that the human mind has finally developed to a point where it can assist in its own evolution It even knows where to look -- inside the cell. So we may expect progress at an ever-increasing rate. Sahtouris believes the human will mature, and this says the same thing.

In the meantime, ecological concern is rapidly gaining momentum. And let's not overlook the bacteria again. They are doing everything they can to clean up after this heedless human. We all know about the micro-organisms that feast on oil spills. But recently one was discovered in a waste-dump engaged in breaking down contaminants like dioxin and chlorophenols." [24]

Chapter 15

Viewpoints -- their Fall-out for the Planet!

(Comments on the interrelatedness of all life. Why such inter-relatedness cannot be understood using the reductionist procedure. And why the Gestalt systems approach is preferable.)

"Since this is our last lecture session," I commented, "I'd like to spend the hour rounding out some of the broader aspects of our subject, issues skipped over hastily, and other loose ends. Possibly the best place to begin is by discussing the different outlooks with which scientists approach problems. Methodology can seriously influence whether one is successful. There are two major categories. One is orthodox reductionism -- which I call the *'tinkertoy'* approach, and the other is the Gestalt systems method.

The differences between them arose long ago. Let's start with reductionism. It is the older of the two. In ancient Greece there were those who declared that all things are made up of small pieces called atoms. As luck would have it, they turned out to be correct. Moreover, the idea meshed quite nicely with the thinking of the industrial revolution which came much later. Pieces (gears, bolts, levers, etc.) could be put together in various ways to make useful contrivances called machines. Thus, our culture was nurtured on the basic assumptions of reductionism. These implied that to understand how something works all one had to do was disassemble it and see how the pieces fit together. All things were made up of units of one type or another. To create something new, the process was simply reversed. One took the necessary pieces and put them together.

People tended to overlook the fact that creating something new first required one to visualize the *whole* and how it operated. However, the attitude persisted. Similar approaches were later applied to information.

It was assumed that if one accumulated enough information, however blindly collected, he would ultimately end up with all the answers. Ridiculous as it sounds, reductionism worked beautifully for much of engineering. With a little covert visualization, miracles of machinery were produced. It was a program which provided most of our know 'how,' even though it resulted in only meager knowledge of the 'what' or 'why.' [25]

Needless to say, the life sciences tried to emulate this success story of physics and engineering. But here they hit a snag. For some reason the basic assumptions would not work. Whether dealing with plants, people, brains or societies, nothing organic could be constructed out of parts. The parts simply could not be put together effectively. And worse yet, none of the organic systems could be reassembled once they had been reduced to parts. It was often better just to forget the pieces entirely. All too frequently they were artifacts of arbitrary dissections or classifications. What provided understanding were the *functions!* And these were not parts They were events -- sometimes relations. The problems encountered were somewhat akin to the differences between gross anatomy and physiology. Anatomy requires only dissection and classification. Whereas, physiology studies how the systems operate, their internal organization and mutual relatedness.

The orthodox reductionist engages in a search for ever smaller bits and pieces. He has his sights set on finding the ultimate quark -- the holy grail of physics. By contrast, the systems analyst examines the system as a whole, including all its input, output, and particularly its relationship to the environment. He then looks for the functions which are important to over-all operation. These may or may not correspond to any particular parts. Dissect an organic system into parts and the functions are lost irretrievably. Functions are relationships, the essence of organization. And it seems quite likely that organization is *mind!*

Our knowledge of the outside world is provided by the senses. Therefore, what we learn is organic by definition. After all, it occurs in our heads! For this reason reductionism cannot be applied to anything in the life sciences. Little or no understanding can be obtained from analysis of so-called parts. True, many discrete anatomical units like cells and organs do exist. But their real significance becomes known to us only through their functions and interrelations with other such units. It does not derive from their being segregated and classified as this or that When it comes to what we see, for example, it is always the patterning, form, or *whole* that registers — not any collage of parts. Allow me to demonstrate.

Take a look at Figure 12. It consists of two pairs of unfamiliar polygons. But it can also be considered four figures assembled out of parts. There can be no question about what constitutes the parts. They are simply straight lines and angles enclosing areas. This makes them easy to analyze, or so it might be thought. But suppose we try to define their shapes in these terms, i.e., define them reductionistically as it were.

Polygon 'A' does not have the same form as 'a', nor does 'B' resemble ' b'. Nonetheless, (1) All have the same area divisible into four equal parts. (2) All have the same perimeter divisible into eight straight lines. (3) The lines are the same number of the same length in each case. In other words, any one figure can be reassembled into any other. And in addition (4), Figures 12 A and a even have the same number of the same internal angles -- and so do B and b. In brief, *all physically given parts of these polygons are identical!*

Like graphite and diamonds, these figures are quite different despite the fact that their atoms or parts are the same. What one sees, therefore, cannot be 'parts.' He sees shape, form, or *patterning*. If he is to analyze what he sees, it is obvious he must deal with something he *cannot* see-- something that is not physically present. Call it mystical if you wish, but this does not change the facts. And as pointed out earlier, this is true of *everything* seen!

Because our inner world is fundamentally an organic world, all prior attempts to understand the mind have been frustrated for precisely these reasons. Sensory data and sensory systems become meaningless when considered simply as combinations of parts. This is true whether the parts are receptor cells of the retina or the sides of polygons. Reductionist methodology will not work in the organic world -- and this is the only world we know!

What distinguishes the above polygons and makes them different is an undefinable something called form, organization, or internal relatedness. In each case, lines drawn from the midpoints of opposing sides, or from opposing angles, will have distributions just as unique as the forms themselves. The intangible pattern of field effects represented by such lines is what organizes the things we see. It is provided by the mind and does not appear with the retinal image.

FIGURE 12. Polygons that differ *only* in shape (organization.)

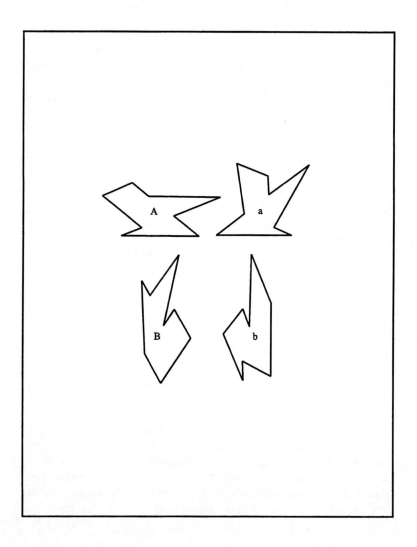

Once again, this observation applies to *everything* we perceive. It has been demonstrated in numerous ways including the perceived similarity of human faces. Apparent facial likeness does not depend on the likeness of facial features. [26] In brief, one's face is not comprised of features. It is a *face!* Though we can focus on such details, they are essentially analytical artifacts like the sides of the polygons -- matters of descriptive convenience.

The argument is perhaps easier to understand with regard to hearing. Ostensibly, music is made up of notes. But is it? It is written in notes and these are usually considered parts. However, the sound arrives at our ears in a continuous pattern, only a small fraction of a tone at any given instant of time. So it cannot be described as serially presented units. Except for some particular infinitesimal moment, all the melody and its patterning is due to memory! The action of the auditory mechanism during that particular instant has no meaning in itself. Moreover, the rhythm also plays an important role in the complex patterning going on in the mind. The melody is almost as easily identified simply by tapping out the associated rhythm.

What one hears, therefore, is the organization or patterning -- much as in the polygons. And this is virtually pure relatedness. Extending the concept to speech, it will be noted that words and possibly whole phrases are often meaningless when taken out of the contextual pattern. That which appears in awareness is actually the *meaning* one's mind attributes to the sentence. Sometimes this can be grasped well before the sentence is finished. We complete the organization as it were.

If this 'imperceptible' relating activity exists and is necessary to organize everything we deal with, then something has to account for it! Some heretofore unrecognized energy has to be operating in the brain. And its operations are doubtlessly what we know as mind. Moreover, it can only be an energy of mutual attraction, a miniature analogue of gravity. Only mutual attraction within and between salient aspects of the patterning could hold them together, interrelate data when we think, create the harmony of melodies, and so on and on. Relating activity produces bonds. This is what the word relating means.

When one casts about wondering what this strange energy might be, some interesting comparisons come to light -- features which distinguish the organic from the inorganic. Let us examine inorganic matter for a moment. Here electrical particles of like kind (including ions) repel each other. In electricity it is always *opposites* which attract each other. Opposite charges, say protons and electrons, equilibrate each other when they form a pair. They lose free energy and become stable. Thereafter they do not change, much less grow.

In the organic world the situation is exactly reversed. Things which are of like kind *attract* each other! They join forces as it were, and do not neutralize or equilibrate. In most cases, any free energy contributes to life or growth. It is only logical to conclude that the energy itself must be one which acts between molecules. We know it is in the brain where memory resides, and memories can only be molecular. This strongly suggests chemical structures, the 'like kind' factor being a matter of stereochemical shape or form.

Now it just so happens that large organic molecules do indeed attract each other. Moreover, they do so in proportion to both mass and likeness of stereochemical shape The phenomenon is known as 'resonance.' It is responsible for virtually all interaction at the cellular level, how viruses connect to cells, how immune cells identify antigens, and so forth. Thus, it could also explain how memory molecules relate to each other, or how they are referenced by sensory input during processes of recognition. [27]

In fact, there is reason to believe that daily perception actually arises from this resonating process which takes place during recognition -- the interaction between sensory input pattern and its identifying memory structure. Why? Because perception seems to be a composite of the two! For example, we have what is known as 'perceptual constancy.' This means that what we see is more like the real object than is warranted from known conditions on the retina. Memory obviously modifies input during recognition in a fashion not unlike that which occurs with Rorschach blots. Or again, if we are hungry we can see food objects much more readily than non-food objects. It is a commonplace that we see what we want to see and hear what we expect to hear. Wants and expectations are also parts of our mental structuring.

If our hypothetical mechanism is correct, and similarity of molecular patterning accounts fox the attraction between like kind, it would have to be extremely common and widespread. The entire perceived world occurs in the brain, and all animals have brains however rudimentary. Further, all are social to some extent, and the socializing certainly is not random! Birds of a feather flock together -- despite the fact that nothing physical extends between the birds. So the attractional agent has to be molecular and in the separate brains of the birds. Most likely, each carries a small molecular template about with him -- a *Suchbild!* And this matches the profile (shape) of birds like him. The same is thought to be true for schooling fish, swarming insects, deer herds, and possibly even certain groupings of humans.

Attractional relatedness of this social type, based on likeness of kind, may be described as a general affiliative tendency. It otherwise passes by a variety of aliases. Depending on manifestation and context, we call it interest, altruism, infatuation, love, belongingness, herd instinct, and similar names. Work by sociobiologists has pretty well established that social altruism among animals at least, coincides with genetic relatedness (also molecular), and is possibly implemented by body scent or pheromones. [28]

Just for the fun of it, let us carry our speculation still further. As the mind of an individual grows it feeds on sensory input. Molecular equivalents of the input are created in memory. The process is known as learning. To all effects and purposes, these resulting memory surrogates of events, people, houses, cars and other objects, extend the mind into the environment. However, the relating itself takes place internally in the brain -- much as occurs with the flocking of birds. It is established by proxy as it were, between representative memory structures.

With respect to property, we often refer to this negatively as greed, hoarding, selfishness, and similar terms. This is when the property belongs to someone else When it belongs to us we take a radically opposite view. We say we collected it because we were interested in it. It provoked 'gut-feelings,' perhaps even love. These things, we declare, are *ours!* They are parts of *our* world! In a literal sense it is true. The relatedness is internal to the mind. But it is no less real than if actual physical bonds existed between ourselves and the objects outside.

To the degree that one treasures something possessed, to that degree he is *possessed by it!* The resulting relationship anchors both ends of the bond -- the owner and his own. This is why he becomes quite emotional if something disrupts the web he has woven. It constitutes a threat to the self. It endangers the integrity of his inner world.

The affiliation and belongingness of social groups also has a dark side. Individuality of any sort tends to set one apart from others. This is what 'individuality' means. Like birds 'of a feather,' it is equally natural for people to flock together. So they divide themselves into cultural, religious, racial, economic, and miscellaneous smaller groups. Unfortunately, such differences often make for conflict. History confirms that in-groups and out-groups have always been disruptive aspects of the larger picture -- never successfully eliminated by either legislation or education.

Social relatedness or bonding would appear to have limits beyond which it cannot extend. One such limit has to do with system size and complexity. When social systems get too large, as in the case of major nations, people are necessarily treated as 'things.' In turn, the people themselves are unable to identify with the system. It becomes just another impersonal faceless bureaucracy. There is nothing with which to relate, only tangles of irrelevant and vague laws having little or no meaning.

As might be expected, our tightest bonds are formed with the immediate family. Looser bonds exist with the extended family of aunts, uncles, and other relatives. The largest such natural group is the tribe or clan. All are genetically related and once provided social belongingness. No more. They have now largely disappeared, and with them has gone the belongingness. For the most part, we are surrounded by strangers. If lucky, there is a friend or two. Thus, one of our most critical present day problems is loneliness. [29] It particularly afflicts the elderly. They hear their names called in the passing mixtures of sound. But they do not look up. They know there is no one to do the calling. People also have meaning only in context.

Let us return for a moment to the outward extension of the mind. It would seem that this is merely another way of describing mental growth or learning. It is growth involving rearrangement and restructuring of brain matter rather than further accumulation of new cells as in the case of body growth. It is wholly internal because the only world we know is internal. In brief, mind is an organizing phenomenon that occurs at a molecular level in the brain. The general features of its developmental process, however, are little different from those of any other growth -- whether that of plants, puppies, or people. Physical growth is an on-going organization of cells. Mental growth is a similarly continuous organization of molecules -- an accretion of patterning pretty much as Aristotle described it to be.

At first thought, this description of growth seems paradoxical. Standard texts picture it as having two aspects: (1) the accumulation or amassing of cells by mitosis, and (2) the differentiation of this mass into various body parts during development. Terms include extension vs differentiation, integration vs. separation, socialization vs. individuation, and so on. For example, a plant not only gets larger, but it sends out branches, leaves, and in general becomes more complex. This latter feature appears inconsistent. If the responsible energy must be exclusively attractional in order to form bonds, how does one account for the 'splitting off' at various stages to make the system more elaborate? It is the age-old question, 'If all life is one, how does the one become so many?' Biologists sometimes refer to it as the problem of 'symmetry breaking.'

A little further study and it becomes obvious that this may not be as paradoxical as it first seems. Any force that pulls things together is necessarily also a force that pulls things apart. Suppose we examine items A B C D E F. Should a force of mutual attraction arise between consecutive pairs, as would occur in A-B, C-D, E-F, then other potential pairs, namely B-C and D-E, would be pulled apart. When the items are components of some perceived visual pattern like a cluster of dots, this grouping occurs according to the Gestalt law of proximity discussed earlier. [30]

If the same forces of molecular attraction were to occur in the leveloping embryo, as one might expect, they could easily account for loci of accelerated growth, gradients of structural stress, and even planes of cleavage -- all manipulable at the cellular level! Perhaps the problem of 'symmetry breaking,' which has plagued embryologists, is not totally insoluble after all!

It might be mentioned that cities (which also grow) follow much the same program. When they reach certain stages of growth, they tend to differentiate into suburbs, shopping centers and such. Often the inner city then becomes dead material like the middle of an expanding fungus ring.

When I began this exploratory study of growth I had a purpose in the back of my head. Call it a hidden motive. Suppose the biosphere (or Gaia) were a living organism in its own right as Lovelock contends. Evolution would then become the developmental aspect of its growth. In short, evolution would be to the biosphere what maturation is to the human body. So my interest was in finding out how well evolution compared with other such growth processes.

By and large, biologists had already suspected that life had become increasingly more complex during the course of geological time. It appears to have branched off every which way. It began with single cells like everything else, and its growth was sporadic much like human growth. Moreover, it was most creative during early youth (the Cambrian period). There is even reason to believe that evolving animals became progressively more specialized and intelligent. All these more general aspects of evolution would seem to be consistent with what we know of human development. Beyond broad observation, however, little more could be said. [31]

Speculation of this sort is 'iffy' at best. The biosphere is far less homogeneous than the cellular components of any organism It is made up of large numbers of overlapping ecological systems which bear little resemblance to each other, much less to body parts or functions. Many feel, and I believe correctly, that it was these ecological systems which evolved, and not just individual species. [32]

It should be obvious that life affects the environmental context in which it arises fully as much as the environment affects life. Traditionally, however, we have always interpreted the fossil evidence solely in terms of species changes. There has been no overview encompassing ecosystems, and certainly nothing involving the whole biosphere. One reads only of separate alterations in separate species.

Such traditional thinking, though possibly unavoidable, takes the species out of context. And little if anything can be understood when taken out of context. For this reason (among others) it appears doubtful that evolution could have been the one-way street it is commonly pictured as being The paradigm of chance mutations ⇨ bodily changes ⇨ natural selection, constitutes a linear program allowing for little symbiosis or other mutually supportive behavior among developing life forms. [33]

By contrast, the very existence of evolution presupposes an ongoing transformation. The very fact that living things have developed one from another, speaks of continuity. It has been described as a ' tree of life,' or perhaps a 'bush.' But in either case, it implies a living entity, an organism in its own right -- one that possibly still carries within itself a wealth of genetic memories concerning the dead past.

A much more realistic picture of the biosphere soon emerges if one shifts mental gears and thinks about relatedness rather than species, things, pieces, and their differences. Viewed from this opposite Gestalt systems perspective, it is soon recognized that the biosphere is *not* hopelessly fragmented as popularly supposed. Living things are so interrelated that the total indeed begins to appear more like one gigantic living organism.

Vital dependencies exist everywhere. The example we remember from childhood is the relation between flowers and bees. The flower is the sex life of the plant. Now one can't do much about sex when rooted in one spot. So flowers need bees to distribute their pollen. Bees, on the other hand, have an equally dire need of flowers to make honey. Neither flower nor bee can exist without the other. This being the case, they are *organically linked*, and could be more accurately described as sub-units of some still larger whole. The world-wide oxygen exchange between plants and animals is another commonly known organic linkage. It takes on special importance with realization that the human brain literally lives on oxygen, more so than any other known organic system.

Once one focuses his attention on the interrelations rather than arbitrarily defined 'parts,' the infrastructure of the biosphere shows up with startling clarity almost everywhere. It forms a particularly dense network holding together the smaller creatures, plants, and (don't forget) the bacteria. Even the trees are organically dependent upon one another. More than a hundred species (alders, pine oaks, larches, etc.) have root systems which form conjoining underground networks. Experiments with radioactive tracers and dyes have revealed consistent nutritional transfer of needed materials up to 43 feet between trunks!

Considering the enormous variety of plants and animals, their dependence on each other can become quite complex. Communal cooperatives emerge involving radically different species, and these may be hooked into still other nets. Literature is to be found under the heading of 'co-evolution.' The new science of ecology also contains large sections devoted to such relationships. The subject is already voluminous and much too intricate to be detailed here. It is obvious that the biosphere is no more 'disconnected' than the modern nation. And much like the nation, it is so large and complex it is nearly impossible to visualize. Biologists are aware of this situation, and many suspect that what we now know may be only the more obvious linkages. There is no way to estimate the total.

Biosphere II has now completed its first mission (Sept. 26, 1993). It is located some 35 miles north of Tucson in a remote patch of desert. Both in conception and size it was a massive project compared with other scientific experiments. It covered 3.15 acres and consisted essentially of a large greenhouse hermetically sealed from the outside world. There was a miniature ocean, 7 carefully selected ecosystems, and about 3800 species of plants and animals -- including 8 humans. The aim of the project was to provide a realistic (though necessarily limited) simulation of the conditions enabling life to exist on earth (Biosphere I). The hope was to uncover some of the more critical hidden variables, and to learn how these interact to sustain the fabric of life. Though designed to last a century, the initial period of isolation was 2 years. Repeated runs were projected to correct unforeseen errors and omissions. [34]

While at the Johns Hopkins Operations Research Office, a now defunct think-tank, I helped engage in some rather extensive war games. These were simulations played on a huge platform laid out with representative terrain. Men and equipment consisted of small pieces which could be moved about as in a chess game. Every effort was made to ensure realism. Nonetheless, no two games ever came out the same way, and the 'answers' we obtained were always somewhat iffy. The trouble lay in the variety of unpredictable variables which kept asserting themselves. These were not only numerous but often incapable of being resolved.

From this limited experience, I would have predicted that Biosphere II would encounter similar problems. It was even larger and more complex. Given that it could operate for a whole century, however, consecutive 2 year scenarios might well have produced continuous improvement in realism The result could have been a highly valuable body of information not otherwise obtainable. But it might not have been exactly the information they set out to find.

Close interdependence of process, together with homeostasis, leads one to think that the biosphere could be a living entity -- difficult as this may be to accept. If accepted, however, it means that man-made changes in various parameters of the system can have far reaching consequences for life on earth. Worse yet, these frequently cannot be foreseen. For example, well-meaning alterations in the course of waterways have produced much more damage than benefit, particularly in Florida. Importations of foreign species such as 'killer' bees have created still different problems. Add to these mistakes the new insecticides and herbicides that wash into the streams and poison wildlife, and the list of thoughtless blunders becomes endless.

Man does not yet fully understand how his own insides work, much less his brain! It is therefore disturbing to realize that modern technology has put him in a position where he can meddle with something which he knows absolutely nothing whatever about. Depletion of the ozone layer and destruction of the rain forests are merely two of the major alterations whose ultimate effects are almost wholly unknown. How fortunate it is that he cannot control the weather!

The earth and/or the biosphere is not a gadget which can be readily repaired or replaced once it breaks down. It is the most intricate manifestaction of life known, and sometimes living things are easily sickened or killed. Since we are a part of the biosphere, organically linked with its fate, it seems foolhardy in the extreme to interfere with any of its basic processes unless we are sure of the consequences. And such certainty is rarely attained. This does not mean we should halt modern 'progress.' We could not do so if we wished. It is growth. Rather, it only asks that we act rationally *before* any catastrophes occur instead of rationalizing afterwards.

In this seething sphere of life which is becoming ever more

complex, we are at the cutting-edge, the growing surface. This is what accounts for our presumably 'superior' intelligence. But it also accounts for our paranoid delusions of grandeur - the idea that everything was 'put here' just for us. It seems degrading to suggest that we may be advancing solely because most of life is advancing. There is no alternative. If life doesn't advance it dies. Life is growth It could be that we don't notice the advancement because perception is relative. Suppose everyone and everything suddenly became five times as smart, or even five times as big. How could we know it happened? If our ruler expands with what we are measuring how can we detect any change?

Consider the social insects again. They outnumber us, even out-weigh us! But they are not ruining the environment. And they have no starvation, crime, or engines of destruction. They have solved most of their more important social problems. We have not. In light of such success, who is to say whether we or they are the more intelligent?

Nobody knows how many of the statements attributed to Chief Seattle are really authentic. But some are truly perceptive. Among them, this one: 'Warn the white settlers that man did not weave the web of life, he is merely a strand in it. Whatever he does to the web, he does to himself.' Whenever we make some species extinct, we degrade our own future to some unknown degree. We narrow our possibilities for adaptation. And because results are unknown, particularly long-term effects, the fabric of life could unravel. The next 'minor' hole in the web might well be our own.

Our most urgent need, it would appear, is a reversal of outlook, a new philosophy of life, one that is appreciative of earth's other life -- at least one recognizing that we are dependent on this other life. We should cease this hacking at our own roots! Our current humanism, buttressed by our Middle East theology, emphasizes humanity to the exclusion of everything else -- including our own future! The environment is considered almost an enemy, something to be 'conquered.' It was 'given to us' to be exploited! Such views may have worked well in the year one. I don't know. But with today's burgeoning overpopulation, they are manifestly disastrous.

Perhaps a more reasonable outlook would be that suggested by the Japanese philosopher, Tsunesaburo Makiguchi. In his *Kachiron,* or 'Philosophy of Value,' he observed that all true value (*soka*) arises from maximizing one's relationship with nature. *Kyosei!* (Living together, symbiosis!) [35] It leads to peace of mind, and it only makes common sense. We are a part of nature. When we consider the environment as antagonist we are merely antagonizing ourselves!

Present day societies confuse value with wealth. This promotes greed and works against harmonious social relations. Ideally, societies should be such that one can belong to both nature *and* society. In belongingness there is freedom -- because they are then *your* nature and *your* society,

To some, the prospect of regaining such rapprochement with nature seems almost laughable. As a friend expressed it, 'man is about as far removed from nature as it's possible to get and still survive. Should he become wholly dependent upon the artificialities of modern civilization, he could well become like some of his own domesticated animals -- unable to survive on his own. Even an electrical outage now paralyzes a whole City!

Man currently has almost no knowledge of the living web from which he believes himself totally excised. He is unfamiliar with either birth or death, being born in the aseptic atmosphere of one hospital and commonly dying in another. The intervening period is also largely artificial. It is spent in fabricated buildings connected by a sheet of tar and cement, pursuing abstractions. Wherever he goes he surrounds himself with chunks of plastic, feeds on ersatz foods, and listens to unnatural noises! He is the only animal which lives in an almost completely artificial environment of his own making. Other animals, finding themselves in such a radically altered environment, have become extinct. But man has not been here long, in geological terms, so we can only wait and see.'

Welladay! As I pointed out to him, it won't be easy for man to re-join the world to which he rightfully belongs. However, I believe it can be done while still retaining most of his toys. As of this writing, it seems entirely possible that the environmental movement, coinciding as it does with the rise of genetic engineering, may result in a more mature mental outlook -- either that, or the overpopulation crisis will force it upon him. I keep my fingers crossed."

Through a Glass Darkly:
The Mechanism of Mind

Chapter 16

Is the Mind Chemical? The Brain and Body are!

(Ten reasons for thinking the operations of the mind may be chemical rather than electrical. Magnetic fields have no effect on us!)

The school year was finished and part of the past -- dead! Final rites had been performed at commencement. Black-robed figures had marched solemnly down the aisles to funereal music. All stood in stark contrast to the ill-suppressed enthusiasm of students, singing birds, and the luxurious green of early summer. I was glad it was over. I had exhausted myself with answering questions and herding people into overcrowded class rooms.. It was now my turn to loll on the back seats in leotards! I was going fishing, somewhere away from it all. A good catfish hole on the Snake River suggested itself. It lay some miles south of Hell's Canyon and was completely isolated.

Let's see, tackle box, poles, bait, . . . just then a knock sounded on the screen door. "Come in!" I yelled without looking up. He came in. It was a colleague from the math. department whom I had not seen since early in the semester.

"I came over to take you up on your offer," he said with a grin.

"What offer was that?" I inquired.

"Well, the last time I saw you, walking home from the game some months ago, you told me that when I had a day or so to spare you would explain how the mind works, that it had to be chemical. I not only have a day -- I have all Summer. Will it take that long?"

I ignored the question and simply pointed out, "Look, I'm going fishing. I am all geared up, gassed up, and ready to go."

He studied the tackle box. "So I see. Where you going?"

"Over to a spot on the Snake."

"But there's no trout in the Snake," he protested.

"I am aware of that," I retorted. "I'm not after trout. I'm going for catfish. And there are loads of them where I'm going -- blue channel cats, big ones -- ten pounds and over."

He studied this for a moment, then asked, "Would you object to my coming along?"

This was not what I had hoped for. But I couldn't see any polite way around it. So I said, "Of course not. It's nice to have someone to talk to."

He promptly left to get his gear, and I returned to taking inventory. When this was completed, with everything brought in, turned off, and locked up, I went into the spare room used as an office. There I rummaged through some files. What I was looking for was a hand-out which I had written for some earlier lectures on brain models. It was more than twenty years old. But very little had been added to the chemical theories since that time -- and certainly none of the problems had been solved! The upsurge of computer models and network theories had pretty well drowned out everything else. So the paper was still quite applicable, fact-ual, and would furnish him with a good overview of the issue. It was brief, I felt, and he could read it en route.

Glancing out the window I noticed he had returned and was busy stuffing tackle into the rear of the station wagon. I went out and handed him the paper.

"What's this?" he inquired.

"It's something I wrote a few years back," I explained. "It summar-izes some of the reasons for thinking the brain is primarily a chemical construct. It is short and can be read while riding. I thought it would save time by providing a common basis for discussion."

"Right on!" he said, stuffing the paper in his jacket. "Let's roll!"

The Chemical Nature of Mind/Brain Activity

Since casual inspection of the brain reveals little more than a maze of intertwined nerves, it is only natural that its functioning should be portrayed in terms of these nerve distributions. The resulting neural network theories have enjoyed almost universal acceptance. Thus, it becomes necessary to explain why a chemical approach should even be considered. As it turns out, there are numerous reasons for suspecting that chemical processes may very well be the prime carrier of information in the system.

Before discussing these, however, I must point out that there is not one scintilla of scientifically acceptable evidence establishing *any* particular information transport system in the CNS -- and especially none for the current belief that neuroelectric impulses are responsible. Though widely accepted, this latter is strictly an assumption. It most likely came about from lack of any known feasible alternatives. Thus, all existing theories about the mind are dependent wholly upon this assumption

So let us consider the logic for a moment. If one defines mental events as communications between cellular structures of the CNS, it would seem almost necessary that the information be in chemical rather than electrical terms. Why? Because virtually all other such communications, where completely identifiable, have turned out to be chemical. Aside possibly from muscular activation, this is true for all mind/body interactions. And it is even true for the larger portion of social communications between animals other than humans. All such facts suggest that as the brain evolved, it would have been simpler for evolution to have extended these more familiar existing chemical techniques. In short, the logic implies that psychological functions should be chemical functions! In addition to this, there are numerous reasons for believing the brain/mind could be just such a chemical system. A few of the arguments may be touched upon briefly.

(1) *All communication between organisms was originally chemical. This continued long after the evolution of neural structures.*

The behavior of simple (unicellular) life forms is obviously mediated by chemical activity. But with multicellularity came the evolution of nerves, and all this was thought to have changed. Nonetheless, if such changes occurred they must have been slow and incomplete. This was demonstrated at the turn of the century by Jacques Loeb. [1] He experimented extensively with primitive creatures possessing nerves, e.g., jellyfish, planaria, earthworms, and the like. Findings showed that much of their behavior remained unimpaired after sectioning (or even excision!) of their neural structures. In a large number of cases, the behavior could be traced directly to membrane chemosensitivity, i.e., data were transmitted and identified chemically by the organism.

Later, and at more advanced levels, creatures developed the use of hormones. These can only be described as chemical messages employed internally for communication within the body. About the same time, a broad spectrum of animal life came up with a closely related chemical signal system intended for external social communications. This involved information-laden odors called pheromones. They are exuded by one individual and usually carried by the wind to others. They have been proved to influence hormone levels, fertility, sexual maturation, mating behavior, social dominance, and territorial marking in creatures as diverse as moths and hyenas.

There is even a body of evidence accumulated showing that humans unknowingly secrete and detect pheromones. These are primarily sex identifiers and stimulants. One cannot otherwise explain the many strategically placed apocrine glands or tufts of hair in genital areas and arm pits. Supporting experiments reveal that human odors taken from one sex are identifiable by members of the opposite sex, and sometimes produce heightened sexual responsiveness. As might be expected, research of this sort also produces heightened responsiveness in the popular press. [2]

All living things still rely on the transmission of information-laden chemicals for control of processes occurring internally. But the human is no longer consciously aware of any organic secretions employed for social communication. As receptors of information, the usefulness of taste and smell is now severely limited. Nonetheless, their basic features such as adaptation, still follow the same general principles characterizing audition, vision and touch.

(2) *The cortex evolved as a further extension of the olfactory lobes, and olfaction is a chemical sense.*

In lower vertibrates the cerebral hemispheres are thought to be little more than chemical detection centers. Their refinement into organs for smell discrimination probably arose from use of the nose as a distance receptor when in search of prey, detection of enemies, or finding a mate. In the human, both vision and audition have long since supplanted olfaction as more accurate means of detecting distant features of the environment. This occurred slowly as man assumed an upright posture, and was accompanied by retrogression of the sense of smell. The atrophy of olfaction was not complete, however. The human brain can still identify thousands of odors.

Experimental evidence establishes that it is the stereochemical shape or *form* of the odorous molecule which is discriminated. Substances having similar molecular *patterning* are perceived as having similar smells. Those having different stereochemical shape have different smells The fact that odors are identified by the brain strongly suggests that the brain's memory somehow records them as specific molecular configurations.

How the nose is able to discriminate these differences of form is not known. In general, form perception is poorly understood. The uncontested fact that it *does* occur in olfaction, however, is highly significant. It demonstrates that neural tissues can detect and conduct patterning qua *patterning!* Many animals, especially bloodhounds, can be shown to discriminate very fine nuances of human odor -- even isomers! There seems no possible way such minute differences of form could be differentiated, learned, and recognized except via direct pattern conduction in the neural tissues of the olfactory system.

There are no elaborate structures in the olfactory epithelium (sensory surface) enabling it to code, transduce, or otherwise modify the molecular patterns. Unlike any of the other senses, the responsible receptors are merely free nerve endings. This means that neurons must have the ability to detect differences of shape and to transmit this pattern-information unaltered to the forebrain. There are no synapses en route as in other senses. Regardless how disturbing it may be to existing theories, the sense of smell requires *direct discrimination of stereochemical form* as well as intact conduction of this form. Since such patterning occurs in at least two dimensions it is totally beyond the capability of the neural impulse as an information carrier!

One of the more intriguing aspects of our smell sense is the fact that the olfactory epithelium is *pigmented!* The retina (which was similarly early to evolve) is equally pigmented -- and it also is an embryological outgrowth of the brain. This suggests that their modes of operation follow the same principles. Indeed, the fact that all our senses developed from a single embryological source (ectoderm) further enhances the thought that they may operate in like fashion. The idea is bolstered by a large literature demonstrating that the senses interact. Normally this interaction simply serves to keep them "in register." However, cross-referencing sometimes occurs, as in cases of synaesthesia. And since all began as an original membrane chemosensitivity, and all channel into the same small brain area (the thalamus), one cannot help but suspect that the brain must speak the same language.

It seems reasonable to assume that if the olfactory system can discriminate form (organization), with intact memory storage of the input, then other senses probably use some modification of the same method. After all, evolution is a continuous process, and chemoreception was the initial rudimentary sense. Originally all senses developed from the skin and operated chemically. The sense(s) of the basic cell are also on the outer membrane (skin) and react chemically to just such molecular shapes.

(3) *Throughout all life stereochemical mechanisms are used for creating, conveying, and storing information within the organism.*

Neuro-transmitters, enzymes, hormones, and related structures are employed to carry chemical messages controlling the performance of many physiological, developmental, and behavioral processes. Molecular information of this sort is always associated with differences of stereochemical patterning. It is highly specific to the particular communicated task, to the species, and sometimes even to the individual. Growth hormones are especially noteworthy by reason of the complexity and serial order of the information transmitted. This is particularly true of insects undergoing metamorphosis. One example is a hormone secreted by the brain of the blood-sucking insect *Rhodnius.* It has been experimentally manipulated to bring about different larval stages of the insect's development. [3]

DNA and RNA are also chemicals. Moreover, they determine a variety of behavioral sequences with the same exactitude shown in their control over the formation of body structures. For example, highly elaborate behavioral routines like the mating dances and courtship displays of birds are completely innate -- transmitted chemically from one generation to the next. Often overlooked is the fact that these elaborate patterns necessitate visual or auditory recognition by the opposite sex to evoke appropriate responses. This can only mean that corresponding "recognition patterns" also have to be present in the inherent memories of the responding birds.

Ethologists speak of these inherent recognition memories as innate releasing mechanisms, or IRMs. They are perhaps best described as *Suchbilden,* or "search models" used to trigger complementary behavior patterns in the responding bird. Their existence would seem to require highly specific and *directly representative* molecular configurations which are sex-related, transmitted by the DNA, and recorded in memory. Such innate memory images provide recognition of incoming sensory signals often experienced for the first time. Therefore, they must possess patterning "tuned'' to that picked up by their sensory systems.

None of this closely interlocked exchange of information would be possible unless the input pattern matched the *form* of the corresponding memory pattern. This implies *resonance* of some sort. There can be no specific neural routes for particular patterns, and shape or form cannot be coded. It further eliminates any thought that individual neurons may be sensitive only to specific patterns or pattern parts, as sometimes suggested for smell or vision.

Experiments in this area are quite numerous, and establish the validity of these innate recognition patterns beyond any doubt. [4] The behaviors themselves involve a broad variety of stimulus features such as spatial designs, color distributions, ritualized movements, tonal sequences of songs, and so on. All are inherent and therefore must be reducible to molecular level inIormation. Their variety suggests that the same mode of operation is present in all senses. They are evidence that memories are not only molecular, but must be referenced by comparably patterned input.

(4) *Learning processes in flatworms (and probably protozoa) have been shown to leave a chemical memory trace.*

One of the responsible chemicals is RNA. This seems eminently logical. DNA might well be described as *racial* memory, and RNA is necessary for its transcription into proteins. Because the system works and was already in operation, one would have expected *acquired* memory to use some modification of the same system. Nonetheless, learning in higher order creatures is popularly thought to be the exclusive prerogative of neural tissues And since the only *obvious* action occurring in these tissues is the neuroelectric impulse, the impulse is assumed to be the carrier of the information used by the system -- and therefore responsible for learning.

This creates numerous paradoxes. If the impulse is the carrier of data in the organism, then it necessarily presupposes the evolution of a new and radically different kind of communication system, viz., electrical impulse coding of some sort -- for there is no way in which the impulse could be directly representative of outer reality. Unfortunately, intact conduction of such data is inconsistent with what we know of impulse transmission. In addition, it is alien to all other organic processes, denies all information transport in preneural creatures, and implies the existence of some mysterious decoding operation. In brief, it appears unnatural in that it does not follow the otherwise general continuity of evolution.

Part of the learning issue hinges on preneural creatures. Whether life forms as simple as protozoans can learn, remains an unsettled question at this time. However, from flatworms (planaria) up the scale of evolution, the existence of learning is now well established. [5] And though the planarian has a minimum of neural tissue (one or two ganglions), it has been demonstrated that memory is acquired and transmitted *without* the ganglions, and that the process involves RNA.

Suppose it should turn out that mammalia possess RNA-related memory structures or, for that matter, chemical memory of any sort. The assumption that impulses carry information would then face a truly serious crisis. Currently there appears no feasible means by which memory molecules could be recorded, much less subsequently referenced by impulse type data. Impulse sequences are too large by several orders of magnitude, and they are serial rather than multidimensional in character. In short, they could not interact with the memory during recognition.

(5) *The CNS is intimately tied in with the endocrine system.*

In many ways the neural and glandular systems seem to be simply different aspects of one integrated control mechanism. This is suggested by a growing body of evidence that neural structures have important glandular (chemical) aspects. In vertibrates as well as invertebrates, neurosecretory cells perform as both nerves and glands. Instances occur where it has been demonstrated that neural control is really neurohumoral. Olfactory nerves have already been mentioned as a case where events surpass the capabilities of any neuroelectrical system. There is no way in which the specific shapes of odorants could be "coded" into any series of impulses.

It should surprise no one if it turns out that CNS operations are primarily chemical, and *not* electrical. After all, the pituitary or "master" gland is essentially part of the midbrain And it has long been known that certain brain structures, particularly the hypothalamus, function more as glandular centers. Even the impulse itself depends upon neurotransmitters in order to bridge the synapse!

As for the glands themselves, there is abundant evidence of their *direct* authority over many aspects of behavior, some of which are quite complicated. For instance, experiments on the rat prove that elaborate copulatory and post-parturitional activity are under the direction of hormones. Both sexual and maternal behavior can be elicited by application of the pertinent hormones to specific brain areas.

Increasing data of the above sort lead one to wonder whether the neuroelectric impulse plays any role whatever in the transmission of information -- and especially intricate sensory information. It seems possible that it may be only a systemic effect produced by cellular metabolism. All cells carry a charge on the outer membrane. In neural cells one would expect it to be disrupted by anything impinging upon the cell, and particularly by changes brought about internally due to passage of some unknown information carrier. In other words, the impulse could be something which frequently accompanies information transport, but is not itself the carrier. It could be an *epiphenomenon*.

Because it is a byproduct of metabolism, the neural membrane potential builds up to a maximum, then discharges. This takes place periodically and spontaneously (as evidenced by the EEG), even in the *absence* of stimulation. Moreover, such spontaneous firing is no different than that induced by stimulation. If the impulse were the carrier of information in the system, one would normally expect the signal to be completely drowned out (masked) by phenomenally perceived tingles, tinkles, and sparkles. Yet none of this white background noise shows up in awareness. Why not?

(6) *Body chemistry is regulated by the brain, and can be altered by learning. In other words, the mind-body interaction can and does occur chemically!*

For example, it has been reported that the hypoglycemic state, which follows insulin injection, can be brought about by pairing it with auditory stimuli -- even in totally depancreatized dogs! Similar claims have been made for "conditioned reflex" hypercholesterinemia. This implies that the CNS can play a very detailed role in regulating body chemistry.

More interesting, perhaps, are reported experiments where learning is shown to influence immunological reactions. [6] Recently at McMaster University in Ontario, they have been able to teach rats to produce allergic reactions (swelling, inflamation, excessive mucus secretion, etc.) in response to light and sound signals. Experiments were attended by immunologists.

Findings of this nature, made largely since 1960, emphasize the relationship between the mind and the immune system. A large body of evidence now establishes that the mind can assume control over almost all facets of the body's chemical functioning, and that it does so by stereo-chemical communication. This being the case, it appears almost foregone that mental operations themselves must be in the same chemical language!

(7) *Stereochemical changes in proteins could provide an information mechanism having almost unlimited capacity -- one far exceeding any thus far proposed.*

Information can only be carried or stored by patterning (modulation) of some conducting medium. If this medium is completely uniform, no information is present. Neuroelectric impulses are all essentially the same, making for little variation -- pretty barren stuff with which to construct our highly variegated mental world! It means that "volleys" of them would be necessary to transmit information, the information itself being a matter of their mutual internal arrangement. Since all are of like sign, no such volley would hold together.

Another apparently insurmountable problem with impulses derives from the fact that they demonstrate very little fidelity during transmission between sense organ and brain. There are usually two synapses en route, and at each of these synapses their effects on the following neuron are probabilistic. Worse yet, when the impulse of the second neuron does occur, it is very likely to be different in all major parameters.

By contrast, if one were to assume that configurational differences in proteins were the prime information carrier and recording mechanism, all the above problems would be greatly simplified, if not eliminated entirely. Protein molecules are known to be replicated with extreme fidelity. And this occurs despite their unbelievable complexity and variety of structure. Moreover, differences of molecular shape have already been identified as responsible for virtually all specific biological reactions. Since proteins possess such flexibility and elaborate structure, potential changes are unlimited. It has been estimated that the approximate number of possible proteins is somewhere in the neighborhood of 10^{2700}! It is a large neighborhood. It could easily record all the reactions which have ever occurred in living things!

(8) *There is an abnormally high rate of protein synthesis in nerves. This suggests some sort of axoplasmic and/or cell-body process over and beyond what occurs with metabolism.*

Protein synthesis usually declines in mature cellular structures of the body. However, adult nerve cells are a remarkable exception. They carry on an intensive and continuous protein synthesis. This cannot be explained on the basis of growth -- as with synthesis in the egg cell. In the adult brain there is little or no numerical increase of cells by mitosis. After an early period in life the brain ceases to grow in the usual sense. It is equally difficult to see how the protein could be used up metabolically. It assuredly is *not* foodstuff for any known process or structure of the brain. Like the testes, the brain subsists almost exclusively on glucose.

One cannot help but suspect that much of this synthesis represents brain growth in the sense of changing organization, I..e., complexification. In brief, it seems possible that it indicates processes of molecular reorganization. Intensive replacement of protein might be necessary because as an information carrier and/or storage mechanism, it becomes degraded, disassembled, or otherwise altered molecularly.

Whatever the final answer, one thing is certain. Major regeneration and/or resupply processes are somehow taking place -- and these are well over and beyond simple metabolism with its resulting neuroelectricity.

Studies performed almost fifty years ago discovered that protein is synthesized in the cell body and flows down the axon at a rate of about one or two mm. per day in a particular nerve of the rat. [7] In the massive CNS of the human, an equivalent rate of production would result in no inconsiderable amount. The responsible processes in the cell body would have to be quite complex. Despite this complexity and rate of production, however, it is noteworthy that memory functions are somehow dependent upon protein synthesis. Intracerebral injection of puromycin, which suppresses such synthesis, causes loss of immediate memory. This and related studies show that protein synthesis is tied in with mental processes in some unknown fashion.

(9) *The disparity between O_2 usage and measurable heat production in the brain suggests unknown chemical conversion processes.*

Adult male brain weight is thought to average approximately 2 grams per hundred grams that of the body. If one estimates 60 percent of the body mass to have minimal metabolism (e.g., bony structures, fat, etc.), one arrives at a brain mass only 1/20th that of the total metabolizing tissue. Now it is known that the brain consumes a fifth of all the O_2 taken up by the body! Regardless of the validity of the loose estimates given here, this is entirely out of proportion to what one might expect.

If this amount of oxygen were used exclusively for purposes of oxidative metabolism, one would be forced to believe (as many have) that 20 percent of all body heat is generated by the brain. However, simple calculation shows that with 1/20th of the mass and 1/5th of the oxidation, brain matter should have a unit-mass temperature about 4 times that of the body, i.e., about 394°F -- enough to cook it in as many minutes! Notwithstanding the fact that the CNS has no private cooling system, nor any other known type of heat-sink, input and output blood to and from the brain have almost no perceptible difference in temperature! Question: What becomes of all the oxygen used by the brain?

Exorbitant oxygen usage is only one of several baffling aspects of brain temperature. Another has to do with psychological processes. These should involve movement of energy. And regardless of the theory espoused, movement of energy in the CNS should result in resistances which are heat producing. In brief, learning, thinking, and related processes should have an important heat function. So far as is known, these demands of theory are not met, at least to any measurable degree. During psychological activity there is no measurable increase in either brain temperature or O_2 uptake. All such factors suggest unknown chemical transformations which bind oxygen and are accompanied by minimal heat production

(10) *Changes in perceived time correspond to changes in brain temperature. Moreover, they follow a chemical law -- the Van't Hoff equation. This fact clearly establishes that brain processes are indeed chemical processes -- theory notwithstanding!*

The Van't Hoff equation states that all chemical reactions (rate of energy interchange) will be speeded up by a factor of about 2½ for every 10 degrees centigrade increase of temperature. The discovery that perceived time follows this law means that the responsible processes are chemical functions dependent on brain temperature!

Since the brain has no separate cooling system, brain temperature is always the same as body temperature. Thus, a serious fever will elevate body temperature and result in delirium. The train of thought gets derailed, so to speak, because of the prohibitive rate of chemical activity. Even a degree or two of fever can alter one's perception of the passage of time.

Francois [8] was the first to note this conformity between phenomenal time and blood temperature. He trained subjects to tap at a fixed rate, then used diathermy to produce an artifical fever. He found that increased body temperature altered the speed with which the subjects responded. The direction and amount of the alteration could be accurately predicted by the Van't Hoff-Arrhenius equation relating temperature to chemical reactivity. This work was later verified by Hoagland [9] who performed careful experimentation extending the concept further. Among cold-blooded creatures like turtles or ants, it is readily observed that movements of the body slow down when the temperature drops. All higher order creatures of course, maintain a constant body temperature. This allows brain/mind processes to elaborate themselves undisturbed.

Chapter 17

Fish, Brain-matter, and unsolved Puzzles

(Perception as a sophisticated liquid crystal display, the enigma of "chemical affinity," the nature of perceived time, and other such mystical quandaries..)

It was late in the day and I was anxious to pitch camp while there was still daylight. He had read the paper I had given him at least twice. As it was being folded and stashed in his pack he commented, "Brief, but very meaty! If passed out to a class they must have been quite an advanced group."

"Graduate students," I replied.

"Tell me something," he said. "Since everyone else seems convinced that the brain is just another tangle of computer circuits, how did you happen on the idea that it is basically a chemical system?"

"It was not a new idea with me," I told him. "In fact, it has quite a history behind it." [10]

"But just what started *you* in this direction?" he insisted.

"Well, for one thing I have been interested in the sense of smell ever since learning that the cortex was believed to have evolved from the olfactory lobes. Smell is a sense which detects odors by the *shape* of their molecules. I am a Gestalt type and have always been interested in the ancient problem of *form*. So I was fascinated by the fact that things which smell alike have molecules shaped alike. And since olfaction is so important to all lesser animals, it seemed to me that further evolution should have continued along much the same lines in the human. By contrast, existing theories required a major break in this continuity. They presupposed the evolution of an entirely new and different mode of operation -- and apparently just for higher order animals.

The olfactory epithelium contains no specialized receptors, you know. It is made up only of free nerve endings which lead directly to the brain. So these neurons, at least, have to be able to discriminate differences of molecular patterning and transmit shape, qua *shape*, immediately to the forebrain. This intrigued me because of my Gestalt leanings. It suggested that the brain might be dealing with *all* sensory inputs in terms of their stereochemical configuration And though this thought was totally un-orthodox, it jibed very nicely with the rest of the body's communications. These also make use of stereochemical shape to carry information.

I might further add something few people seem to recognize, namely, that *shape* or form is not like any other aspect of existence. It is almost as mysterious as God Himself! There is no way in which anyone has been able to measure it! It can be varied infinitely and every variation produces a new and unique form. This feature makes it ideal for transmitting information. Referencing the memory (as in recognition) can then take place by means of shape-similarity without the need of any fixed route or computer address. And to top it off, similarity is known to play this role in such psychological processes. [11] The very fact that one makes mistakes most frequently when smells, figures or sounds are alike, demonstrates that pattern similarity determines recognition. And moreover, this is exactly what determines recognition of molecules by the cell.

Then too, the olfactory receptors are pigmented. The only other pigmented receptor is the retina. And embryologically, the retina is an outgrowth of the cortex! So this led me to wonder whether the retina might not function according to the same principles. In short, I suspected that it might be primarily a *form* detector -- more of a photosensitive surface than any assembly of separate rods and cones. At this point, however, I ran into a problem. The apparent size of the retinal image didn't make sense. It didn't fall within the molecular size range. It appeared much too large. So I dismissed the whole idea and didn't bother with it for several years."

"Interesting. What year was that?"

"Oh, somewhere around the late 50's or early 60's," I replied. "I don't recall off-hand. One doesn't remember blind-alleys -- just successes."

"What followed then?" he asked, pilfering a sandwich from the lunch-basket behind the seat.

"Well, one day I happened to be plodding through some data on visual acuity when it suddenly struck me that the retinal image might be a lot smaller than what it is usually conceived to be. Measurements made at that time, and still undisputed, showed that people can distinguish things no further apart than about 1/20th of the diameter of a single retinal cone! For me at least, this totally wiped out any possibility that the retinal surface was a matrix of cells which acted individually. But more significantly, it brought retinal events right down to the size of larger organic molecules. [12] Those tiny bones of the middle ear are another case in point. The vibrations they produce are fantastically small!

As a result of all this, I concluded that we are actually looking at the world through the focal end of a microscope. Where we are (that is, in our mind's eye), everything is extremely small -- molecular. Thus, the phenomenal appearance of the outside world is magnified. It is made illusorily large.. Before a sensory pattern enters our mental system it is miniaturized. This is crucial because the input has to be reduced somehow if it is to interact with our molecule-size memories. Otherwise there would be no recognition of anything. Our memories would be useless. Finding out about visual acuity didn't entirely eliminate the problem, however, because the majority of retinal images are still much too large to coincide with even the most massive organic molecules."

"Why are you so certain that memories have to be molecular?"

"There are a variety of reasons," I replied. "First, I expect the organic world to be consistent. All other information in the body is molecular and chemical. And much, if not all of it is subject to control by the mind. This requires that the mind speak the same language.

Secondly, no matter how information is sensed or carried to the brain, this latter contains an enormous amount of detail which must be recorded within a limited volume. Divide one into the other and the unit of occupied space becomes molecular in size.

Thirdly, insects like termites and ants have very meager neural equipment. They not only perceive and learn, but they often exhibit extremely complicated behavior which has to be recorded somewhere. So the same problem arises with insects. Of course, if it is conceded that preneural creatures like protozoa can learn, as I feel certain they can, then memory can't be anything except rearranged molecules.

Fourthly, an unbelievably large amount of information is known to be stored in DNA -- which is molecular. They may use the term 'code,' but it is actually transcribed as duplicate patterning by the RNA It definitely is not interpreted somehow as the word code implies. Further, this genetic system might well be called *racial* memory. It works. So why should Mama Nature change such well-established procedures to accommodate newly *acquired* memory? For all we know, this distinction between genetic and acquired memory may be largely a convenience of classification. All genetic memory had to have been 'acquired' at one time or another.

Finally, there is a sizeable bulk of experimental work which clearly demonstrates that RNA is somehow linked to memory acquisition and storage. And I might add that there is not a shred of evidence supporting any other type of memory mechanism. Everything else is strictly assumption."

"Zut Alors! Looked at that way, it is French! There can't be any argument!" He brushed away the crumbs from his sandwich, then added, "So memory *has* to be molecular! Therefore, any sensory data which the memory recognizes or retains has to be much the same size. This means it has to be miniaturized somehow! Is this where your force of attraction comes into play?"

I looked at him with increased respect. "One up for you! It took me quite awhile to recognize that point! The attractional energy which relates things during perception and thinking is the same energy which acts to reduce the size of the sensory input. It pulls it together. That way it can be part of the system and react with memory. . . .

Hold it a minute! Here's our turnoff! We'll have to set up camp pretty fast. The sun is already down."

I whirled the wheel and pulled in under an overhanging grove of trees. We got out, stretched our legs, then began hauling gear out of the wagon. I pumped up the Coleman lantern while he spread out the tent. As usual, some pegs were missing and we had to search the wagon. Finally, with the tent up and the car unloaded, we relaxed on the bed rolls. It was still too warm and too early to turn in, but too dark to try the river.

"What I am really interested in," he remarked as he munched another sandwich, "are those forces of mutual attraction. Just what the devil are they?"

"They are called London - Van der Waals energies," I answered. "They act between molecules with intensity proportionate to their mass. And many organic molecules can be truly massive. They might be looked upon as a sort of gravity for the world of small things. [13] To understand their significance, let's go back to the cell. You'll recall that its evolution took five times as long as all the rest of life combined. My hunch is that such lengthy development was necessary for the cell to learn how to custom~make and manipulate large complex molecules. This required the use of energies in the small range.

Much later when the cells developed more extensive societies some sort of government became necessary. We know it as a brain. This is why the same energies and the same techniques became a part of the brain's repertoire. It was a talent which turned out to be quite handy when neural cells had to communicate with each other as well as with body cells. Sometimes this took place over relatively long distances. They grew lengthy axons and extended fibrils. But there was still no way of transmitting information over such distances. Chemical diffusion was out of the question. It was ponderously slow. There was a charge on the outer membrane, and this provided an ionic impulse, but it couldn't be used for anything except a yes-no signal. And besides, it was much too erratic and unpredictable for the complicated and often critical information provided by the senses."

"O. K. Never mind the drama. I'll bite. How did the nerve cells solve their problem?"

"Their one area of expertise," I reminded him, "was their ability to create and manipulate large information-laden molecules. So to make a long story short, they came up with something very like what our electronics people use for displays on watches, calculators and the like. They invented liquid crystals!

Liquid crystals are really little more than long, polarized, rod-like molecules. Most often, they are free-floating to some extent. This mobility enables them to change position and polarity with extreme speed. [14] Furthermore, they are known to attract each other to a point where they frequently move in swarms. It has to be remembered that the brain is not a fixed solid like the bones. It is a gelatinous mass with an extremely high water content. This makes an ideal matrix for them."

He looked me incredulously. "You mean to tell me the brain actually contains liquid crystals?"

"Indeed it does," I answered. "The white matter of the brain, called myelin, is a perfect example -- and there is more of it than there is neural grey matter. It has a very intricate microstructure not unlike that of the retinal rods and cones. Theorists largely ignore it. Since it is fatty material, they assume that it is merely insulation for their neural 'wires.' Nonetheless, it was proved long ago to be somehow vitally related to both sensory activity and learning. [15] Of course I don't mean to imply that the myelin conducts information in the system, only that it is a good example of existing liquid crystalline states."

"Liquid crystals are pretty hard to believe," he countered.

"Well, it's easy enough to experience them directly," I responded. "And I can't think of a more forthright demonstration that they are immediately involved in what we see."

Again that look of incredulity. "And just how would you go about that?"

"Elementary, my dear Watson. Just press your finger against the eyeball or send a mild current, preferably AC, anywhere through the optic system. When you do, you will experience what are called 'phosphenes.' These are often beautifully geometric designs of lights, sometimes accurately symmetrical, and totally unlike the hodgepodge of neural tissue in which they occur. [16] Since they don't correspond to anything neurological, but do have distributions quite like those found in crystals, there appears no other way in which they could be explained."

"I am familiar with them," he confessed. "But considering the status of modern electron microscopy, doesn't it strike you as strange that something so obvious has not been thoroughly investigated?"

"Not at all! When people are blinded by belief in a theory," I pointed out, "they don't notice anything except what fits the theory. They live in their own little private dark ages. But as to your question, there might be some recent work on molecular pattern changes in the retina. I honestly don't know. The only relevant experiments I am aware of were reported back in 1969. These suggested that stimulation can indeed produce just such molecular changes." [17]

"Since you have stated that the retinal image has to be reduced to molecular dimensions in order to be recognized by memory, exactly what happens when one sees something?"

I paused to consider this for a moment, then replied, "You know, I 'm not trying to dodge your question. But I have that very issue written up in a brief paper. It's at home in my desk. And I couldn't possibly do as well if I tried to explain it orally. So let's temporarily bypass that point, and when we get home I'll give you the paper -- O.K.?" *

I noticed he was trying to suppress a yawn. "Sure, just as well. That ride about wore me out. I think I'll turn in. You'll probably want to be up early in the morning -- how early?"

"'Day-break," I announced. "Dawn and dusk are best for this fishing business."

---

*Colleagues who read this manuscript advise me that this particular discussion is "a tad too technical" for inclusion in any book tailored for the general public. Therefore, it is appended as a final entry to the notes. Refer to the Addendum: *A Penny for your Thoughts.*

The following morning I awoke to the invigorating aroma of coffee and frying bacon. Apparently he had preceded me and was busy getting breakfast. As I pulled myself out of the bag and rolled it up I noted that the sunlight was already being filtered through the trees.

"Look who's alive!" he chided. "I won't have to go for the coroner after all!"

I ignored the remarks. "There's some flapjack flour in the back of the wagon if you want it," I told him. "It's in the quart can."

We ate, strung the poles, put the dishes in a bag so they could be rinsed in the river, and took off for a small embankment which extended into the water. Having settled ourselves in a pair of folding chairs I had brought along, he lighted up his pipe and asked, "has anyone identified these liquid crystals in neural tissue?"

"Well, yes and no," I responded. "I feel pretty sure they are there, largely because of diffraction studies and such. But nobody has actually seen them. Practically everything we know about protoplasm has come from discovery of staining techniques. And there are no stains that would make them visible, at least to my knowledge. Without any way of differentiating them it would be like trying to photograph a flock of white birds against an arctic landscape."

"Suppose we just admit they exist," he said. "I have another question that's been bothering me. It also has to do with communication between cells, but is somewhat different."

"What's that?" I asked.

"Chemical affinity," he replied. "I've heard you use the phrase on several occasions. And I've tried looking it up, but couldn't find anything about it. What is it?"

I reeled my line in and replaced the bait with a small piece of chicken liver. After wiping my hands on the burlap bag, I cast out toward the middle of the stream. "No one knows. It's a loose phrase. I've gotten into the habit of using it as a 'catch-all' for longer-range interactions I don't understand. Call it the chemical equivalent of what physicists term 'action at a distance' -- mysterious stuff."

"Mysterious in what way?"

"Several ways. But the most troublesome are the numerous cases where cells behave as if they could sense things at a distance. I know such statements sound downright silly. There is no evidence of any sensory receptors other than their chemosensitivity, much less distance receptors. But that's the way it looks anyhow."

"For example?"

"Well, suppose a leg is grafted onto the back of a salamander and hooked up at random to some branch of the local nerve supply When healed it will perform synchronously with the other legs much as if it were properly located. This happens even though movements make no sense in this new position. Question: how does the brain's message find the leg muscles in such an unnatural location using a totally different route?

Even more mysterious is the fact that sperm cells will home in on the ovum though they may be a considerable distance away. Similarly, haploid yeast cells of different sex will attract each other despite being relatively far apart. Or again, immune cells will locate and identify an antigen from among millions of other moving cells. Actions of this sort are not only puzzling, they are downright creepy! It were as if they had some kind of intuitive foresight -- or were perhaps using ESP." [18]

"How is it explained?"

"Actually, I would say that such issues are side-stepped rather than explained. In the cases of individual cells like the sperm and yeast, it is usually assumed that a sort of chemical road-map is used. There is said to be a shape-specific molecular energy pattern on the surface of the one cell, and that this acts as a 'call-number' for the other. Copies are diffused into the surrounding medium and constitute a chemical gradient. The second cell senses the molecular pattern and homes in on the gradient." [19]

"What's wrong with that?" he inquired. "It sounds logical to me."

"For all I know it may be correct," I admitted. "But it certainly leaves a big bag full of mushy questions unanswered."

"Such as?"

"Well, for one thing, the action often takes place over what, for the cell, would appear to be prohibitively long distances. Secondly, it requires the rapid manufacture of large quantities of exudates for which no source is apparent. And thirdly, these secretions would have to be propagated by slow diffusion through a medium which is sometimes in rapid motion like the bloodstream.

Suppose we consider an antigen, say a virus bent on sabotage -- its chances of actually bumping into an immune cell are pretty slim. So how does it get detected? Unless it is suicidal, it surely isn't going to use exudates to advertise its presence to the immune system. Viruses are so small and simple they can't even reproduce themselves, so how could they print out thousands of copies of a chemical road map? As for cases like the activation of the displaced salamander leg, answers are even more difficult."

"What's your opinion -- do you see any possible solution?"

"Nothing I can think of off-hand. That's why I say it's mysterious. Whatever the mechanism may be, it looks like it can act over long distances and is based upon molecular shape-specificity. I suppose it could be related somehow to the much shorter range resonance known to occur between large organic molecules of like kind. Mebbe -- I dunno. When I can't answer such things it doesn't disturb me too much. I have never been blessed with that blissful God-like conviction that we already know everything, and that all existing energies have long since been discovered. As I see it, there may be a lot of very basic stuff out there that is still unknown. History tells me that today's theories always get filed under tomorrow's 'primitive beliefs.' In other words, all sacred cows ultimately end up at the bologna factory."

"Look at your pole!" he yelled, waving an arm toward my left side.

I whirled around and grabbed the pole just as it was about to go into the river. Flicking the lock off the reel, I let the line play out a distance before trying to turn the fish downstream. No soap! He decided to come back toward shore! I had to reel in line like crazy. Back and forth and around, until finally he was towed peacefully in where he could be hauled out of the water. He was beautiful -- about 20 inches long, dark blue skin, and the barbels on his face looked for all the world like a beard! I stared into his beady little eyes and told him, "You're having dinner with us tonight!"

The stringer was handed to me, and together we slipped it through his gills and tossed him back in the river. By sunset there were six or seven more on that stringer, one even larger than the first. Back at camp that evening we stretched out on top of the sleeping bags. A red glow from the setting sun turned the few clouds into strange figures. He was silent for a period, then remarked, "You know, there's one thing about your Gestalt position that still escapes me."

I made no comment, so he continued, "It has to do with the clouds up there. Suppose I accept your thesis that we perceive all organization, form, harmony, and such attributes directly. You might even claim that it constitutes some sort of vital link between an 'inner' and an 'outer' mind. And since all information is carried solely as modulations or changes in the patterning of some medium, information is also form In fact, the word 'in*form*ation' almost implies as much So our senses provide us with immediate in*form*ation about the outside world.

If I understand you rightly, our inside world automatically grows to fit the world outside. It *has* to fit because everything we know about it has to be inside our heads in order to be known at all! So the perception of space, which led the philosopher Kant on such a merry song and dance, is really straight-forward. All shape involves space by definition. Space is necessary for it to be shaped. The result is that we also see space directly when we see the form, don't we?"

"Couldn't have put it better myself," I replied. "But what has that to do with the clouds up there?".

"It's the obvious *distance* of the clouds that puzzles me," he said in a bemused tone. "How can we explain distance or the third dimension? It can't be extensions of any field effects due to shapes. There aren't any shapes between us and the clouds! For example, that tall fir tree dead ahead is almost an exact 200 yards. So we can also see the space between ourselves and other things rather accurately. Since there are no structures of any sort between us and the tree or the clouds, how do we manage it?"

"You are overlooking the fact that we have two eyes," I reminded him, "and these provide slightly different images. Field effects occur not only *within* perceived figures to hold them together, but also *between* figures. They are particularly strong between the images from the two eyes because of their close similarity of shape The angular difference between these two images is proportional to the focal distance of the object seen. Consequently, when the images fuse they create what might be called a gradient of stress or intensity-difference along this third dimension This is what provides apparent depth

Unfortunately, this is a rather difficult subject to explain verbally, and I can't very well draw pictures to illustrate it here. But if you can take my word for it, depth perception is readily explainable in terms of these image differences. Details of the process were carefully worked out almost forty years ago by Linschoten. [20] And so far as I know, this is the *only* feasible explanation. There is no way in which any retinal 'points' on one retina can be brought into alignment with the corresponding points on the other. It has to be the *shapes* that attract each other! [21] This naturally disturbs network theorists. They don't even like the idea that shapes can be seen."

"What about holographic pictures?" he asked. "Would his explanation apply to these?"

"'I admit that holographs appear in 3-D even though the viewing distance remains constant for different parts of the picture," I replied. "But this is because the differences of shape are photographed with two separate light sources and are printed within the same picture. These printed relations then shift with the angle of perspective when viewed.

The end result is something closely akin to what happens normally with fusion of the images from the two eyes. These latter are also provided by two light sources.

Relations of this sort are the stuff that organizes itself into patterns. And the identification of everything we see or hear depends upon just such patterning of sensory input. What the input carries is a distribution of energies corresponding to contours and surfaces of the world outside. Frontal aspects of these enable us to see forms. On the other hand, the perceived distances or depth (space), or duration (time), are always correlated with the *intensities* of the patterning. As explained, gradations of intensity are the visual gradients responsible for stereoscopic effects. It can even be experienced rather directly. For example, when stimuli are bright or loud (more intense), they are usually interpreted as being close to us. When small, dim, or barely audible, they seem further away. In brief, what we recognize as space and time are the intensities involved when things are perceived.

The entire concept is not all that different from the manner in which Einstein described physical space. As he pictured it, interastral space was actually the field effects of matter. Depending on the mass of the astral bodies present, the surrounding space became distorted in a predictable fashion much like visual illusions distort our micro-world -- and for much the same reason. There is gravity outside and London -Van der walls forces inside. Both are matters of attraction and the attraction is a function of relative mass in both cases. In other words, the inner world is an exact organizational form-analogue of the perceived outer world.

As you have no doubt guessed, this intensity/space reciprocity is most pronounced in hearing and vision -- our distance receptors. Here the transmitted sensory data must achieve a figure-ground effect in order to have something with which to match memory for recognition. This figure-ground effect is a consolidation process resulting in image formation -- the creation of what we recognize as shapes. It is not necessary for the sense of smell. The molecules responsible for smell are already configured, so no figure-ground differentiation is required for their structuring. Result: there is no awareness of space or time associated with smell. Aromas are more like feelings. They occur personally and immediately. This is probably also true of our more abstract mental structures. The ideas and concepts we use in thinking are usually not accompanied by any awareness of space or time."

He sat quietly for a moment, then asked, "Just what *do* you do with the experience of time?"

"Now that's not so simple as the question of space," I cautioned, "chiefly because we can't *see* it. To explain, let's go back to Newton and Einstein. The essential difference between them was that Newton judged everything from unchanging coordinates which were outside the observer and independent of the universe itself. Quite by contrast, Einstein put his coordinates in the observer -- hence the term 'relativity.' Everything was relative to whomever did the observing, his position, his motion, and so on.

In a very real sense, therefore, Einstein brought about a marriage between physics and psychology. It was extremely logical because the outside world is also the inside world. Unfortunately, psychology still considers it an illicit affair. One of its consequences has to do with time. Whether time is a physical reality outside the observer really doesn't matter much. It can't be known except through the observer, and it has to be subjective because he is the subject doing the measuring. [22]

I'll skip over the question whether all time would disappear if the human disappeared. That is to say, whether time is something which exists in its own right apart from our awareness of it. The issue would get quite messy and couldn't be answered anyhow.. What we do know is that everything we experience necessarily occurs in the brain, and we experience the passage of time. So it *has* to correspond to some process in the brain. Given this point, let's confine discussion to our awareness of it -- O.K.?" [23]

"I think I follow you, so carry on."

"I'll start with a blunt statement. What we experience as time is a direct function of the rate of energy interchange in the brain/mind system -- its intensity. I don't mean metabolism. The brain maintains its own metabolism and it is steady. What I am referring to is the speed with which the brain's chemical processes take place. Some of the experimental evidence for this was mentioned at the end of that paper you read while coming here.

But again, there is plenty of direct evidence which we experience daily. You'll remember that as a child, time passed very slowly. It seemed forever till Saturday or recess came. You moved at a good clip, processes were fast, and by contrast, clock time seemed unbearably slow. When you arrive at my age this relationship with the clock will be reversed. Time will appear to zip away because the clock is still moving at the same speed, whereas you are slowing down. Relativity again.

It should be mentioned that phenomenal time is not entirely a matter of such basic physiology. In fact, anything that alters the speed of mental activity will also change the apparent duration of that activity. Thus, if you are engrossed in a book or anything else that is highly interesting, the hours will slip by without notice. But if you are waiting for someone, and particularly if you are in pain, time will seem interminable. And I might add that certain drugs will similarly distort one's awareness of the passage of time. It was this plasticity of experienced time which the surrealist painter, Salvador Dali, tried to suggest with his melted watches and clocks.

The outside world is a swirling of various energies accompanied by their field effects. They represent a broad range of patterning, density and intensity. As a total we sometimes refer to it as *change*. We say that change is the only unchanging thing. But is it? Physics informs us that there is nothing constant about the changes going on in the outside world. For example, elements undergo radioactive decay in a very predictable fashion. But the rate of decay differs from one element to another. The same appears true of everything. Granite does not disintegrate as rapidly as sandstone. People do not age at the same rate, and neither do other living things. The lifespan of social entities is even more variable.

We picture the rate of energy interchange (its velocity or motion) as equal to space divided by time. The classical equation is: $V=S/T$. With space constant, this says that time is inversely related to velocity or, in the terms used here, rate of energy interchange. It is a relationship which characterizes both the physical and organic realms. It has been particularly well documented in human perception. [24] It constitutes a formidable argument that the outer and inner worlds are structured alike.

Since phenomenal time depends on our age, what we are doing, and numerous other factors, it can be quite elastic. The same would appear true of changes in the external world. They seem to alter with whatever conditions prevail. Thus, time must be as variable as the energies giving rise to it. The apparent constancy with which it flows ever onward is illusory. The fact that we can sit in New York and call Los Angeles at an agreed hour, say 11:05 AM, merely indicates the great care taken to assure the synchronization of clocks. But clock time is artificially stabilized. It can be moved forward or backward arbitrarily. Similarly, in our mental world the passage of time also seems constant. But again, this largely reflects the fact that brain-body temperature is extremely well regulated. It is so predictable that 'normal' temperature of 98.6°F can be printed on thermometers for use by anyone anywhere. None of it has anything to do with an outside physical continuum of time, if indeed one exists."

"Since Einstein treats space-time as something external and physically given, doesn't this put you at odds with relativity theory?"

"On the contrary," I remonstrated, "there is no quarrel with Einstein. As mentioned, he achieved a sort of merger between physics and psychology by using the observer as a coordinate system. Thus, whether space-time exists externally, internally, or both, has no meaning in this context. Everything known comes by way of the observer's brain, and here time is variable. This is why clock time does not always agree with what we experience. You know, 'Oops! I didn't realize it was so late!'"

Chapter 18

How Cells converse in Chemical Chinese

(Mind as a living communications and control net which uses a stereochemical language somewhat analogous to the ideographs of Mandarin. Why the world is inside, or the inside outside and vice versa.)

The following morning we finished breakfast, struck the tent, and prepared to leave. He packed the station wagon while I went down to the river to rinse dishes and gut fish Upon returning he stared at the fish a moment then remarked, "There are different ways to skin a cat That I am aware of. But what about catfish? They look pretty slippery to me."

"You don't skin them in the usual sense," I replied.

"Well, you sure as hell don't scale them." he retorted. "They don't have any scales!"

"No, it's really very simple," I explained. "You just get yourself a pail of boiling water and a rough cloth like this burlap. Scald the fish in the water for a second or two, and it is easy to wipe the skin away. There's no fish faster to clean than a catfish."

"I'll try it when I get home," he commented. "Thanks."

With everything stowed haphazardly in the wagon, we pulled out on the road toward home. I expected him to bring up some biological issue once we were settled comfortably. It was an area of mutual interest and would help pass the time. I was not disappointed.

"If you don't mind," he finally commented, "I'd like to get back to that brief talk we had while coming home from the game several months ago. At that time I gathered that you felt the cell, and primarily its DNA, was the root source of the individual mind -- that the intelligence of living things simply expanded outwardly from the cell as this gave rise to multicellular life forms. Does that state it correctly?"

"That's the way I see it -- pretty much like life in general. All organic entities originate from seeds in this fashion, so why should the mind be any different?"

"I'll admit it sounds logical," he replied. "But to me at least, it also sounds weird. I have trouble with the idea."

"Why, may I ask?"

"Well, for one thing, I can't quite relate the individual mind with that 'mind-in-general' which seems to be implied.. It's not a question of one being alive and the other an abstraction. You say that all of it is alive! If I have the picture right, the individual mind is simply much more complex, locally concentrated or 'condensed,' and therefore personal. Mind at large is more diffuse and generalized. However, both are said to be on-going organizational processes which possibly interact with each other. Could this interchange between them explain those weird effects which are claimed to occur in quantum physics -- you know, the so-called interactions between experimenter and subatomic events?"

"To be frank, I haven't carried my thinking that far," I conceded. "Nor have I tried to deal with issues such as psychic phenomena or ESP. The only thing I am really certain about is that 'I' contribute to the overall patterning outside myself -- probably via a more loosely organized social mind. And in turn, 'I' am able to partake of that contributed by others. In brief, there is a sort of give-and-take with something I call mind. This being the case, all of it has to be pretty much the same stuff.

Though admittedly far-fetched, I sometimes think it possible that the highly reactive nature of the human mind makes it a multi-faceted sense organ. To borrow a phrase from the late Alan Watts, perhaps the biosphere 'peoples' in the same sense that an apple tree 'apples,' and that the 'I' is merely the means by which it 'I's itself. [25] This would imply that life does not begin at birth, nor at conception, but at myth-conception -- the myth being the belief that all our minds are absolutely separate. I honestly can't say. And worse yet, I can't see any way of answering such questions."

"Sounds like oriental philosophy," he remarked. "How in the name of Zen could one ever account for cellular intelligence using this view?"

"It would be difficult," I admitted. "But maybe the difficulty arises from our definition of intelligence. I am totally convinced that the inner workings of the cell cannot be mere matters of fixed DNA transcription -- all taking place according to mechanical principles. The processes are much too elaborate. They are almost as complicated as the workings of our own brains! I agree that our brain/mind system is an outstanding advancement beyond what is present in the cell. But since our personal minds bear almost no relationship to our brain physiology, it seems likely that they are some still higher level of complexity, a step further -- a living communications net made up of the cells themselves.

In brief, the appearance of mind could be much like the similar appearance of multicellular life in the animal world. Nothing new or unique was added when the cells decided to socialize. But the end result was the emergence of something totally new and different -- multicellular organisms. Among brain cells similar socializing, plus communications among themselves, is most likely what defines a mind. It was a mind that could faithfully portray the outside world, thus bringing over-all complexity full cycle. The biosphere could now 'I' itself -- something which Gödel's theorem says we, as individuals, cannot do.

Confusion about the nature of mind is partly owing to our definitions of intelligence. These are grossly inadequate. For example, intelligence is usually identified with the ability to assign symbols (mostly words) to our memory images of things and events, then to manipulate the symbols mentally. But this is a highly specialized talent. So far as we know, it is a recent acquisition almost uniquely human. And judged by his behavior, the human is certainly *not* the only intelligent creature. Man can talk and he can symbolize, but these may be his major distinctions."

"What would be a preferable definition?"

"I am not sure it can be defined with any scientific rigor, but I am convinced of one thing. This abstract aspect of intelligence, occurring in the human cortex, can only be a further outgrowth of other CNS operations -- something which permitted greater variability of behavior. What controls the movements of our eyes or hands (volitional) cannot be fundamentally different or separate from what controls our hearts or intestines. These latter are now largely autonomic, and non-mental. Nonetheless, most of such internal processes can be brought under voluntary (mental) supervision by means of biofeedback, hypnosis, and similar techniques.

Procedures of this sort establish that the same control principles are used throughout. So intelligence had to have originated with organic control operations. Its present-day capabilities are elaborations upon more primitive 'instinctive' methods used to supervise and coordinate internal and external behavior. In other words, the new brain is quite literally an extension of the old brain Comparative brain studies confirm this. Therefore, our everyday picture of intelligence as something uniquely abstract, and wholly removed from the rest of the body's functions, is unjustified -- inconsistent with what we know of physiology.

When examined from this broader perspective, the enormously elaborate control functions occurring inside the cell demand the existence of intellect -- possibly a mind of greater complexity than that of any other known system save our own minds. Stop and think about it. Our brains themselves were assembled by neural cells, and our minds arose within this neural complex. One would therefore surmise that the cellular intellect, microscopic though it may be, would have required a long, long time to evolve. And this has proved to be the case. As mentioned earlier, its evolution took five times as long as all the rest of life put together!

Considered logically, any arguments based upon differences of size are untenable. They ignore the fact that we are judging from a position somewhere in the middle of a size scale ranging from the infinitely small to the infinitely large. Everything is relative to us (Einstein). And that is why we are in the middle of this particular size scale. We can't even imagine the vast regions of internal space. Nevertheless, it is here that matter is manipulated at its most basic and pliable level, namely, that of molecules."

"I don't wish to change the subject," he said, "but this question of size brings up a philosophical issue that's been bothering me. Since countless transformations are known to occur during growth, what's the difference between a predetermined creationist doctrine and a predetermined DNA code? In either case, all growth would be following a fixed program whose details are dictated to us and probably beyond our knowing. Wouldn't this be just another example of name-switching (DNA for destiny) -- what you would call 'verbal musical chairs'?"

"I hadn't thought of it in that context," I laughed. "Certainly, those who believe the cell follows fixed iron-clad principles -- that it doesn't make any decisions -- turns it into an automaton. Therefore, any 'guidance' would have to come from above. As long as DNA is looked upon as a pre-determined code, there really wouldn't be much difference. When we speak of the serial patterning of the DNA as a 'code,' however, we not only imply a 'decoding' procedure and alphabet, but some sort of cryptographic system which enables it to be translated into proteins. As I see it, no such 'decoding' function is either necessary or possible -- or perhaps I should say that none is known at this time."

"What do you mean?" he asked. "Aren't protein molecules simply direct transcriptions of the initial sequences present in the DNA ?"

"Only in a superficial sense," I replied. "The copying by the RNA is a duplication at the outset, yes. But this is only at the beginning of the process. The final form of the proteins, as well as their functions, is far removed from this initial sequence. To look upon them as simple transcriptions is a little bit like trying to describe an automobile by listing the order in which its various parts (wheels, fenders, pistons, etc.) come off the assembly line. True, the car is made up of these parts. But the final product bears little resemblance to a parts list, particularly one serialized in the order of manufacture.

Both the nucleotides of the DNA, as well as the amino acids comprising the list (comparable to wheels, pistons, and so forth) probably achieved their status as molecular construction units because of their combinatorial properties, their versatility at merging into new and different intramolecular energy patterns. This conclusion appears virtually foregone. The amino acids, for instance, are few in number-- only about twenty. But the resulting proteins possess almost infinite variety."

"I still don't see what you mean," he muttered in a puzzled voice. "How can the final form of the proteins be so different?"

I couldn't help grinning. "We are back to that Gestalt issue of the difference between graphite and diamonds," I observed. "The serial or *primary* structure of a protein, say that of an enzyme, is 'printed out' as a long ribbon of amino acids. As it comes from the ribosome it twists itself into a coil-like figure called its *secondary* structure This long coiled ribbon then further contorts itself into a more three-dimensional shape by bending, folding, and doubling in upon itself. It ends up looking almost like a wad of ticker-tape. Such ultimate compacted forms place the amino acids in totally new and different relationships to one another. And it is this final *tertiary* structure which provides the molecule with all its properties.

The functions of the protein molecule derive from the highly specific (uniquely shaped) energy configurations which are created when it folds. These bear little or no resemblance to the original primary sequencing. In fact, science has been unable to deduce one from the other. As of this date at least, we have found no way of predicting these more important final forms simply by using the so-called 'codes' with which they started."

I slowed the car so I could fill my pipe and light it, then suggested, "Let us go back to the question of cellular intelligence and the role it plays in embryonic development. The number of different cell types has been estimated at more than 250, and the different proteins somewhere above 100,000. Present-day belief has it that all this diversity arises from the switching on and off of specific genes. This is thought to occur mostly at those points where DNA patterns are transcribed into RNA. Since we all begin as single cells, and since the DNA of all body cells appears to be the same, the thesis seems logical enough. However, it does bring up the question of what orchestrates all this fantastic control activity."

"How do our current theorists deal with that issue?"

"I haven't kept up with the literature as well as I should," I replied. "But the latest I have is that there are quite a few different views. All picture it as a very complicated process. In other words, activating and deactivating genes is not like turning a light on or off. One well-known researcher used the phrase 'smart genes' for this functioning of signals (presumably molecules) transmitted from one location to another. [26] The process itself seems to suggest both cooperation and communication between molecular entities -- either that or enormously elaborate and detailed instructions from somewhere in the cell.

There are usually numerous sites on the DNA where such 'switching' takes place, and these may be as far apart as 40,000 nucleotide pairs! So it is difficult to see how any sheer mechanical transfer process could be so free of error -- much less how it could take place by slow chemical diffusion. When as many as 20 different proteins may be active in a given regulatory operation, intracellular communication of some sort appears inescapable. William McGinnis, now at Yale, is reported to have remarked that the longer the problem is studied the more convinced one becomes that these regulatory processes involve intelligence. [27]

Despite all this localized complexity, it should be kept in mind that neither genes nor their protein 'assistants' are viable self-sustaining organisms in their own right. The cell alone holds that distinction. Thus, in final analysis it has to be the cell itself which orchestrates its own immensely complicated internal processes. And this necessarily presupposes the existence of an intracellular communications system of equal complexity. One may call it whatever he wishes. I prefer to use the term 'language.' It points to a cell which, if a robot, must be an intelligent one!

When mind is considered synonymous with the process of organization, there has also been a further interesting development. By any definition, organization is the opposite of *chaos* -- a little-understood condition of state which has recently become a new toy in the scientific bin of playthings. Anyhow, this rephrases mind (organization) as 'anti-chaos.' Now, it so happens that one of our more prominent biologists has recently proposed the existence of a widespread phenomenon which he calls anti-chaos, or in other words, *organization!* He states that it can arise spontaneously in various systems, both organic and inorganic, and that it plays a prominent role in biological development as well as evolution. If this turns out to be true, I submit that it could well be interpreted as an argument for mind. Details of the theory are not in print at this time, so I can't really say much about it." [28]

He stared at the roadside for several minutes before commenting, "I had no idea it was all that complicated! How does it fit in with your picture of a chemical language thought to be used by the cells?"

"That's the odd thing -- because it appears to dovetail *perfectly*," I responded. "But first let me state that some kind of language, regardless how it is defined, *has* to be operative. It is even possible to identify some of the properties it can and cannot have. For example, we know it can't be any code made up of symbolic units. That is to say, it can't necessitate some kind of decoding process. The meaning must be intrinsic to the structure itself, not something inferred from any 'parts.' It can't be symbolic, alphabetic, phonetic, nor confined within the straight-jacket of any known grammar. So -- its 'words' have to be discrete entities unto themselves. I would describe them as three-dimensional, stereochemical, molecular energy patterns each with its own unique form or organization.[29]

The fact that such a language is being used is one of the reasons for suspecting that considerable specialized intelligence must be involved. There is no way in which intracellular events can be understood as serialized chemical processes -- which is the common description. They can't be fixed in lock-step fashion. Creativity would be required to devise new patterns. And each would have to have exactly the right distribution of molecular and atomic energies needed for the task. Further, we know that elaborate pattern-making of this sort *does* occur routinely during anti-body formation, and it has to be original and creative whenever the antigen is new. I have often wondered whether this, or something quite like it, might take place in the brain cells when we learn. It is suggested by observations that permanent memory consolidation requires an incubation period not unlike that needed to create new antibodies."

"Positively occult!" was the comment. "Pass me the coffee, will you please? The thermos is tucked in behind your seat." I handed it to him, and as he poured the coffee he asked, "is there any other language even remotely similar to this?"

"Not really," I responded. "But Mandarin Chinese started out this way. It had no alphabet or grammar and was not phonetic. It consisted only of monosyllabic words. There were several hundred of these pictographs, each portraying some commonly encountered object such as man, clouds, moon, or the like. They were not symbolic. Instead, they were directly representative of outer reality.. As you are aware, I am convinced that our sensory input is also directly representative.

Later modifications and combinations were added to symbolize certain ideas. These became subject-related drawings usually referred to as ideographs. Much as in the chemical language, each word of Mandarin is an individual unit or 'molecule.' It is not a part of speech, nor can it be spoken, spelled, parsed, or otherwise analyzed. It carries its own unique root-idea or meaning. The reader simply 'plugs it in' to produce the intended mental state. Only recently has this written language been adapted to the different spoken dialects by further introduction of 'phonograms.' You can imagine what a hodgepodge current Chinese must be -- what with the technical jargon of today's world!"

"Sounds horribly complex!"

"It is. But the basic pictographs are at least finite in number and easily learned. Whereas, the analogous stereochemical configurations are almost infinite. What I find most provocative about the analogy is the identification of form with function. Pictographs in Mandarin represent things, whereas those in stereochemistry represent functions. But as any physicist will affirm, things *are* their functions!

Just as in Mandarin, one can classify stereochemicals to some degree according to their structural patterning. And within-class members are usually related by comparable similarities in their properties. As you are doubtlessly aware, such structural similarities are used to create new 'designer drugs,' as well as experimental medicines. All in all, it makes for a fascinating analogy."

"Maybe so. But I would hate to think that my brain cells were communicating with each other in Chinese. Mixed with English it would come out Pidgin!"

I laughed. "Not to worry. As I tell my class, there's no way in which the mind can step outside itself to interpret what is going on inside. So who or what would translate the Pidgin? There's no homunculus upstairs. That's why you can only sense the mental action directly, qua *action*, and can't identify what's doing the acting! One gets the feeling and the meaning, but nothing of the mechanism.

Thus, the objects you see appear outside. Much the same thing occurs when you read. The words don't go flipping about through your head. Only the meanings appear in awareness. Words merely serve as trigger-symbols to activate them. The activity itself is the movement of attention."

He rode along quietly for several minutes before stating, "You are over my head with this cellular communications business and how it is tied in with the shape of protein molecules. I can see how it would work in the case of hormones, pheromones, the activity of the immune system, and possibly even the communications of social insects. But to me at least, the human mind appears to require something beyond this."

"That's a perfectly normal reaction," I informed him. "Chemical theories have always met with immediate disbelief. The current passion for electronic gadgetry may be responsible for part of this. But much of it also stems from the fact that chemical processes are usually very slow, as in the case of diffusion -- not all of them, but most of them. Thus, despite the problems and paradoxes it creates, it is nonetheless generally assumed that the neuroelectric impulse somehow carries the information in the brain-mind system. There is no proof of this, mind you, none whatever. It's just that the impulse is easy to identify, and casual inspection doesn't turn up anything else."

"Don't you feel that the neural impulse plays any role at all in the transporting of information?"

"It's possible that it may be active in the *output* side of the system," I replied, "specifically messages to the muscles. I don't know. It is true that muscles react to electricity, even to electromagnetic fields. But the events taking place at the neuromuscular junction are still not fully understood. Furthermore, signals to the muscles largely act as triggers. Muscles contract en masse with a graded response, and these gradations might correspond to the variable intensities possible with impulse volleys. I can't honestly say.

Anyhow, there are reasons for suspecting that the output and input sides of the CNS may have different techniques for handling information. Obviously both make use of nerves, but the tasks they perform are markedly different. The input side (senses, midbrain and cortex) is far more specialized and intricate than the output side which manages the muscles. This latter has not changed much since nerves first evolved. Lizards, for example, are real gymnasts compared to humans. During evolution it was the sensory features, and particularly their cortical processing, which underwent development. The neuromuscular features changed but little..

It is noteworthy that coordination of the muscles is even consigned to a completely separate part of the brain, namely, the cerebellum This is structured somewhat differently than the cortex However, the most important distinction between the two sides of the system is the myelin or fatty substance of the brain. Its microstructure is quite complex Those nerves leading to muscles have almost no myelin at all compared with those of the senses and their processing centers. And it has been known for over a century that this myelin is somehow closely tied in with both sensation and learning. It has even been shown to be related to the embryology and evolution of these processes. Such facts strongly suggest important differences in the operation of the two sides of the system."

Compared with the output to the muscles, the input or sensory side is enormously complicated. Take vision, for example. Not only do the separate images from the two eyes have to fuse to provide depth perception, but the images themselves have to be precisely that -- *images!* They are sensed and transported as exact replications of the patterning of the outside world. And I might add there is no conceivable way this could be accomplished by neuroelectric impulses. What happens is perhaps best illustrated by some paintings of the Belgian surrealist, René Magritte.

Magritte painted several pictures which carried the same message, namely, that what we see inside our heads can be mapped point-to-point on what exists outside our heads. In these paintings an artist's easel is portrayed. It is located in front of a window. The picture on the easel corresponds exactly with the outer world seen through the window. In other words, removal of the painting would leave the scene unchanged. He notes that this is the way the world is perceived. It appears outside ourselves despite the fact that it can only be a representation of reality. [30] I call the process 'projection.' The senses act almost as if they were mirrors."

"The correspondence does seem to be exact," he admitted. "But is there any way of proving it?"

"I'm afraid not," I replied . "Everyone is restricted to the contents of his own skull. Logically, however, it is inescapable. Suppose we place ourselves inside the Magritte picture. Look upon it as if it were our own mental imagery. We are gazing out the window. One can then take a rifle and aim it at some point in the outside world. This aiming is done, you realize, completely from within the mental representation. . However, the bullet will hit exactly where it is aimed outside. The hole will appear in the outer world, and it will be faithfully matched by the hole which we see inside. Prediction is perfect. This could *only* happen in a point-to-point representation."

FIGURE 13. René Magritte's *Les Promenades d'Euclid*. (Courtesy of the Minneapolis Institute of Arts.) Because of its title and the juxtaposed cones differing in perspective, it seems likely that Magritte was suggesting that perceived space is basically Euclidean.

"For some reason or other," he remarked, "this strikes me as having an oriental flavor. Could it have anything to do with your penchant for Zen philosophy?"

I chuckled. "Your intuition is really sharp today," I told him. "Zen states that the inner and outer scenes, the picture and the vista from the window, are actually only one scene. One and the same reality gets ex-

pressed in two different conceptual systems -- the outside (material) and
the inside (psychological). But it must be remembered that this is a matter
of mental stance, that this outside is *also inside!* I admit that trying to
visualize the idea will almost turn one's thinking inside-outside. Full
awareness of it is dumbfounding -- *satori!* We refer to this nexus of the
two as the HERE and NOW. And we correctly observe that this is all that
can possibly exist. So there can be only one such world, *ours!*.

Instead of being alert to the here and now, however, people live
largely in the *there* and *then*. [31] They allow themselves to be victimized by
their own memories. Their inner scene then becomes cluttered and
camouflaged by the nonexistent, and especially by symbols and words.
True reality gets 'painted out' as it were. Enough of this and it seems that
the senses provide nothing but junk mail -- that 'there is nothing new
under the sun' Not so! Everything everywhere is new and different every
instant. They have simply canceled themselves out and become unlisted
numbers.

To illustrate what I mean, consider the child. It lives wholly in the
present. Its mental world or memory is not highly structured like ours has
become. So when it sees a rose, the inner and the outer are identical --
much as in the Magritte painting. There is only the immediate rose. Its
childish wonder finds the rose a thing of beauty: the colors, spiraling
petals, and delicate fragrance. For the child, all life is *wonder*ful. But
when you or I look at the same rose we simply recognize it and pass on.
For us a rose is a rose is a rose is a rose. All the childish wonder is gone."

"Why does this have to be so?" he asked in a puzzled voice. "Why
should the adult have to lose so much of his immediate awareness of the
many things about him?"

"Actually, the Zen people say he doesn't have to -- that it *isn't*
necessary," I replied. "As for the 'why,' it's really pretty simple. The mind
is a growing thing, and as it learns and grows it gains structure in the form
of memories. It becomes complexified. For the adult, this means that
virtually all perceptions then become recognitions. In other words, all
sensory input references memory. The older one gets and the more he
learns, the greater the amount recognized. After awhile, he simply accepts
the identification from memory as the true reality, and more or less
dismisses the input. It becomes 'old hat,' as it were."

"What determines this recognition -- whether what is seen is actually
the same as what was seen before?"

"It's a matter of similarity or likeness of form," I explained. "The
sensory patterning of the things we see or hear can only be identified by

how well this patterning matches that of the memory structures. If it is exactly the same. . . ."

"It resonates!" he exclaimed. "The patterns match. Patterns of like kind attract each other! So do people of like kind -- birds of a feather! The whole concept is beginning to fall into place for me! I see what you mean. That's why poetry uses rhyme and rhythm, why wave patterns of tones are alike and pleasant, whereas those of noise are disorderly and ugly. It's why things that are symmetrical are attractive -- even the word 'attractive' fits into the picture! It not only explains why the savage beats his drums, but why the baby is lulled to sleep by the mother's heart beat! Likeness of patterning gels things together!"

"I admire your enthusiasm," I responded. "And you are quite correct. It's very basic to life, perhaps life itself. It's not just the means we use to recognize things. It's the paradigm by which the entire mind works! Even in logic and mathematics things have to 'hang together' as it were. They have to 'fit.' When we hear the matching of patterns it makes music, and when we see the matching of patterns, it looks pleasant and orderly. If the pieces of our puzzle match together, it makes sense. It is rational So I call it *mind*."

I pulled into the driveway at my place, and while he was gathering his gear from the wagon, I hurried the fish inside to the freezer. Upon returning I noticed he was sitting on the tail-gate jotting something on a slip of paper. I continued to unload, and when he still hadn't moved after some minutes, I inquired whether anything was wrong.

Without looking up he asked, "What would be a good night for you?"

I set the tackle box down and stared at him. "Good night for what?"

"Fish fry and a big stomp, as they used to say in Louisiana. I feel like celebrating."

"Hell, any time's O.K. for me," I laughed. "I'm not much at stomping, but I'm long on fish! I'll contribute my share of the catch -- that is, all but one. I would give you that one except I promised him he would have dinner with me!"

REFERENCES AND NOTES

(References are selected on the basis of relevancy, primacy, validity, and if possible, public library availability. Recency of publication is *not* stressed. Too often, it merely reflects existing theoretical fads. In general, explanatory notes are preferred. To avoid triple digits, they are packaged in terms of section heading.)

PREFACE

1. KHAYYAM, Omar, The *Rubaiyat*, E. Fitzgerald trans., 5th version, 1889, verse 27.

2. EDDINGTON, A. S., *The Nature of the Physical World.* Folcroft, Pa.: Folcroft Library Editions, 1935; and JEANS, J.,*The Mysterious Universe*, Cambridge, Eng.: Cambridge Univ. Press, 1935.

3. VONNEGUT, K., The term "foma" is from his small book of essays: *Wampeters, Foma, and Grandfalloons.* N.Y.: Dell Publ. Co., 1974.

I. THE MIND/BODY RELATIONSHIP

1. There is certainly no dearth of theorizing about the mind -- over 8000 years' worth! The various philosophies and religions are stuffed with all manner of "answers." For those in search of mental adventure, one extreme case might be mentioned: OUSPENSKY, P. D., *Tertium Organum*. trans. by N. Bessaraboff & C. Bragdon, 2nd ed., N.Y.: Alfred A. Knopf, 1923.

Ouspensky suggested that mental operations made use of the fourth dimension! People good at visualization can often see into and behind such things as stacks of blocks, recognize unfeasible symmetrical rotations, acquire insights into events seemingly unrelated, and otherwise perform in ways that appear alien to our three-dimensional world. It were as if the mind had access to some sort of hyperspace enabling it to act in "out of the body" fashion.

There are even theories about why we have no basic answers! One of these has to do with Gödel's theorem discussed later. It says we can never get all the facts about mind, life and matter because that is what we *are*! By this view, evolution provided man with a questioning mind, but denied him all access to the final answers. As a result, there is a ceaseless jousting with windmills and a flaunting of fable for fact. The spectacle would be amusing were it not for the unhappy consequences. Whenever one mistakenly identifies some fiction for fact, he gold-plates it and adds it to his sanctuary for idols. It becomes TRUTH! The door gets slammed shut on any further opinions about it. And forever thereafter, his mistakes will be inversely proportional to the validity of these hallowed assumptions.

2. NILSSON, L., Becoming (Rare portraits of the early weeks of human development)., *Science '83*, 1983, 4, 7(Sept.), 44-49. So far as I can determine, this periodical is now defunct.

3. HALL, G. S., Some aspects of the early sense of self., *Amer. Jour. Psychol.*, 1898, 9, 351-396. Hall made the first systematic study of this developmental process in human behavior. Since that time, there have been numerous others -- none of which have deviated significantly. It is noteworthy that the tactual space layout in the cortex is greatest for the hands.

4. FAY, J. C., & SETTLAGE, P., Cerebrospinal fluid pressure adjustment to change in body position., *Neurology*, 1953, 3, 916-921.

5. Probably the most thorough book on the relative independence of brain and body processes remains an older work: GELLHORN, E., *Autonomic Regulations*. N.Y.: Interscience Publishers, 1943. Much of the material presented here originated with Gellhorn and has since been confirmed by others.

6. These observations are from a classical study on malnutrition: JACKSON, C. *The Effects of Inanition and Malnutrition upon Growth and Structure*, Philadelphia: Blakiston, 1925.

7. HIMWICH, H. E., *Brain Metabolism and Cerebral Disorders*, Baltimore: Williams and Wilkins, 1951.

8. CANNON, W. B., *The Wisdom of the Body*. N.Y.: W. W. Norton, 1939. When a system uses feedback to compensate for fluctuations of the environment, thus achieving constancy of operations, it is said to be homeostatic and independent of the environment to that degree. The brain exhibits more such homeostatic independence than any other system, whether organic or inorganic. No energies enter or leave the CNS during operation, only information. Sensory stimulation merely triggers rearrangement of energies already present in the receptors. The same is true for output to the muscles. However, the CNS has no separate control for its own temperature maintenance, and no storage facility for oxygen. Otherwise, it is essentially a closed system, self-regulated.

9. Most of the data cited in this paragraph is to be found in: RICHARD BERGLAND, M.D., *The Fabric of the Mind*. N.Y.: Viking Press, 1985. Also pertinent is an article by SARAH HRDY, Daughters or Sons? *Natural History*, 1988, 97, 4(Apr.), 63-83. Further, see: RIDLEY, M., A boy or a girl? Is it possible to load the dice? *Smithsonian*, 1993, 24, 3(June), 113-123.

It will be noted that sex selection of offspring is common among a large segment of animal life. This is currently "explained" by sociobiologists as a result of the need to produce sexual proportions favoring further offspring. Since it seems unlikely that the animal figures this out for herself, where is the decision made?

The strange idea that the sex glands are somehow uniquely isolated from the remainder of the body originated with August Weismann (1834-1914), a German zoologist. Nonetheless, there is considerable indirect evidence suggesting interaction. The germplasm and/or sexual activity influences basic biological parameters such as the life-span of organisms. Veterinarians are well aware that neutered or spayed pets live longer. Female lab rats and mice, if not allowed to breed, will significantly outlive their reproductively active siblings. Plants are similarly affected. Clip the flower buds from annuals as they appear, and the plants will continue living for years. One might further note the influence of gland transplants and hormonal therapy on effects of aging, the increased growth rate at puberty, and the genetically programmed death of many creatures (notably salmon) following breeding.

Being parts of the glandular system, testes and ovaries derive from the ectoderm the same as the brain and other parts of the body's control system. One interesting aspect of this was announced by the *New York Times News Service*, 7 *Jan., 1994*. They cite Dr. Roger Gosden, a research scientist at Edinburgh Univ., to the effect that a ten-week-old human female fetus "has already made all her eggs, about 6 to 7 million of them. If a fetal ovary is implanted into a woman, the ovary grows to adult size . . . after which the eggs mature naturally." (Note that this is remarkably consistent with the fact that brain growth also occurs almost entirely *in utero*, and implies a very close relationship between brain and germplasm. One wonders if any similar feature is true of male sperm cells.)

10. PENFIELD, W., *The Mystery of the Mind*. Princeton, N.J.: Princeton University Press, 1975.

11. Because of its morbid romanticism, literature on this topic is truly voluminous. Three representative samples: PARKES, C., et al., Broken Heart, a statistical study of increased mortality among widowers. *British Med. Jour.*, 1969, Vol. 1(5646), March, 740-743. INMAN, W. S., Emotion, cancer and time: coincidence or determinism? *British Jour. Med. Psychol.* 1967, 40(3), 225-231. HOLT, W.C., Death by suggestion. *Canadian Psychiatric Assoc. Jour.*, 1969, 14(1), 81-82.

12. COUSINS, N., *Anatomy of an Illness.*, N.Y.: W. W. Norton, 1979.

13. Again, a huge mass of literature which increases almost daily. The following selected list of references includes both technical and popular items:

ADLER, R., ed., *Psychoneuroimmunoloqy.* N.Y.: Academic Press, 1981. BORYSENKO, J., *Minding the Body, Mending the Mind.* Reading, Mass.: Addison Wesley Publ. Co., 1987. HALL, S. S., A molecular code links emotions, mind and health, *The Smithsonian,* 1989, 20, 3(Jun), 62-71. HAMMER, S., The mind as healer, *Science_Digest,* 1984, Apr., p. 47 ff. JANET, P., Our immune system: the wars within, *National Geographic,* 1986, 169(6), 702-734. PEARSALL, P., *Superimmunity.* N.Y.: Fawcett Gold Medal Bks., 1987. PERT, C., et al., Neuropeptides and their receptors: a psychosomatic network, *Jour. Immunology,* 1985, Aug. SIEGAL, B., *Love, Medicine and Miracles.* N.Y.: Harper & Row, 1986.

14. Cited examples of historical sources for psychoneuroimmunology include: MIKUSHKIN, M. K., *Dokl. Akad. Nauk, SSSR.,* 1960, 132, 1454-1457 (In Russian). DZHMUKHADZE, A. P., et al., *Zh. vyssh. nervn. Deiatel.,* 1960, 10, 559-605 (in Russian). ALVAREZ-BUYLLA, R., & CARRASCO-ZANINI, J. Buenos Aires: *Acta Physiol. Latinoamer.,* 1960, 10, 153-158 (Spanish).

Those familiar with the history of psychosomatic medicine will recall EMILE COUE (1857-1926), a French therapist. His statement, "Every day in every way, I am getting better and better." became known as "Coue ism." Coue formulated no underlying physiological rationale. But he did insist that if his technique were to be successful, the patient had to actually *believe* it. And in such cases, indeed it frequently worked!

15. WADDINGTON, C. H., *Biology, Purpose, and Ethics.* Worcester, Mass., Clark Univ. Press, 1971.

16. TITCHENER, E. B., *Lectures on the Elementary Psychology of Feeling and Attention.* N.Y.: Macmillan, 1908, p. 173.

17. Though many studies of this sort have been done, the ones referred to are: ANAND, B. K., CHHINA, G. S. & SINGH, B., Studies on Shri Ramanand Yogi during his stay in an air-tight box. *Ind. Jour. Med. Res.,* 1961, 49, 82-89. IDEM., Some aspects of electroencephalographic studies in Yogis. *Electroencephalography_& Clinical Neurophysiology,* 1961, 13, 452-456. And RAO, H. V., et al., Some experiments on a yogi in controlled states.,*Jour. All-India Inst. Ment. Health,* 1958, 1(2), 99-106.

18. Credit for this observation goes to BYKOV, K. M., & GANTT, W. H., *The Cerebral Cortex and the Internal Organs.* N.Y.: The Chemical Publ. Co., 1957.

19. KAMIYA, J., Conscious control of brain waves. *Psychology Today,* 1968, 1(11), 56-60. IDEM., Operant control of the EEG Alpha rhythm and some of its reported effects on consciousness. In: TART, C. T., ed., *Altered States of Consciousness.* N.Y.: John Wiley & Sons, 1969, 507-517. KAMIYA, J., et al., eds., *Biofeedback and Self-control: an Aldine Reader on the Regulation of Bodily*

Processes and Consciousness. N.Y.: Aldine. 1972. NOWLIS, D. P., & KAMIYA, J., The control of electroencephalographic alpha rhythms through auditory feedback and the associated mental activity. *Psychophysiology*, 1970, 6(4), 476-484. NOWLIS, D., & MACDONALD, H., *Rapidly Developed Control of EEG Alpha Rhythms through Feedback Training with Reports of Associated Mental Activities.* Stanford, Calif.: Stanford Univ. Press, 1970. HART, J. T., Autocontrol of EEG alpha. *Psychophysiology,* 1968, 4, 506.

As of this writing it has been further demonstrated that the brain (mind) can learn to manipulate its EEG so accurately the brain wave signals can be used to control external equipment such as TV sets, or even steer wheelchairs and boats! See popular account by DAVISS, B., Brain powered, *Discover,* 1994,15, 5(May), 58-65.

20. Further references on the use of biofeedback in the learned control of autonomic responses: DICARA, L., Learning in the autonomic nervous system. *Scientific American*, 1970, 222, 1(Jan.), 30-39. MILLER, N., & DICARA, L. V. Learning of visceral and glandular responses, *.Science*, 1969, 163, 434-445. BENSON, H., et al., Behavioral induction of arterial hypertension and its reversal. *Amer. Jour. Physiol.*, 1969, 217, 30-34. ENGEL, B. T. & HANSEN, S. P. Operant conditioning of heart rate slowing., *Psychophysiology,* 1966, 3, 176-187. BUDZYNSKI, T. E. et al., Feedback-induced muscle relaxation: application to tension headaches. *Jour. Behavioral Therapy & Exper. Psychiat.,* 1970, 1, 205.

As to the merchandising, a sales brochure was received Feb. 21, 1972, from Cambridge Cyborg Corp., 4 Brattle St., Cambridge, Mass. 02138, describing what they called a "cyborg." It was an electronic feedback device for monitoring internal body variables and relaying the information back to the user. Accessories included items for monitoring EEG, EMG, and similar functions. All came complete with instructions and training materials.

21. BERNSTEIN, M., *The Search for Bridey Murphy.* N.Y.: Doubleday, 1956. For an account of this famous hoax, see: MARTIN GARDNER, *Fads and Fallacies in the Name of Science.* N.Y.: Dover Publ , 1957, Chap. 26.

22. ERICKSON, M. H., A special inquiry with Aldous Huxley into the nature and character of various states of consciousness.*Amer. Jour. Clinical Hypnosis,* 1965, 8, 17-33.

23. PENFIELD, W., The interpretive cortex.*Science,* 1959, 129, 1719-1725. IDEM., *The Mystery of the Mind.* Princeton, N.J.: Princeton Univ. Press, 1975. IDEM., Some observations on the functional organization of the human brain. *Proc. Amer. Philosoph. Soc.,* 1954, 98, 293-297.

24. Representative studies on hypnotically induced skin effects: ULLMAN, M., Herpes Simplex and second degree burns induced under hypnosis. *Amer. Jour. Psychiat.,* 1947, 103, 828-830. PAUL, G. L. The production of blisters by hypnotic suggestion: another look. *Psychosomatic Med.,* 1963, 25, 233-244.

MASLACH, C., et al., Hypnotic control of complex skin temperature., *Proc. Ann. Convent. of Amer. Psychol. Assoc.,* 1971, 6, (pt.2), 777-778. CHAPMAN, L. F., et al., Changes in tissue vulnerability induced during hypnotic suggestion. *Jour. Psycho-somatic Res.,* 1959, 4, 99-105.

25. Personal communication.

26. THOMAS, L., *Late Night Thoughts on Listening to Mahler's Ninth Sym phony.,* N.Y.: Viking Press, 1983. (See also his: *The Medusa and the Snail.*)

27. We are prone to think of growth as change of size -- becoming larger while keeping the same shape or identity. However, growth can occur in another way. Things can remain about the same size, but become more detailed and intricate internally. Think of computers -- once the size of moving vans, but now the size of typewriters. In a sense, computers have "complexified." If organic, we would say they have grown internally, are more versatile and efficient. Both the culture and the mind obviously tend toward greater complexity. The body also becomes increasingly more complex. But the change is not too noticeable until the colloids start to settle out and the free energy declines to a minimum. We then realize we are growing old.

28. HEBB, D. O., *The Organization of Behavior.* N.Y.: Wiley & Sons, 1949.

29. SICKLES, W. R., *Psychology: A Matter of Mind.* Dubuque, Iowa: Kendall Hunt Publ. Co., 1976.

30. WEISS, P. A., Knowledge: a growth process. *Science,* 1960, 131, 1716-1719. It would now appear that there are two interactive but distinct types of learning. (1) There is the selective accumulation of information referred to here. This continues throughout life, is *overt*, occurs with full awareness, and furthers mental growth by adding to one's system of beliefs. In general, the rate of this growth is inversely related to age. The grade-schooler can absorb a foreign language or become a computer maven much more readily than can an octogenarian. The totally new is easier to learn with an uncluttered mind.

(2) Underlying this, there is an earlier and more primitive type of learning akin to imprinting. This latter is largely *covert* and usually occurs without awareness -- mostly during early years. It is what provides the basic assumptions, values and role models which go to make up the core of one's belief system. After all, man is a primate, and primates learn largely by immitation -- monkey see monkey do. Once established, such belief systems tend to determine basic behavior patterns as well as the course of further learning. For all the idealism of teachers and preachers, education and "rehabbing" seldom change the basic character of people. Education can only contribute information enhancing their belief systems. For example, an educated sociopath is simply a more efficient sociopath. Trying to change ingrained behavior with verbiage is much like telling

your cat to be nice to mice.

31. Except where it bears on clinical issues, the subject of curiosity is now more or less on a back burner. However, some earlier representative studies would include: BERLYNE, D. E., Stimulus intensity and attention in relation to learning theory. *Quart. Jour. Exper. Psychol.,* 1950, 2, 71-75. IDEM., Attention to change., *Brit. Jour. Psychol.,* 1951, 42, 269-278. IDEM., Curiosity and exploration., *Science.* 1966, 153, 25-33. HARLOW, H. F., et al., Manipulatory motivation in the infant rhesus monkey., *Jour. Comp. Physiol. Psychol.,* 1956, 49, 444-448. MILES, R. C., Learning in kittens with manipulatory, exploratory, and food incentives. *Jour. Comp. Physiol. Psychol.,* 1958, 51, 39-42.

32. Scientific theories and religions are sources of "standardized" beliefs and have much in common. For example, (1) both are in search of absolute TRUTH and assume its attainability. (2) Both begin with assumptions which usually cannot be verified, and these range from the pathetic through the hype-pathetic to the well-supported. (3) Both tend toward orthodoxy with authority figures and established dogma. And, (4) both are vigorously promoted and defended emotionally, with dissident opinions either refused a hearing or openly repressed. In these respects, scientific tolerance is no more common than religious tolerance. Few genuinely new and different scientific papers get past the so-called "peer" review.

As noted by Socrates, no man makes a mistake purposefully. Each is convinced he is right else he would change his mind. What is important to people is not any absolute TRUTH. This can rarely be determined. What one necessarily lives by is what he *believes* to be true. Thus, everyone is badly shocked when told a truth he doesn't want to hear. Often it is vehemently rejected in order that some cherished assumption may be saved.

Despite all this, the tendency to believe is considered both normal and healthy. Uncertainty is mental insecurity -- a source of stress. The mind has to have answers in order to grow, and those who can accept and understand one level of answer often can't comprehend the other. If there are are no ready answers the mind weaves one whole-cloth. As described by Gazzaniga, "The human mind leaps in to interpret everything, from overt behavior to covert 'needs' . . . Our conscious system jumps in and generates a theory. . ." (GAZZANIGA, M., *Mind Matters*. Boston: Houghton Mifflin, 1988, p.93). Apparently, there are extremely few who can follow the admonition of C. S. PIERCE that "Belief ought to be proportional to the weight of the evidence." Things either "fit" with what they already believe, or are summarily rejected.

33. DAVID HUME (1711-1776) was intrigued by the enormous amount of relating activity which occurs during perception, learning and thinking. He concluded that such 'association' was the most important feature of mind. Moreover, he recognized that some sort of energy had to bring it about. He described this latter as an ". . . attraction in the mental world" whose effects are not unlike those produced by gravity in the outer universe.

34. There is also an opposite to this being "buried in thought." It is what Zen people speak of as "no-mind" -- meaning that the mind ceases to influence the course of attention. The "spot of light" in one's head is freed from having to constantly shuttle between memory structures as in thinking, dreaming, recognition, etc. Instead, it is channeled exclusively into sensory awareness -- the HERE and NOW. The resulting state, variously called satori, samadhi, or tun wu, is described in Zen terminology as "enlightenment." It is difficult to achieve. Thinking can only be thinking *about*. But enlightenment is full and immediate awareness of all aspects of the perceived scene, unedited, and without cognitive evaluation. Thus, Zen is sometimes jokingly referred to as the religion which helps people "go out of their minds."

35. The programming of behavior, achieved via attention, is best understood as a further development of the learning process. Mental simulation (set, foresight) is a natural extension of anticipation -- as in Pavlov's dogs. To anticipate something, or *expect* it, as dogs reveal by salivating, is tantamount to predicting its occurrence. They foresee the reward (food). For the dog, payoff is usually immediate. But for humans there are often long time delays. Such extensions of simple learning obviously require the larger brain of the mammal. They also suggest that animals can "think" to some degree.

As might be anticipated, the best sources of information on attention and related phenomena are texts antedating behaviorism, preferably those 50 years or older. In the exact sciences, anything so "out of date" would have long since been incorporated into the body of the discipline, superceded, or discredited. Unfortunately, this is not possible in psychology. The total absence of any coherent and unifying theory means there can't be any criteria with which to assess relevance. Thus, older experiments are just as pertinent and valid as more recent work -- and frequently more so. This is particularly true of subjects like attention. Accordingly, references will be omitted in this case.

36. Set is a technique used for diverse ends. It does *not* assure that the human will always be rational. For the most part, thinking is recreational: day-dreaming or musing about people, things and events. Serious thinking seldom occurs except when necessary -- when there is no appropriate set, precedent or habit available. There has to be a *need* to think, some goal to be attained, problem solved, or question answered. And all too often, these goals, problems or questions are themselves unrealistic, e.g., "How many angels can dance on the head of a pin?" Contrary to popular thought, man is *not* primarily a rational animal. He is first and foremost a *believing* animal. He then rationalizes his beliefs and behavior.

Instances of thinking "just for the sake of thinking"are most likely peculiar to humans. It might be called *abstract* reasoning. The ideological content of such thought includes assumptions, beliefs, concepts, and other second-order constructs. It may be contrasted with *applied* reasoning -- of which other animals are also capable. The ideological contents of the latter are largely direct perceptions and memories of the same. All deal with the HERE and NOW.

The above distinction is nicely demonstrated by most believers of abstract doctrines. Their beliefs are like the teenager's concept of death. The teenager knows that death occurs, but it applies to others -- not him. It is only an abstraction. Sim ilarly, the majority of sincere religionists strongly believe in their abstractions. But like the teenager, they have no direct awareness of them as realities. And since the beliefs have no direct reality, they can be (and frequently *are*) circumvented at will. Your pet dog, by contrast, has little comprehension of anything which cannot be verified by the senses, i.e., perceptually.

37. BALDUS, K. Experimentelle Untersuchungen über Entfernungslokalisation der Libellen *Aeschna cyanea. Zeitschr. für vergleich. Physiol.*, 1926, 3, 475-505. Baldus found that the larva of the large dragonfly, *Aeschna*, was quite precise at siezing prey within reasonable distances. While watching prey, it kept its victim on an axis in the medial plane of vision symmetrical for both eyes. When blinded in one eye, size was confused with distance and it struck at far but large objects -- indicating impairment of stereoscopic depth perception. Note that the dragonfly is a very ancient insect -- a relic from the past like the horseshoe crab. Because of its great antiquity, *vision can only be direct form perception.* I am disinclined to think that the trilobite of Cambrian times -- at the very beginnings of multicellular life -- assembled coded impulses from its compound eyes, then somehow translated these "blips" in its "brain." Vision must have preceded the brain -- perhaps even the nerves themselves. A good example is *Anomalocaris.* This creature swam the Cambrian seas in search of prey, and may have reached a length of 2 meters! It had prominent bulbous eyes mounted on stalks, and most likely possessed excellent vision, possibly even depth perception. All this, mind you, without any brain of significance, much less a mind to interpret what it perceived. See: DEREK E. G. BRIGGS's report in *Science*, May 27, 1994.

38. Anableps is one of many such oddities described by MILNE, L. J., & MILNE, M. J., *A Multitude of Living Things.* N.Y.: Dodd, Mead, & Co., 1945.

39. WEISS, R., *Science News,* 1988, 134, 23 (Dec. 10), p. 374. Reports on on experiments by MRIGANKA SUR and coworkers at MIT. Cells in the auditory cortex were found to "transform" data from the eyes into "oriented rectangular receptor fields" hitherto identified only in the visual cortex. This implies that there is nothing intrinsic about the auditory cortex which makes it auditory. The response of different cortical areas depends upon the input received. In essence, this confirms K. S. LASHLEY's earlier finding that cortical areas possess what he called "equipotentiality," i.e., one area can do the task of another if necessary.

40. Von NEUMANN is cited by DEWAN, E. M., *On the Mechanism of Permanent Memory.* Bedford, Mass.: Air Force Cambridge Res. Lab., Electron. Res. Dir., *Research Note No. AFCRL-62-521,* 1962. *ASTIA DOC. NO. 285-792.* All such estimates are very "iffy," including my own.

41. The outer world is *not* fractured into bits, nor is our perception of that world. Even the computer itself uses bits only as a medium with which to mold patterns -- much as it displays pictures in pictels or points of light. The differences in *bit-patterns* , and the relations between such patterns, are what provide both identity and meaning for the computer. To describe something in bits would be like describing a building in terms of bricks, or a tapestry in terms of threads.

42. MOROWITZ, H. J., *Mayonnaise and the Origin of Life*. N.Y.: Berkley Books, 1986, p. 179.

43. The 10^{35} snowflake figure is attributed to CHARLES KNIGHT of the Nat'l. Ctr. for Atmospheric Res., Boulder, Colo., according to Harper's Index, *Harper's Mag.*, 1988, 276, 1652(Jan.), p. 11. According to my notes, the 10^{79} figure was arrived at by EINSTEIN. However, I have been unable to locate the specific source.

44. JAMES, W., 1890, *The Principles of Psychology, Vol. I,* N.Y.: Henry Holt, 1890, p. 279.

45. This serially progressive nature of attention also influences learning. This is why it is much easier to learn something new than to "unlearn" something old -- such as a well-established habit. It is also why backward conditioning is extremely difficult to establish. The mind grows *forward* in time.

46. See: GAZZANIGA, M. S., *Mind Matters*. Boston: Houghton Mifflin Co., 1988, pp. 11-14. This operation, which separates the two hemispheres of the brain, is performed in cases of intractable grand mal epilepsy to limit the spread of siezures.

47. A few of the numerous views on the nature of consciousness:
It is an illusion: HARNAD, S., Consciousness, an afterthought. *Cog. Brain Theory,* 1982, 5, 29-47.
It is an artifact of social development: HUMPHREY, N. K., The social function of intellect. In: *Growing Points in Ethology*, P. P. G. BATESON & R. A. HINDE, eds., N.Y.: Cambridge Univ. Press, 1976. (JAYNES, J., *The Origin of Consciousness in the Breakdown of the Bicameral Mind,*, 1977, proposes a similar argument.)
It is a statistical state of brain activity: WALKER, E. H., The nature of consciousness. *Mathematical Biosciences*, 1970, 7, 131-178.
It is an internal feedback system of the brain: THATCHER, R. W., & JOHN, E. R., *Foundations of Cognitive Processes*. Hillsdale, N.J.: Erlbaum, 1977.
For still others, including consciousness as a computer program, as a soul (material), and soul (non-material), etc., see popular reviews of the subject by GLIEDMAN, J., a psychologist at Empire State College, SUNY. These appeared in *Science Digest,* 1982, 90, Nos. 4 & 7.
More recently: HORGAN, J., Can science explain consciousness? *Scientific American,* 1994, 271,1 (July), 88-94. CHALMERS, D. J., The puzzle of conscious

experience, *Ibid.,* 1995, 273, 6(Dec.), 80-86. IDEM., *The Conscious Mind,* N.Y.: Oxford Univ. Press, 1996. And GREENFIELD, SUSAN, *Journey to the Center of the Mind. Toward a Science of Consciousness.* N. Y.: W. H. Freeman, 1995. Indeed, there is now even a journal dedicated to the subject! Needless to say, as the opinions proliferate the few facts become ever more obscure.

II. HOW IT ALL BEGAN

1. .Representative studies of periodic (cyclic) phenomena: AYENSU, E. S., & WINFIELD, P., eds., *The Rhythms of Life.* N.Y.: Crown Publ., 1982; PLAYFAIR, G. L., & HILL, S., *The Cycles of Heaven.* N.Y.: Avon Bks., 1978; DEWEY, E. R., & MANDINO, O., *Cycles, the Mysterious Forces that Trigger Events.* N.Y.: Hawthorne Bks., 1971; CLOUDSLEY-THOMPSON, J. L., *Rhythmic Activity in Animal Physiology and Behavior.* N.Y.: Academic Press, 1962. (This one contains 500 references!)

2. In subatomic physics the "complementarity principle" of NIELS BOHR states that light can be either particle (photon) or electromagnetic wave (ray). In the former case it acts as a "thing," and in the latter it is more of an event (function). The contention here is that this is a general principle with broad applications in the macroscopic world. In other words, orderlines of structure and periodicity of function are merely different aspects of the same phenomenon. If one looks for them, he soon discovers that the outer world is a veritable museum of periodic (e.g., organized) phenomena where function expresses itself as form, and vice versa.

It is easy to prove for oneself that periodicity and rhythm create orderliness of structure. Try the following. Mount a metal plate, thin enough to vibrate, on a violin. Scatter it with powder or fine sand. When the bow is pulled across the strings, beautifully symmetrical and ornate patterns will emerge. These are called Chladni figures, after ERNST CHLADNI (1756-1827), a German physicist interested in sound. His work was extended to include various media and sources of sound by H. Jenny, a Swiss doctor and scientist. Cf., JENNY, H., *Cymatics, I & II..* Basel, Switzerland: Basilius Press AG, 1966. Such phenomena will become important later when the relationship between mind and organization is discussed.

In addition to the order-rhythm identity, there is still another argument that the appearance of complex organization was inevitable. This is somewhat abstruse and has to do with the basic physics of the earth. When pictured as a semi-closed system subject to a flux of energy from the sun, material organization becomes unavoidable due to the nature of matter itself. For a simplified discussion of this point, see: CHURCHLAND, P. M., *Matter and Consciousness.* Cambridge, Mass.: M.I.T. Press, 1984, Chapter 8.

3. I have no recent publication on the structural properties of water. Much of the information presented here comes from an excellent but brief earlier source: FOWLER, R. H., & BERNAL, J. D., Note on the pseudocrystalline structure of water. In: *Faraday Society Symposium on Liquid Crystals and Anisotropic Melts.* London: Faraday Society, 1933, 1049-1056.

4. This estimate of the huge number of possible proteins was made by Von BERTALANFFY, L., *Problems of Life*. N.Y.: John Wiley Sons, 1952, page 103. I have no idea how he arrived at it.

5. BEUTNER, R., *Life's Beginning on Earth*. Baltimore: Williams & Wilkins Co., 1938, preface. It should perhaps be mentioned that silicon also has some of these strange and valuable properties, but not nearly to the extent of carbon.

6. The most common elements in outer space are hydrogen, carbon, oxygen and helium. Infrared astronomy has found evidence for polycyclic aromatic hydrocarbons in space. SAMUEL EPSTEIN (Cal. Tech.) and JOHN CRONIN (Ariz. State Univ.) analyzed a ¼th oz. piece of the Murchison meteorite, a 180 lb. rock that exploded over Murchison, Australia, in 1969, and found 55 different amino acids with succinct evidence that these were of astral rather than earthly origin. In addition, it has been estimated that dust from Halley's comet (picked up by Russian and European spacecraft) contained as much as 20% organic matter in terms of mass.

7. AMATO, I., RNA offers clue to life's start., *Science News*, 1989, 135, 24(June 17), p.372. Reports that JACK W. SZOSTAK, together with JENNIFER DOUDNA, both at Mass. Gen'l Hosp., Boston, were able to modify an RNA molecule found in protozoans until it could copy parts of itself almost unassisted. Thus far, they have not gotten it to copy itself completely.

8. The hypothetical boundary between the living and non-living has been further blurred by discovery that the scrapie virus (causing a fatal disease in sheep), and the Creutzfeld-Jakob virus (causing brain disease in humans) have no detectable DNA or RNA whatever! DR. STANLEY B. PRUSINER (Univ. Calif., San Fran cisco Hosp.) has spent years studying these. They are chemicals a hundred times smaller than a virus, said to be immune to both heat and radiation, yet seemingly alive. Cf., *Reader's Digest* article, Feb., 1985, p. 128 ff. LEWIS THOMAS refers to them as the "fourth wonder of the modern world." *Late Night Thoughts on Listening to Mahler's Ninth Symphonv*. N.Y.: Bantam Books., 1984, p. 58.

9. The only legitimately "improbable" feature of evolution possibly would be nitrogen fixation, a process essential to all life. It is accomplished by less than 100 species, mostly bacteria, and involves the enzyme nitrogenase. This latter is a highly complex metalloprotein uniquely dependent upon the metal molybdenum. Since molybdenum is relatively scarce on earth, and life cannot exist without it, some notable figures have suggested that earth life may have been "seeded" from some other planet where it was more abundant.

10. MARGULIS, L., *The Origin of Eukaryotic Cells*. New Haven, Conn.: Yale Univ. Press, 1970. For a popular account: MCDERMOTT, J., A biologist whose heresy redraws earth's tree of life. *Smithsonian Mag.*, 1989, 20, 5(Aug.).

This merging of individuals to create still larger individuals is a process which has occurred over and over again throughout the history of life. One of the central theses of the present work is that this not only characterizes the cell and human, but may be logically extended to include various other symbiotic assemblies such as insect and human societies -- possibly even the biosphere as a whole. Life is almost synonymous with growth, and the term growth means continuous self-empowered expansion and complexification. Regardless of its manifestation, life constantly tries to transcend itself -- as noted by the philosopher Hegel.

11. PORTER, K. R., & TUCKER, J. B., The ground substance of the living cell. *Scientific American,* 1981, 244(3), 56-67.
It might also be mentioned that the cell has something roughly akin to an immune system. When under stress due to heat or toxins, it manufactures what are called "stress proteins." See: WELCH, W.J., How cells respond to stress, *Scientific American,* 1993, 268, 5(May), 56-64.

12. Personal communication with staff member assisting the biologist, GUENTER ALBRECHT-BUEHLER, who tracked the cells with a scanning electron microscope, March, 1979. A brief popular account of the procedure and results appeared in the L.A. Times-Washington Post Service, Feb. 2, 1979.
Notable among others who have similarly studied cell movements is D. LANSING TAYLOR of the Center for Fluorescent Research in Biology. Carnegie Mellon Univ., in Pittsburg.

13. Selected studies from the heyday of protozoan education (titles omitted): METALNIKOW, S., *C. R. Soc. de Biol.,* 1913, 74, 701-703; BRAMSTEDT, B., *Zeitschr. für vergleich. Physiol.,* 1935, 22, 490-515; GELBER, BEATRICE, *Jour. Comp. Physiol. Psychol.,* 1952, 45, 58-65; IBID., 1956, 49, 590-599; IBID., 1958, 51, 110-115; IDEM., *Jour. Genet. Psychol.,*1956, 88, 31-36; IDEM., *Science,* 1957, 126, 1340-1341; IDEM.,*Psychol. Rec.,* 1962, 12, 165-192; JENSEN, D. D., *Science,* 1957, 125, 191-192; IBID., 1957, 126, 1341-1342; BERGSTRÖM, S. R., *Scand. Jour. Psychol.,*1968, 9(3), 215-224; APPLEWHITE, P. B., & GARDNER, F. T., *Physiol. & Behav.,* 1970, 5(3), 377-378; GARDNER, F. T., & APPLE-WHITE, P. B., IBID., 713-714.

14. For conditioned neurons in the brain of the monkey, see: FETZ, E. E., Operant conditioning of cortical unit activity. *Science,* 1969, 163, 955-957. For the mollusk *Aplysia,* see: BERLUCCHI, G., & BUCHTEL, H. A., Some trends in the neurological study of learning. In: GAZZANIGA, M. S., & BLAKEMORE, C., eds., *Handbook of Psychobiology,* N.Y.: Academic Press, 1975, 481-498.

15. I am aware that lymphocyte learning has also been contested -- it being assumed that the cells are born with the ability to recognize all possible antigens. But whether considered a matter of learning specific antigens, or simply "self" versus "non-self," it presents problems. The ability to construct specific antibodies to counteract the non-self antigen, still involves recognition of detailed differences of stereochemical configuration.

Consider the trypanosome carried by the tse-tse fly. Reputedly, it can change its coat of antigen seemingly at will, and does so to pass undetected by immune cells of the infected host. Apparently the immune cell must not only detect these new differences of stereochemical shape, but must retain (learn) them if it is to manufacture antibodies having a counteractive configuration. Moreover, recent research (*Nature,* 1995, May 11) indicates that the T cells of the immune system have receptors capable of a much broader range of discrimination than assumed.

No matter what the theory, once details of the process are taken into account, learning on the part of the cell becomes logically inescapable. The very existence of *acquired* immunity presupposes learning. And when considering cellular learning at whatever level, the phenomenon of molecular resonance becomes highly significant. Given an electrically sensitive cellular membrane, resonance with the alien electronic pattern could account for the cell's reaction to an antigen. It would further explain antibody formation as an induced mirror image (electrical isomer of opposite sign) capable of "neutralizing" the antigen.

Any chemical theory of brain functioning, where memories are necessarily considered molecular, involves the same problems. Sensory input must resonate somehow with memory molecules in order to achieve recognition. And this is much too rapid to be considered anything except a physical (electronic) process.

16. The work of JACQUES LOEB is a gold mine filled with studies of many primitive creatures and their reactions to natural energies of the environment. Moreover, his conclusions are just as pertinent today as they were then. References: LOEB, J., *Comparative Physiology of the Brain and Comparative Psychology.* N.Y.: G. P. Putnam's Sons, 1900; IDEM., *The dynamics of Living Matter.* N.Y.: Lamcke & Buechner, 1906; IDEM., *Forced Movements, Tropisms, and Animal Conduct.* Philadelphia: J. B. Lippincott Co., 1918.

17. On the centipede, *Scutigera,* see: LISSMAN, H. W., Proprioceptors. In: *Symposia of the Society for Experimental Biology, IV. Physiological Mechanisms in Animal Behavior.* N.Y.: Cambridge Univ. Press, 1950, 35-59. On the cross-amble of crabs, etc., see: Von BERTALANFFY, L., *TheProblems of Life.* N.Y.: John Wiley & Sons, 1952, p. 115.

Along these same lines it is important to recognize that human motor skills (learned patterns of muscular motion) have been shown to be stored in the brain as *patterns* -- and *not* as any stimulus-response linkages involving specific muscles. One can learn a complex pattern of movement using, say the left foot, then duplicate the pattern with the other foot or either arm. In brief, the pattern exists independently of the muscles used to execute it. In the jargon of psychology, this has often been called "transfer of training." However, naming something does not explain it.

18. SEEDS, N., A brain rewires itself in a test tube. *New Scientist,* 1972,

January 6th.

19. Much of this work was done by Paul Weiss. Like Loeb, his many definitive experiments have gone largely unnoticed because results (and conclusions) often ran contrary to orthodox opinion. For example, he presented evidence that signals sometimes get conducted in the organism with almost total disregard of the neural distributions involved. Presumably, the routing of messages takes place on the basis of chemical affinity -- a phrase which suggests some sort of long-range resonance between stereochemical configurations of like shape. See: WEISS, P. A., Erregungspecificität und Erregungsresonanz. *Ergebn. Biol.* 1928, 3, 1-151; IDEM., The so-called organizer and the problem of organization in amphibian development. *Physiol. Rev.,*1935, 15, 639-674; IDEM., *Chemistry and Physiology of Growth.* Princeton, N.J.: Princeton Univ. Press, 1949; IDEM., Interactions between cells.In: *Reviews of Modern Physics,* 1959, 31, 449-454.

In my opinion, the thinking of Weiss has been ignored (not disproved) simply because he was 50 years ahead of his time. Like the Gestalt movement, which occurred in the same time-frame, he refused to conform with the dogma-of-the-day.

20. ROGER SPERRY of Cal. Tech. fared much better than either Weiss or Loeb, above. He even received the Nobel prize! Nonetheless, much of his work (including that cited here), is just as disruptive to existing theory. See: SPERRY, R. W., Effect of 180° rotation of the retinal field on visuomotor coordination. *Jour. Exper. Zoöl.,* 1943, 92, 263-279; IDEM., Optic nerve regeneration with return of vision in anurans. *Jour. Neurophysiol.,* 1944, 7, 57-69. IDEM., Restoration of vision after crossing of optic nerves and after contralateral transplantation of the eye. *Jour. Neurophysiol.,* 1945, 8, 15-28.

21. It should be obvious that our various genetic determinants (genes) do not "mutate" at the same rate. If they did, then older established structures such as the vertebral column, would also undergo change, and the very foundations of the organism would be destroyed. A moment's reflection tells us that continuities of this sort are a strong argument against evolutionary change being either constant or randomly directed. Indeed, there are times at which it even appears *meaningfully* directed!

22. Man gained dominance over other life largely by use of cunning and strategy. Thus, he is further unique in that he is born with little or no instinctive controls for his social behavior. One result is that individuals have no assurance their leaders will wield power for any purpose other than self-aggrandizement. Other social animals can (and do) employ hierarchial power structures for social control. They are assured of consistent (genetically determined) treatment. But if the human is to possess a stable culture he must resort to some form of democracy. In turn, this is biologically unnatural in the sense that it emphasizes the commonality of people -- whereas life in general advances only via deviations from this commonality. To be the average John Doe, nameless and uninspired, frequently means security. But it does not advance the culture. This requires the *rare* individual. The value of anything is at least partially due to its rarity -- its differences from the average. If diamonds were as common as gravel they would be used for fuel.

23. There are several of these theories which aim at explaining the progressive differentiation which occurs embryologically. Examples of recent efforts: EDELMAN. M., Topobiology. *Scientific American,* 1989, 260, 5((May), 76-88; and HOLLIDAY, R., A different kind of inheritance. IBID., 6(June), 60-73.

In the meantime, work is progressing on the genes involved. These are called "homeobox genes" and apparently are used by the cell during different stages of the infant's development. They occur in different regions of the DNA and seem to perform similar roles for all creatures so far examined. This suggests that the genes of any one species may carry the history of all species preceding it. Interestingly enough, these homeobox genes are sequenced in the same cephalocaudal order as embryological development itself, viz., from head to tail of the organism.

24. NEEDHAM, J., *Order and Life.* New Haven, Conn.: Yale Univ. Press, 1936; IDEM., *Biochemistry and Morphogenesis.* N.Y.: Cambridge Univ. Press, 1942.

25. Central to our thinking here is the cell's ability to create elaborate, new information-laden molecules as needed. This ability, believed peculiar to living cells, would be especially helpful to plants. Being rooted in one spot severely limits the diversity of materials available to them. As a result, some have proposed that certain plant root cells may have acquired the ability to even change one element into another -- something the alchemists failed to do! See: TOMPKINS, P. & BIRD, C., *The Secret Life of Plants*, N.Y.: Harper and Row, 1973, pp. 275 ff.

26. MOROWITZ, H. J., *The Thermodynamics of Pizza.* New Brunswick, N.J.: Rutgers Univ. Press, 1991, 241-244.

In today's literature there is much talk about "the chemical language used by the cell." However, there is little mention of its properties or potential translation because this would necessitate that the cell be considered intelligent -- something contrary to scripture. Of course, translation of a sort *does* continue in the sense of identifying the influence of one molecule upon another, or upon the organism as a whole. But this tells us little about the relationships between stereochemical shape and meaning for the organism, i.e., what might be called the chemical syntax.

27. This theory, in which the genes control virtually all behavior either directly or indirectly, is known as sociobiology. Perhaps the most extreme statement of the doctrine is provided by DAWKINS, R., *The Selfish Gene.* Oxford, England: Oxford Univ. Press, 1976; IDEM., *The Blind Watchmaker.* N.Y.: W. W. Norton,

1986.

To me at least, sociobiology is much more logical than preceding theories attributing most organic change (particularly child behavior) to the environment. Nonetheless, Dawkins' version would seem to credit the gene with intelligence and perhaps even foresight. This is awkward in that the gene is not even a viable entity. It is only a small, and sometimes arbitrarily determined portion of the cell's chrom osomes. The cell is the minimal organism.

28. Until quite recently there were merely three studies of identical twins reared separately. Then, in 1979, a study was started by THOMAS BOUCHARD, JR., a psychologist at the Univ. of Minn., Minneapolis. This group is well staffed, and to date has examined 77 sets of reunited twins reared separately.

Some of the findings of the group are truly amazing -- being much too phenominal to be matters of coincidence. For example, one pair had the same sideburns, moustache, glasses, gestures, much the same personality, drank the same brand of beer, were both bachelors, and even worked at the same job -- both were firechiefs. For a popular summary of the study, see: ROSEN, CLARE, M., The eerie world of reunited twins. *Discover Magazine,* 1987, 8, 9(Sept.), 36-46.

29. LAPICQUE, L., Sur la conscience psychologique considérée comme intégrale d'eléménts cellulaires de conscience. *C. R. Acad. Sci.,* Paris, 1952, 234.

30. Such design "defects" are numerous and largely due to upright posture. They clearly indicate that cells are incapable of long term planning. They lack foresight and cannot play the game of "what if . . .?" Instead, the cellular society called a human simply *grew.* It necessarily maintained detailed cumulative memory records (in DNA) of its phylogenetic past as well as its own growth history. If it hadn't, repair, regeneration, or sexual replacement of the society could not occur.

As the brain enlarged, new behaviorally-induced features occurred. These made many earlier adaptations disadvantageous. They became "design defects" in light of the new use of the body. However, by that time it was too late for any corrections in the basic structure. For the cell, there can be no editing of the past nor planning for the future -- only adaptations in the HERE and NOW.

According to the Bible, creation was accomplished at enormous speeds. This would not have allowed for extensive foresight. Nonetheless, God looked over each day's work and "saw that it was good." It can only be concluded that He was using a rating scale ranging from very poor to excellent. In which case, most physiologists would give the human a similar rating -- a "B" perhaps, but certainly not an "A."

31. BIERENS DE HAAN, J. A., *Die tierischen Instinkte und ihr Umbau durch Erfahrung.* Leiden: E. J. Brill, 1940. (He also used the concept to explain spider-web construction.)

32. Search models or "blank schemas" are common devices used unknowingly during everyday problem solving. They are necessary to assist in unaided recall, or when engaged in search when the object of search is not fully identified. For example, I can hunt for someplace to hang a picture, something with which to punch a hole, or some tool capable of prying off a can lid. All require visualizations (of an indefinite sort) with which to evoke memory (recall), or to identify items in the environment (recognition). The greater the similarity between the search model and object, the easier the problem is solved. Please note that this requires that memories consist of *patterns* that are referenced by their similarity with the input pattern. See: DUNCKER, K., *On problem solving* (Trans. by Lynne S. Lees). Washington, D.C.: Amer. Psychol. Assn., 1945. *Psychol. Monogr.*, 1945, 58, No. 5, Whole No. 270.

33. JOHN CAIRNS and colleagues JULIE OVERBAUGH and STEPHEN MILLER, at the Harvard School of Public Health, Boston, worked with *E. Coli*. They report that when threatened with starvation, this bacterium can, in effect, recognize its predicament and mutate in ways enabling it to survive. They showed that the life-saving mutations were produced in response to the stressful situation and were not naturally-occurring variations that simply turned out to be helpful.

More definitive evidence of directed mutations was provided a few months later by BARRY G. HALL, Univ. Rochester, and published in *Genetics*. BERNARD DAVIS, Harvard Medical Sch., has contested the thesis of non--random mutations and offered what was essentially a rationale "that may save the established biological dogmas." This was published in *Proc. Nat. Acad. Sci.* In turn, CAIRNS has come up with a rebuttal which he says disproves Davis's theory. And so it goes. See: CAIRNS, J., et al., *Nature*, Sept. 8, 1988. A good summary of the debate is given by RENNIE, J., Hungry to evolve. *Scientific American*, 1989, 261, 5(Nov.), 20-22.

34. For a good but brief popular review of chromasomal variance between species, see: MONTAGU, A., *Human Heredity*. N.Y.: American Library Publ. Co., 1960, Chap. 2.

35. Possibly one reason the cockroach has survived for such a fantastic period is that it has been found to have a highly sophisticated immune system. This was discovered quite recently by RICHARD KARP, an immunologist at the Univ. of Cincinnati. See: OLIWENSTEIN, L., The bug that can say no. *Discover Mag.*, 1992, 13, 4(Apr.), 26. This runs contrary to the dogma that invertibrates do not have "true" immune systems. Since it would contribute heavily to survival, one wonders how many other "living fossils" may be similarly endowed.

36. It should be recognized that the DNA of the chimp is arranged differently from that of the human. There are inversions and change of location as well as chromosome fusion. However, if the DNA is considered only an assemblage of individual genes, why should differences of location be critical? Question: could such differences relate to the neotony present in the human? There are at least 20 different ways in which features of the adult human virtually duplicate those of the foetal chimpanzee. See: BOLK, L., *Das Problem der Menschwerdung*. Jena: Gustav Fischer, 1926.

37. EDWARDS, D. D., Human genetic map: worth the effort? *Science News,* 1987, 131, 9(Feb.), p. 134. DAWKINS, R., *The Blind Watchmaker.* N.Y.:W. W. Norton., 1986, p. 116, estimates the amount of information in human DNA as equivalent to 3 or 4 times that of the 30 vol. set of the *Encyclopaedia Britannica*. Of the total only about two percent is said to have been identified.

My own guess (for whatever it is worth), is that the human genome project will unveil a vast amount of data valuable to the medical profession, but that there will be an equal amount which will be totally beyond comprehension.

38. FINE, P. E. M., Lamarckian ironies in contemporary biology. *The Lancet,* 1979, June 2, pp. 1181-1182.

According to an *AP* news release, dtd. 1/1/90, RNA does not necessarily transport gene information ad verbatim. "We now have three examples in which more than 50% of the gene has been edited." states KENNETH STUART, Seattle Inst. Biomed. Res. By "editing" is meant that missing features of a gene, taken from DNA, are restored by the RNA during transit.

39. Arizona State Univ. physicist, STUART LINDSAY, has used a scanning tunneling microscope to examine naturally wet DNA. Resulting photography reveals that the DNA is not the neat uniform helix commonly pictured. It has ridges, curves and kinks strongly suggesting that it may undergo changes of form related to its function. -- note in *Discover* Mag., 1989, 10, 10(Oct.), p. 18.

Given this observation, and considering the dimensions of DNA, the number of potential molecular energy configurations (assumed to be manipulated by the cell) becomes essentially infinite.

40. One well-known proponent being STEPHEN J. GOULD of Harvard. See his: *The Flamingo's Smile.* N.Y.: W. W. Norton, 1985.; IDEM., Not necessarily a wing: which came first, the function or the form? *Natural History,* 1985, 94, 10(Oct.), 12-25.

41. See comments on "Trans-Kingdom sex" in *Scientific American,* 1989, 261, 4(Oct.), 34-35.

42. Microbiologists SORIN SONEA and MAURICE PANISSET, Univ. Montreal, have proposed that all bacteria are interrelated into a vast communications network that is planet-wide. It is said to constitute a single large gene pool interconnected by virus-like organisms. Accordingly, it promotes life in all possible niches of the planet by bringing about different genetic permutations wherever conditions are favorable. See: *The Smithsonian,* 1987, 18, 8(Nov.), p.116 ff.

There is rapidly emerging evidence that horizontal transfer of genetic material can occur between radically different species such as mites and fruit flies.

"Jumping" genes hitch rides between species. See: RENNIE, J., DNA's new twists, *Scientific American,* 1993, 266, 3(Mar.). 122-132. The extent and variety of ways in which genes may be shuffled about among bacteria, are to be found discussed in: BEARDSLEY, T., La ronde, *Ibid.*,1994, 270, 6(June) 26-29. He states "that a blizzard of genetic material blows freely through the microbial world," and suggests that this may also involve multicellular plants and animals as well.

There are now a number of studies revealing that the large population of marine bacteria are mostly held in check by equally extreme numbers of viruses. All in all, the oceans are highly active microbiological arenas. For details, read: SIEBURTH, J. M., *Sea Microbes.* N.Y.: Oxford Univ. Press, 1979.

43. This finding by Norwegian scientists was reported in *Der Spiegel,* Hamburg, Germany, and carried in "Science Notes"in the *World Press Review,* 1989, 36, 12(Dec.), p. 69.

44. Virtually all biologists have become interested in slime molds at one time or another. But in my opinion the best reference is still: BONNER, J. T., *The Cellular Slime Molds, 2nd. ed.,* Princeton, N.J.: Princeton Univ. Press, 1967.

45. There is a very large literature on colonial life forms which typify the transition period between unicellular and multicellular life. Some of my favorites are: ALLEE, W. C., *Animal Life and Social Growth,* Baltimore: Williams & Wilkins, 1932; BONNER, J. T., *Cells and Societies,* Princeton, N. J.: Princeton Univ. Press, 1955; and WILSON, E. O., *Sociobiology,* Cambridge, Mass.: Harvard Univ. Press, 1975.

46. KROPOTKIN, PETR (1842-1921) was a Russian libertarian philosopher of noble lineage who was always on the front edge of any socialistic movement. His *Mutual Aid: A Factor of Evolution* (London, 1902) was written largely in rebuttal to T. H. Huxley's advocacy of the "fight to survive" aspect of Darwin's theory. Kropotkin contended that evolution was furthered more by cooperation than competition. See the brief discussion by GOULD, S. J., Kropotkin was no crackpot. *Natural History,* 1988, 96, 7(Jul.), 12-21.

It should be noted that E. O. Wilson (of Harvard) attributes the advanced civilization of social insects (ants, bees, termites, etc.) To their unwavering cooperation with each other. They will compete with, and even war against members of other tribes -- much as do humans. But unlike the human, they never compete with members of their own tribe. Here, cooperation is absolute. As a result, they have no need for laws, lawyers, police, and other governmental bric-a-brac.

Impedimenta of this latter sort are crucial for the human because he has no social instincts. He is forced to perform a balancing act between total competition (each for himself) and total coöperation (one for all). The creative side of his nature builds his culture, and the competitive side destroys all but the most durable. There is no evidence for Kropotkin's theory more clear-cut than this. For more recent arguments against the negativism of Neo-Darwinism, refer to: GOODWIN, B., *How the Leopard changed its Spots,* N.Y.: Chas. Scribner's Sons, 1994. Goodwin is of the opinion that Darwin short-changed us all -- both scientifically and ethically.

47. NIETZSCHE, F., Letter to Peter Gast from Marienbad, July 18, 1880. *Selected Letters of Friedrich Nietzsche.* OSCAR LEVY, ed., Garden City, N.Y.: Doubleday, Page & Co., 1921, p. 127.

48. LAMARCK, J. B., Homme. In: *Nouveau Dictionnaire d'Histoire Naturelle, New Ed.* Paris: Déterville, 1817, 15, 270-276.

49. The term "mutation" is unfortunate. It merely means change. Whether epigenesis or evolution, nothing is explained as simply change. Both are consistent growth phenomena. Being so, there must be record-keeping of that growth. Without it, the result would be what statisticians call a "random walk." The same mistakes would be repeated haphazardly. There could be no overall directedness nor consist ency, much less heredity. Thus, the very existence of DNA records implies that very little that is organic happens by chance. Neither does it truly disappear. It is latent in the structure, still in existence as information -- in a world where everything is information.

50. This estimate of all species past and present, was made by LEWONTIN, R. C., Adaptation., *Scientific American,* 1978, 239(3), 213-230. Please note that this is a very modest estimate. Others, e.g., Harvard zoölogist ERNST MAYER, places the total figure at approximately 50 billion! Cf.: *Science News,* 1996, 150, Sept.7.

51. Given that there are 4 billion nucleotide pairs in human DNA, the probability of a stray atomic particle irreparably altering a specific nucleotide (e.g., radiation induced mutation) begins at the minute value of one eight-billionth! Because of the many body cells, cancer becomes a reasonable possibility. But in the more limited (and protected) germ cells, the expectation of mutant births becomes almost negligible -- as demonstrated by the much-studied aftermath of Hiroshima.

52. Sad to relate, the origins of life would seem to have many possible explanations. Here are the six most prominent:
(1) Except for past extinctions, life has always been. Theories about origins merely reflect our unfounded assumption that all things necessarily have a beginning and an end.
(2) Some Super-doer personally created them (for reasons unknown), including 200,000 species of bacteria, 300,000 species of beetles, and unknown numbers of dinosaurs. Congratulations to Him, Her, It, or whatever.
(3) Despite their enormous complexity, everything living assembled itself by chance. Inefficient assemblies simply failed to survive by reason of adverse

environmental conditions.

(4) Living things emerged (grew) from more primitive structures with at least some innovation and selectivity exercised by preexisting materials (e.g., cells).

(5) Everything was planted here from another planet -- possibly via comets. This merely shifts the problem to some unknown elsewhere.

(6) The entire issue is ridiculous because everything is made up of mental ephemera and has no material justification anyhow.

53. Though possibly irrelevant, the art works of ancient Egypt, Greece, and Rome often portray facial features somewhat different from those of today's inhabitants. The forehead is more aligned with the nose. It makes a straight line, with the bridge of the nose quite shallow, almost level with the brows. It is to be noted that the forehead is the locus of the frontal lobes of the brain (those most involved with intelligence), and that slanting of the forehead is conspicuous in hominids preceding H. sapiens. Whether this indicates any frontal lobe changes is unknown. It seems more likely to have been merely stylistic features of the art at that time.

54. KRECH, D., et al., Effects of environmental complexity and training on brain chemistry. *Jour. Comp. Physiol. Psychol.*, 1960, 53, 509-519. See also BENNETT, E. L., et al., Chemical and anatomical plasticity of brain. *Science,* 1964, 146, 610-619.

55. BOWER, B., IQ's generation gap. *Science News,* 1987, 132, 7(Aug. 15th), 108-109. Reports work of JAMES R. FLYNN (Univ. of Otago, Dunedin, New Zealand), author of *Measurement: Realism and Objectivity.*, FORGE, J., editor, Reidel Publ. Co., 1987.

Data were collected from numerous developed countries. It was found that the average IQ of Dutch draftees increased 20 points from 1952 to 1982. Totally independent studies elsewhere in the world showed single generation IQ gains ranging from 5 to 25 points in 13 developed nations. In the case of the Dutch , IQs of over 150 (roughly genius) increased by a factor of 60! "Ironically, the greatest IQ gains occurred in the 'culture-fair' tests."

As expected, Flynn's observations were irksome to certain theorists. For a recent summary, refer to: Science and the citizen -- a long-term rise in IQ scores baffles intelligence experts, *Scientific American,* 1995, 273, 5(Nov.), 12-14.

56. See the massive and scholarly work of E. O. WILSON, *The Insect Societies.*, Cambridge, Mass.: Harvard Univ. Press, 1971.

57. GRASSÉ, PIERRE-PAUL, La reconstruction du nid et les coordinations interindividuelles chez *Bellicositermes natalensis* et *cubitermes sp.* La théorie de la stigmergie: Essai d' interpretation du comportement des termites constructeurs. *Insectes Sociaux,* 1959, 6(1), 41-83.

IDEM., Nouvelles expériences sur le termite de Müller (*Macrotermes mülleri*) et considérations sur la théorie de la stigmergie. IBID., 1967, 14(1), 73-102.

58. And that's not all! The dinosaur which reputedly evolved into a bird also had a problem. Part of a wing, or rudiments of a wing would not provide any lift in flying. It would seem that wings could not have evolved as a series of small chance mutations, all in the same direction, each furnishing additional survival value. Thus, Neo-Darwinians of the Mendelian persuasion go to some lengths trying to explain such features. But the evolution of wings is only one of the more obvious instances. The problem itself is quite extensive. It includes virtually all the behavior of social insects, elaborate instances of insect mimicry, as well as equally elaborate cases involving symbiotic behavior commonly described as "co-evolution." So far as I know, none of this has been resolved to everyone's satisfaction.

For a brief but very readable treatment of the dilemma, see: GOULD, S. J., Not necessarily a wing. *Natural History*, 1985, 94, 10(Oct.), 12 ff. Gould's explanation for the appearance of wings may be feasible. But there is no way of extending it to the many other instances, particularly metamorphosis.

59. There are various experiments on this theme. One of the classical ones dealing with the blood-sucking insect, *Rhodnius*, was performed by biologist WIGGLESWORTH, V. B., Growth and form in an insect. In: *Essays on Growth and Form, presented to D'Arcy Wentworth Thompson*, W. E. LeGROS CLARK & P. B. MEDAWAR, eds. Oxford, Eng.: Clarendon Press, 1945.

III. JOURNEY INTO NO"THING"NESS

1. In Zen Buddhism, as in most Buddhistic beliefs, it is recognized that the world we know is only a mental fabrication. See: *Zen and Zen Classics (Selections from R. H. Blyth),* FREDERICK FRANCK, ed., N.Y.: Vintage Bks., 1978. On page 104 it is noted that this brings up complications for our concept of death. If all things known to the mind are constructs of that same mind, then they are illusions (Maya). By the same token, death itself becomes illusory. The individual mind, which is all we know, was never a material "thing" to begin with. So how could the materially non-existent go out of existence? Tsk! Tsk!

2. EINSTEIN, A., & INFELD, L., *The Evolution of Physics.* N.Y.: Simon & Schuster, 1938, p. 31; EDDINGTON, A., *The Nature of the Physical World.* Cambridge, Eng.: Cambridge Univ. Press, 1931, p. 332.

3. The problem of form (patterning) and how it is perceived, dates back to the writings of ARISTOTLE (384-322 BC). In *De Anima, II,* 12, 424, he described sensory perception as "that which is receptive of the forms of things sensible without their matter, much as wax receives the imprint of a seal without the iron or gold of which the seal is composed."

In the 2300 years since, different metaphors have been used. Beyond this, we have not advanced significantly.

4. There is no quarrel with neural network theory insofar as the term "network" is concerned. Interrelated neural structures of this sort obviously occur. The difficulty arises when one considers how they operate -- and particularly the neuro- electrical impulse assumed to be the information-carrier. It is made up of ions, and ions can't behave in the fashion they assume.

Despite the highly touted comparison, operations of the CNS bear little resemblance to those of computers. These latter depend wholly on the controlled flow of electric currents and their magnetic field effects -- in short, *electrodynamics.* The ability to control them enables one to predict the exact energy distribution patterns and their influence upon subsequent events. This makes it possible to accurately manipulate the differently patterned paths taken by currents, and thus create reliable networks.

Contrariwise, neural impulses have little or no predictability beyond what occurs in each of the billions of separate neurons. Any patterning which evolves in the overall distribution can only arise from statistical effects. Impulse energy flow is *not* conducted in the electrodynamic sense. In each case, the next neuron (following a synapse) will have different pulse intensity, timing, velecity, and may or may not fire. In a network of such neurons, stimuli simply set off what is perhaps better described as a spreading electronic disturbance. Since no two results of stimulation will be the same, there can be no signal fidelity -- only noise. This difference between totally predetermined and predictable energy flow patterns (in computers), and flow patterns predictable only within separate neurons (the CNS), is highly significant. The former allows for elaborate and reliable networks either by hard wiring or software. Whereas comparable networks cannot be created in neural assemblies if the information carrier is considered the impulse. All impulses have the same negative sign and mutually repulse each other.

5. KOFFKA, K., *Principles of Gestalt Psychology.* N.Y.: Harcourt, Brace & Co., 1935.
Static electricity reveals an interesting analogue to what is proposed here. It will distribute itself in exact proportion to the *shape* of a conductor. Furthermore, it will emphasize the contours and salient features of that shape. The distribution of the charge will be identical with that on any other such shape (say a square) regardless of conductor size, or absolute amount of charge. In brief, it is *shape-sensitive!*
In the case of electrostatics (per above), the energy is mutually self-repellent, the same as the ions of the neuroelectric impulse. Mathematically, however, an energy which is mutually attractional would perform in exactly the same manner. It also would be shape-sensitive. And furthermore, it would tend to consolidate the shape and become stable, rather than leak away as in electrostatics. Such energies of mutual attraction are thought to operate in our visual systems where direct perception of shape is mandatory.

6. WERNER, H., Dynamics in binocular depth perception. *Psychol.. Monogr.,* 1937, 49, No. 2.

7. The immediately given data provided to our senses *have* to be relations. Otherwise, there would be no way of explaining sensory adaptation. For example, when the eyes adapt to the dark, the objective is to produce better contrast -- and contrast is a relationship, not a thing. Visual perception is constantly enhancing contrast, else the perceived world would soon blank out.

8. WERTHEIMER, M., Experimentelle Studien über das Sehen von Bewegung., *Zeitschr. f. Psychol.,* 1912, 61, 161-265.
The perception of motion where none exists physically, i.e., the direct perception of *relations,* was known to occur earlier. Exner, for example, had done similar studies in 1875. But Wertheimer did the first truly systematic study of it. Since then, comparable phenomena have also been shown to occur in the senses of touch and hearing.

9. MACH, E., *The Analysis of the Sensations* (trans. by Williams, C. M.), 5th ed., Chicago: Open Court Publ. Co., 1914. JAMES, W., *Principles of*

Psychology, Vol. II. N.Y.: Dover Publications, 1950, p. 149. Perhaps the most concrete statement of Lashley's position is found in LASHLEY, K. S., & WADE, M., The Pavlovian theory of generalization. *Psychol. Rev.*, 1946, 53, 72-78.

10. WUNDT, W., *Lectures on Human and Animal Psychology.* N.Y.: Macmillan Co., 1907. We stare at the river and soon feel ourselves moving upstream. We look at a waterfall for a period and the trees on either side appear to move upward. Man is the measure of all things -- *literally.* The coordinates are within us. In these cases, the origins of the coordinate system shift internally. But they illustrate why relativity theory assumes everything measured relative to the observer.

This perspective brought the observer into physics. Nonetheless, psychology (which presumes to deal with the observer) has persistently ignored the implications. In a somewhat different sense, so has subatomic physics. The continuing search for ultimate particles is, in effect, a search for absolutes. Some physicists have recog nized this. For example, Fritjof Capra, Univ. Calif., Berkeley, states that the quest for ultimate particles should be abandoned. We are dealing with patterns in energy, he says. The universe is better described as a web of energy relations, not a scatterment of "things." See: CAPRA, F., *The Tao of Physics,* N.Y.: Bantam Books, 1977.

11. To illustrate the Weber-Fechner law suppose we begin with two lights, A and B. Both are set at intensity 10. Our task is to increase B until it is just noticeably brighter than A. Let's say it has to be turned up to 12, a full fifth brighter, before we see any difference between the two. From this we could predict that if A were set at 30, B would have to be raised to 36 before being seen as brighter: 10/12 = 30/36 = 40/48, etc. What determines our perceived differences is not any absolute value of the brightness, but rather, the relationship (ratio), or relative brightness.

12. FISHER, P., Untersuchungen über das Formsehen der Elritze. *Zeitschr. f. Tierpsychol.*, 1941, 4, 219-233. Taught minnows to distinguish certain letters of the alphabet printed on cardboard rectangles indicating location of food. When letters were grouped, minnows responded to the form as a whole rather than letter parts. Thus, where WL would indicate food, LW would not bring about any response.

Instead of minnows, TINBERGEN, N., & KRUYT, W., studied the homing behavior of the digger wasp. See their: Über die Orientierung des Bienenwolfes *(Philanthus triangulum Fabr.)* III. *Zeitschr. f. vergleich. Physiol.*, 1938, 25, 292-334. They demonstrated that the wasp did not orient itself by any given stimulus, but to the total configuration. Landmarks were moved about to confuse the wasp, but it flew to where the nest should have been relative to the new configuration.

Between 1926 and 1929, Mathilda Hertz performed a series of experiments establishing the same behavior in jay birds, ravens, and bees. Refer: ELLIS, W. D., *A Source Book of Gestalt Psychology.* London: Routledge & Kegan Paul, Ltd., 1938, pp. 228-263.

13. RAUSCH, E., *Struktur und Metrik figural-optischer Wahrnehmung.* Frankfurt am Main: W. Kramer, 1952, pp. 11-13.

14. SICKLES, W. R., Experimental evidence for the electrical character of visual fields, derived from a quantitative analysis of the Ponzo illusion. *Jour. Exper. Psychol.,* 1942, 30, 84-91. (NOTE: this does not mean that the fields *are* electrical, but rather that they have the same *character,* i.e., they follow the same rules and therefore act as if they were electrical.)

15. FISHMAN, R., & TALLARICO, R. B., Studies of visual depth perception: II. Avoidance reaction as an indicator response in chicks. *Percept. Mot. Skills,* 1961, 12, 251-257; BALL, W., & TRONICK, E., Infant responses to impending collision: Optical and real. *Science,* 1971, 171, 818-820.

Studies of this sort bring up the question whether we can perceive causality, the argument being that to perceive the relation is to perceive the cause, i.e., they are one and the same. Thus, a number of scientists have contended that causality is a direct and immediately given experience. Among these is Maine de Biran (1766-1824), and more recently the well known physicist, Alfred North Whitehead.

More to the point, A. Michotte performed a series of experiments tending to show that we do, indeed, perceive causal relations directly. See: MICHOTTE, A., La causalité physique est-elle une donée phénoménale?, *Tijdschr. Phil.,* 1941, 3, 290-320; IDEM., La causalidad fisica, Es un dato fenomenico?, Madrid: *Rev. Psicol., gen. apl.,* 1946, 1, 11-58; IDEM., La perception de la causalité., Louvain: *sup. de Philosophie,* 1946, 296 pp., 180 fr. *Belges. Etudes Psychol., Vol. VI.*

16. There are dozens, perhaps tens of dozens of experiments demonstrating perception of proportionality (transposition). Only one will be described. The behaviorist D. O. Hebb worked with rats (sic!). He trained them to discriminate brightness and size differences. Stimulus 2 (twice that of stimulus 1) was successfully learned. The rats were then presented with a choice of stimulus 2 or stimulus 4 (twice that of stimulus 2 which had been rewarded). They chose # 4. Thus, what was learned was the magnitude *relationship,* not the magnitude itself. See: HEBB, D. O., The innate organization of visual activity. II. Transfer of response in the discrim ination of brightness and size by rats reared in darkness. *Jour. Comp. Psychol.,* 1937, 24, 277-299.

Other experiments on transposition in rats: SALDANHA, E. L., & BITTERMAN, M. E., Relational learning in the rat. *Amer. Jour. Psychol.,* 1951, 64, 37-53; LAWRENCE, D. H., & DE RIVERA, J., Evidence for relational transposition. *Jour. Comp. Physiol. Psychol.,* 1954, 47, 465-471. Transposition in the chick: BINGHAM, H. C., Size and form perception in Gallus domesticus. *Jour. Anim. Behav.,* 1913, 3, 65-113. In the canary: PASTORE, N., Spatial learning in the canary., *Jour. Comp. Physiol. Psychol.* 1954, 47, 288-289; IBID., 389-390. In goldfish: PERKINS, F. T., & WHEELER, R. H., Configurational learning in the goldfish. *Comp. Psychol. Monogr.* 1930, 7, No. 31; PERKINS, F. T., Study of configurational learning in the goldfish. *Jour. Exper. Psychol.,* 1931,

14, 508-538.

17. Following the work of Von Ehrenfels (see next note), Meinong recognized something that was difficult to believe, namely, that the interrelations making up a form actually had to exist independently of the particular items into which the form was analyzed -- regardless what these items might be! For example, the "squareness" of a square consisted in its internal relatedness, not in the four lines of which it consisted. This was the only possible explanation of the facts of transposition later publicized by the Gestalt psychologists working at Berlin. Reference: MEINONG, A., Zur Psychologie der Komplexionen und Relationen. *Zeitschr. Psychol.* 1891, 2, 245-265.

18. In an obscure paper published in 1890, Von Ehrenfels may well have been the earliest of the Gestalt psychologists. He worked with musical melodies and pointed out that their interrelatedness or patterning was the only feature crucial for their recognition. Every note and rest could be changed by using a different key and tempo, and the melody would still be recognized. On the other hand, all the original components could be presented in a different order, or the same order backwards, without recognition. See: Von EHRENFELS, C., Ueber Gestaltqualitäten. *Viertel-jahrschrift f. Wissenschaftliche Philos.*, 1890, 14. This was later revised and printed as a monograph: *Das Primzahlengesetz entwickelt und dargestellt auf Grund der Gestalttheorie*. Leipzig, 1922.

WERNER, H., Musical "micro-scales" and "micro-melodies." *Jour. Psychol.*, 1940, 10, 149-156. Found that the patterning of a melody was independent of the "size" of the musical scale, much as in the case of optical figures.

REINERT, J., Akustische Dressurversuche an einem Indischen Elephanten. *Zeitschr. Tierpsychol.*, 1957, 14, 100-126. Revealed that the Indian elephant could also learn and recognize simple melodies independently of pitch, timbre, and rhythm.

19. "If the life span is 90 days in *Drosophila* and 90 years in *Homo*, we may say that the physiological clock of the fly runs about 365 times as rapidly as that of man." BRODY, S., *Bioenergetics and Growth.* N.Y.: Reinhold Publ. Corp., 1945, p. 712.

20. This is an ad verbatim quotation from the Egyptian *Book of the Dead,* trans. from the *Papyrus of Nu*, British Museum No. 10,477, Sheet 2.

21. We have trouble understanding motion for two reasons. (1) Our assumption of "thingness" leads us to classify it only as a property of the things in motion. (2) Our perspective is necessarily restricted by our use of ego-centric coordinates. Everything is judged from our own position and time as point zero. As a result we cannot conceive of motion occurring in more than one direction at a time. Since three dimensions are necessary to provide any substantiality, it therefore seems unreal.

However, if we muse on the matter for a moment, we soon realize that motion has many simultaneous dimensions. For example, the earth is (A) spinning west to east once every 24 hours, (B) moving about the sun every 365+ days, and (C) sharing the motion of the solar system through the galaxy. Moreover, all are happening at the same time we seem to be standing completely motionless. Plotting this as a single complex spiral proves nothing because spirals also require three dimensions in order to exist.

22. Language probably co-evolved with thinking -- the one providing positive feedback for the other. Thus, it should not be surprising that we tend to think in subject-predicate fashion. If there is movement (verb), some "thing" (noun) has to be moving. It is assumed that movement can't exist without things. How this affects our view of the subatomic world was noted by E. S. Brightman long ago:

"Even the most modern science usually speaks of an electron as a charged 'particle.' The status of the particle is, however, obscure. Either it does work and is through and through active; or it does no work and so is superfluous. If the particle performs no function other than to be a bearer of energy, it is otiose. . . The particle may be a crutch to the imagination. It is only a stumbling block to the understanding. All the work done by 'matter' is energy; the particle makes no difference. Its presence adds nothing; its absence would not be noticed." BRIGHTMAN, E. S., *An Introduction to Philosophy*. N.Y.: Henry Holt, 1925, p. 121.

We usually think of matter (substance) as equivalent to mass. So suppose we look at Einstein's equation $E=mC^2$ in these terms. It says that the energy represented by any mass (m) equals the mass multiplied by the square of the speed of light (C). Mass can therefore be expressed as $m=E/C^2$. When transposed in this fashion it becomes obvious that mass (matter or substance) is only energy moving at enormous velocity. And since energy itself is an event, not a "thing," the substantive nature of matter is recognized for what it really is -- pure *motion* which can be defined only relative to our personal coordinates, size range, and perspective.

23. I searched my notes for some time trying to find where I had picked up this pithy remark of Pribram's. I located it in an interview conducted by a popular magazine: Interview: Karl Pribram. *Omni*, 1982, 5, Oct., p.129.

24. If the perception of "thingness" is a construct of the senses, as strongly suspected, then it is an immediately given experience and would result in numerous secondary assumptions. For example, "things" are enclosed. They have contours. Thus, we assume that everything real must have an inside and an outside, beginning and end, a unique identity, and preferably solidity. Most assumptions of bipolarity (the either-or, in-or-out, yes-or-no, black-or-white, good-or-bad, etc.,etc.) relate to thingness and the division made by contours. One side always presupposes a second side -- moebius strip notwithstanding.

Thus, there is only "me" and "not me." I have contours. The entire universe has contours. Accordingly, it must be a universe, not a multiverse, and there has to be something outside it and inside it. Also, it must be made up of particles. Anything less than particles would have no existence. Further, it had a beginning (Big Bang), and must have an end. The same is true of time. If it really exists, then there had to have been a preceeding period when it did *not* exist.

Note also that our knowledge of "things" is strung out sequentially in this "time." So we are constantly in search of the origins and causes of events. Otherwise, they are not events. This is the only way we can comprehend them. The world as known is in the brain of the knower and can't be understood without such assumptions. This, however, does *not* make them true -- only unknowable.

25. Being an organizing process, the mind does not age as does the body. Unless the brain becomes diseased (e.g., Altzheimer's), the mind continues growing until the senium. At this time, when body cells start failing to reproduce adequately, the mind loses efficiency. The body, being a material structure, necessarily ages and dies. In doing so, it takes with it the material portion of the mind. But remember that form (organization) has been proved to exist *independently* of the material formed (See discussion of Meinong). The important question is this: just how much of the mind is form (patterning process) and how much is material (brain-substance processed.) There seems no ready answer.

26. SPINOZA, B., *Ethics* (trans. by A. Boyle). N.Y.: E. P. Dutton & Co., 1910, pt. 1, Appendix, p. 263.

27. LINDSAY, R. B., Entropy consumption and values in physical science. *Amer. Scientist*, 1959, 47, 376-385; SEIFERT, H. S., Can we decrease our entropy? IBID., 1961, 49, 124A-134A.

In other words, cleanliness may be next to Godliness. But orderliness *is* Godliness!

28. BORING, E. G., *A History of Experimental Psychology*, 2nd. ed, Appleton Century, 1950, p. 611.

29. LASHLEY, K. S., Cerebral organization and behavior., *Res. Publ. Assoc. Nerv. Ment. Dis.*, 1958, 36, 1-18.

Mind considered as organization explains a variety of psychological disadvantages afflicting human thinking: (1) The tendency toward orthodoxy. (2) The felt necessity of systematizing all observable facts into the straightjacket of some theory. (3) The tendency to oversimplify and to reduce everything to a common denominator. (4) Undue generalization, stereotyping, and similar rigid thinking. All these can be traced to the felt need to organize at all costs.

The concept of organization as intelligence (mind) also has a positive side. The more intelligent individual is systematic. He doesn't have to waste time figuring out where to start projects, doesn't have to search for objects (puts them back), doesn't look up items (has them listed), and so on. Thus, for a given total amout of memory, he has a greater proportion of *free* memory.

30. ATTNEAVE, F., Some informational aspects of visual perception. *Psychol. Rev.*, 1954, 61, 183-193.

31. COTTRELL, A., Emergent properties of complex systems. In: *The Encyclopaedia of Ignorance*, R. Duncan & M. Weston-Smith, eds., N.Y.: Pergamon Press, 1977, p. 131.

32. SICKLES, W. R., & HARTMANN, G. W., The theory of order., *Psychol. Rev.*, 1942, 49, 403-421. See also: SICKLES, W. R., The psycho-geometry of order. IBID., 1944, 51, 189-199.

33. SICKLES, W. R., *Probability, Perception, and Form.* (Doctoral dissertation), Dept. Psychology, Univ. Calif., Berkeley, Sept., 1955.

34. LIVSON, N., & KRECH, D., Dynamic systems, perceptual differentiation, and intelligence., *Jour. Person.*, 1956, 25, 46-58.

35. CALVIN, A. D., et al., The effect of exposure time on the relation between perceptual organization and intelligence. *Amer. Jour. Psychol.,* 1958, 71, 573-577; PICKREL, E. W., Levels of perceptual organization and cognition: conflicting evidence. *Jour. Abnorm. Soc. Psychol.*, 1957, 54, 422-424.

36. RASHID, M. A., Rhythmic perception, age, intelligence, and musical perception. *Pakistan Jour. Psychol.*, 1970, Vol. 3(1-2), 3-15.

37. SPEARMAN, C. E., *The Nature of Intelligence and the Principles of Cognition,* 2nd. ed. London: Macmillan, 1927.

38. Notable among these are: ALLPORT, G. W., *Personality, A Psychological Interpretation.* N.Y.: Henry Holt, 1937; LECKY, P., *Self-consistency, a Theory of Personality.,* N.Y.: Island Press, 1945; FESTINGER, L., Cognitive dissonance. *Scient. American,* 1962, 207, 93-107.

One of the most compelling demonstrations of how consistency influences perception may be shown in recognition. Suppose one prints a list of colors: blue, red, green, etc., but in each case uses ink of a color different than that named. The resulting inconsistency makes the list quite difficult to read. This has been widely investigated and is known as "The Stroop Effect." Try patting yourself on the head with one hand while rubbing your belly in circles with the other. Some also find this quite difficult.

Need for consistency frequently causes us to overlook data which do not fit into our belief system, or fail to comply with our expectations. Most often it occurs without awareness, and just as often it distorts any conclusions which result. See: ROSENTHAL, R., *Experimenter Effects in Behavioral Research.,* N.Y.: Appleton-Century-Crofts, 1966; IDEM., Covert communication in the psychological experiment. *Psychol. Bull.,* 1967, 67, 356-367.

39. EHRENSVÄRD, G., *Life: Its Origins and Development*. Minneapolis: Burgess, 1962.

40. HEDGES, E. S., *Liesegang Rings and other Periodic Structures*. London: Chapman & Hall, Ltd., 1932

41. Evolution is commonly understood to mean that skeletal remains of earlier organisms reveal progressive transformations predictive of later organisms. However, from the standpoint of etymology, the term literally says "unrolling" and expresses continuity of process, an unfolding from within -- progressive tranformation, or *growth*.

42. LAMARCK, J. B., *Zoological Philosophy.*, trans. by Hugh Elliot. Chicago: Univ. of Chicago Press, 1984. (It seems everyone is quick to criticize Lamarck, but few have the time to read him.)

If one sticks strictly to the species concept, and thinks only of individuals, then there are indeed some creatures which have become structurally simpler during the course of evolution A large proportion of these are parasites -- most notably the 200 species of *Rhizocephala*, or "root heads." These parasitize crabs and actually become part of the crab's anatomy. However, any living creature whose vital processes have become so modified it must depend solely upon another species to survive, can scarcely be called an organism in its own right. And in this case, the "root heads" cannot survive independently. Furthermore, "crab-plus-parasite" is a much more complex structure than either taken singly. Refer to: GOULD, S. J., Triumph of the root-heads, *Natural History*, 1996, 105, 1(Jan.), 10-17.

Note that the above situation pertains also in many instances of "co-evolution," as well as in quite a few cases of domesticated plants and animals. And it applies equally well to social evolution. For instance, man-as-farmer is a social assembly far more complicated than man-as-hunter-gatherer.

43. TEILHARD DE CHARDIN, P., *The Phenomenon of Man.*, trans. by Bernard Wall. N.Y.: Harper & Row, 1975.

The concept of ever increasing complexity does *not* assume any preordained and God-given superplan for all life. This latter thesis, which is theological by definition, has been put forth by many. The latest proponent is probably DAVIES, P., *The Cosmic Blueprint*. N.Y.: Simon & Schuster, 1988. Rather, increasing complexity simply denies that organic events are random. It assumes that evolution "is working upon some definite law that we do not yet fully comprehend," as stated by WILLIS, J. C., in: *The Course of Evolution*. Cambridge Univ. Press, 1940.

In my own opinion, this "definite law" is only a corollary of the second law of thermodynamics. If energy always follows the path of least resistance, it cannot lead to randomness except in gaseous systems. In structured systems (such as the organic world), it will be guided by the existing structure. This will tend to extend the structure further, i.e., make it larger and more complex. And indeed, it does so during crystal growth.

Inasmuch as increased complexity coincides with increased information, another way of expressing complexification is to say that information accumulates exponentially. This would be expected in any growing system possessing memory. Put in these terms, it doesn't sound quite so mysterious. Morover, it would fit the facts of cultural growth as depicted in Figure 11.

44. JERISON, H. J., *Evolution of the Brain and Intelligence.*, N.Y.: Academic Press, 1973.

45. LEIBOWITZ, H., Some observations and theory on the variation of visual acuity with the orientation of the test object. *Jour. Opt. Soc. Amer.*, 1953, 43, 902-905.

46. Cited by HARTMANN, G. W., *Gestalt Psychology*, N. Y.: Ronald Press, 1935, p. 44. (footnote).

47. LAYMAN, J. D., The avian visual system. I. Cerebral function of the domestic fowl in pattern vision. *Comp. Psychol. Monogr.*, 1938, 12, 3.

Perhaps the most difficult to explain (by any existing theory) is the visual system of jumping spiders. These are only about 5 mm. long and possess eight eyes arranged in a semicircle around the fronts of their heads. Nonetheless, excellent depth perception is demonstrated by the accuracy of the leaps they make. Mistakes are rare. Even some sort of thinking is suggested by their behavior when stalking prey. For a brief descriptive article with beautiful photography, see: MOFFETT, M. W., All eyes on jumping spiders. *National Geographic*, 1991, 180, September, 43-63.

IV. MINDING THE OVERMIND

1. It would be unfeasible to present the original arguments of BELL, J. S., published in *Physics,* 1964, 1, 195-200, and later revised and extended. The same would be true of the earlier paper by Einstein and coworkers. (Note # 5, below) To attempt either would require getting into detailed discussion of particle physics. Fortunately, there are several semipopular works which cover the story rather adequately. One of the better articles is D'ESPAGNAT, B., The quantum theory and reality. *Scientific American,* 1979, Nov., 158-181. For a good up-to-date review, see: CUSHING, J. T., & MC MULLIN, E., eds., *Philosophical Consequences of Quantum Theory.,* Notre Dame, Ind,: Notre Dame Univ.Press, 1989.

2. There are at least six separate experiments dealing with Bell's conclusions as of this date. For a history of these and their implications, as well as additional references, see the excellent non-mathematical treatment of GRIBBEN, J., *In Search of Schrödinqer's Cat.,* N.Y.: Bantam Books, 1984.

3. BOHM, D., Quantum theory as an indication of a new world order in physics: (B) Implicate and explicate order in physical law. *Foundations of Physics,* 1973, 3, 139-167; BOHM, D., & HILEY, B., On the intuitive understanding of non-locality as implied by quantum theory. IBID., 1975, 5, 93-109. For something somewhat easier to read: BOHM, D., *Wholeness and the Implicate Order.* Boston: Routledge & Kegan Paul, 1980. See also: ALBERT, D. Z., Bohm's alternative to quantum mechanics., *Scientific American,* 1994, 270, 5(May), 58-67.
Bohm refers to this intangible type of relatedness or "action at a distance" which permeates the universe, as the implicate order. This is contrasted with our experienced or "explicate" order. In essential details, his position is compatible with that of Bell.

4. The linkage between oriental philosophy and this new outlook in quantum physics is made particularly understandable by ZUKAV, G., *The Dancing Wu Li Masters.,* N.Y.: Bantam Books, 1979; and CAPRA, F., *The Tao of Physics.,* N.Y.: Bantam Books, 1977.

5. EINSTEIN, A., PODOLSKY, B., & ROSEN, N., Can quantum-mechanical description of physical reality be considered complete? *Physical Review,* 1935, 47, 777-780.

6. KOESTLER, A., *The Roots of Coincidence.* N.Y.: Random House, Vintage Books, 1973; IDEM., *Janus: A Summing Up.* N.Y.: Random House,

1978.

Koestler is very readable and has a healthy skeptical attitude toward standardized 'thinking' of any sort. For example, he bluntly states his doubts that mutations have had any influence whatever on the course of evolution. He feels that somehow mind has to be active in the evolutionary process. And if it is, it would be reasonable to assume it might also underlie the appearance of phenomena we call coincidences.

JUNG, C. G., *Synchronicity.* Princeton, N.J.: Princeton Univ. Press,1973. (Also: *Collected Works of C. G. Jung. Vol. 8.* N.Y.: Pantheon Bks., 1959.) In terms of readability, Jung is the opposite of Koestler. But he is rewarding in terms of depth. His primary interest was with the "collective unconscious" -- which might be called a sort of subconscious aspect of an overmind. While working with the well known physicist, W. Pauli, he formulated the concept of "synchronicity." This is very similar to what Koestler meant by coincidence. The role played by the mind is evidenced by the fact that synchronous events are said to be related by a common *meaning.* Coincidences, of course, are meaningfully related in order to be considered such.

KAMMERER, P., *Das Gesetz der Serie* (The Law of Seriality). Stuttgart & Berlin: Deutsche Verlags Anstalt, 1919. Kammerer was an Austrian biologist who, even more than Koestler, endured a life of ridicule from orthodox theorists. He was interested in the apparent clustering of events in everyday life, events which were not causally related and not necessarily meaningful, but nonetheless alike in some respect. He proposed that there was an unknown acausal principle operative in nature, and that this tended to organize things. An excellent unbiased treatment of his views may be found in Koestler, above.

7. For a brief discussion of these proposed superluminary communication links and their implications, see ZUKAV, G., Note # 4, above, p. 295 ff.

8. HUSSERL, E., *Philosophie der Arithmetik.* Halle-Saale: C. E. M. Pfeffer, 1891, Chap. 9. Other comparable terms used for this figural fusion effect include "perceived numerosity," "subitizing," and "creative synthesis."

At that time almost everyone in psychology was involved with these relational phenomena. For example, Wundt found that only about 6 regular metronome beats could be apprehended without counting or rhythmic grouping. With grouping (but not counting) the number rose to 16, comprised of 8 pairs, or 4 groups of 4 each. The largest such grouping effect was reported by Dietze -- 40 beats given at 4 per second, and perceived as 5 groups of 8 each. See: WUNDT, W., *An Introduction to Psychology.*, trans. by R. Pintner., N.Y.: Macmillan Co., 1912.

It seems remarkable that despite all this investigation, no one concerned himself with the fact that such organizational processes presuppose energies of attraction. Also overlooked was the identity between temporal periodicity and structural orderliness. Among today's psychologists all such issues are largely ignored.

9. HAYFLICK, L., The limited *in vitro* lifetime of human diploid cell strains., *Exper. Cell Res.*, 1965, 37, 614-636. Showed that cells went through the usual life cycle and died after about 50 ± 10 serial mitotic passages. MADELINE GRIGG, *Arch. Neurol.*, 1987, 9, 948-954 recorded brain wave activity after death. She found that for brain cells at least, individual cellular death was quite variable. All multicellular creatures also have a limited lifespan of course. The oldest documented living creature was a marion's tortoise (age 152+ years) which lived on Mauritius island. Next in line was a Japanese citizen named Shigechiyo Izumi who lived from 1865 to 1986.

10. As with quantum physics, it is not feasible to discuss Gödel's theorems in any detail. For those mathematically inclined, reference is made to DE LONG, H., *A Profile of Mathematical Logic.* Reading, Mass.: Addison-Wesley, 1971; and SCHOENFIELD, J. R., *Mathematical Logic.* Reading, Mass.: Addison-Wesley, 1967. For a small readable book: NAGEL, E., & NEWMAN, J. R., *Gödel's Proof.* N.Y.: New York Univ. Press, 1958.

Translated into English for the lay reader, Gödel demonstrated that no system can be proved complete or consistent using only the axioms of the system itself. Stated differently, if one is restricted to what is known within a system, he can never be sure that his description of it is either consistent or complete. The drama critic cannot be objective and simultaneously play a role in the drama.

Similarly, the human mind cannot step outside itself and watch itself in action. Because you are the person whom you see yourself to be, you can never fully know the person whom you really are. Socrates' admonition to "know thyself" is tantamount to "lifting thyself by thine own bootstraps." A given mind can no more understand itself than an eye can see itself or a fist strike itself. Things can only be known in context as a figure-ground effect. The mind is isolated with no context. In like manner, therefore, the cell can never know the human because it is a part of that human, and the human can never fully understand his own society for the same reason.

Referring back to our comments (in the Preface) about how very little we have been able to learn concerning mind, life or matter, one is troubled by a question. Could this also be a result of Gödel's theorem? After all, we are made up of these!

KÖHLER, W., *The Place of Value in a World of Facts.*, N.Y.: Liveright Publ. Co., 1938, dismisses all such arguments as "meaningless nonsense." Physicists and mathematicians, he noted, are themselves physical entities. Such arguments would therefore make physics meaningless. And since everything known is mediated by the mind, psychology would be hopeless.

I am unsure of Köhler's syllogistic logic in this instance. It would have seemed preferable simply to note that Gödel's theorem also has a *positive* aspect. It implies that no system, whether brain, math, or the universe, can be considered completely closed. Result: this constitutes a passport for exploration and expansion into the new, different, and undreamed of -- an open gate to hope and imagination. The pot of gold, indeed the whole rainbow, simply continues to recede in front of the seeker.

11. All of us have a natural passion for classification. It is necessary for organization (mind). Sometimes, however, we refuse to recognize that *we* did the classifying, not Nature. One such case is the species concept. I am not alone in doubting its validity. Others have had similar misgivings. Among them is J. B. S. HALDANE, perhaps the century's most noted evolution theorist. See his: Can a species concept be justified? In: *The Species Concept in Paleontology*, P. C. Sylvester-Bradley, ed., London: Systematics Assoc., 1956, Publ. No. 2, 95-96. He describes the species concept as little more than "a concession to our linguistic habits." More recently: RENNIE, J., Are species specious? *Scientific American*, 1991, 265, 5(Nov.), p. 26.

As should be obvious, some sort of classification system is necessary. But as currently determined, species classifications are often arbitrary, inconsistent and misleading. For example, black and white people are said to be the same species, and minor differences are explained as adaptations to the climate of origin. But black and white bears from equally different climates are also much alike, and they are said to be different species. Could this be ursine racism? Bear bigotry?

Homologies of skeletal structure are only a few of many features differentiating animals. Paleontologists are forced to use them as criteria because our sole remnants from the geological past are bones. However, they do not necessarily correspond to other and frequently more salient features. Thus, in the current system differences between races are often greater and more significant than those between species. In every meaningful sense, the German shepherd and husky dogs are very like the wolf (different species), and very unlike the Mexican Chihuahua or pekinese (same species). To sum up my objections to the present system, it seems highly arbitrary. No matter what system is used, it should be consistent.

12. Early psychologists insisted that contiguity of stimuli was necessary for their "association" during learning. (See: McGEOCH, J. A., *The Psychology of Learning.*, N.Y.: Longmans, Green & Co., 1942, p. 540) But why should association occur at all unless one also assumes their mutual attraction (bonding) as in the Gestalt law of proximity? Indeed, contiguity *means* proximity. Also please note that the intensity or strength of these learned relations (associations, bonds) has been shown to vary consistently with the space-time intervals between respective items. Learned lists of nonsense syllables even acquire internal organization and a sort of "contour" in which first and last syllables dominate. (IBID., p. 109)

13. A student presents the following argument. Given that the human is a growth phenomenon constructed by the cells, it seems possible it could also be destroyed by them. Should human behavior become disadvantageous to continuance of the species, as in homosexuality, it is conceivable that corrective biological action might occur at the point source of the problem -- as it did with AIDs. I admit this seems far-fetched, but AIDs has now been shown to be of human origin, and it was not knowingly devised by the human mind. Is it not logical to suspect the cell?

14. . SPENGLER, O., *The Decline of the West, Vols. I & II.*, trans. by C. F. Atkinson. N.Y.: Alfred A. Knopf, 1926. For Spengler, the social organism was the *culture*-- a much more restricted concept than a society based simply on shared language. A culture was defined by its ethos. Besides the common language, this included folklore, customs, mores, and a relatively homogeneous citizenry. It had common mythology, religion and general outlook (*Weltanschauung*). Examples: Gothic Germany, Periclean Athens, or pre-1900 Japan. Cultures were different-iated from civilizations (e.g., ancient Rome or the U.S.A.). The latter were said to be heterogeneous and lacking any unifying ethos. Instead, they were held together by economics. This glorified the role of money to where wealth replaced other values.

15. Though necessary to some degree, legal restrictions (laws) can neither give rise to a culture nor sustain it in illness. Cultures are living things, and when mores get crystallized into laws they reduce variability, are restrictive, and often oppressive. What prevents crime and holds a culture together is not any body of laws. It is a common ethos which grows from within. It cannot be successfully imposed from the outside by legislation. Thus, it has often been noted that as soon as a small percentage of the public consistently disobeys any given law, that law becomes impossible to enforce.

16. The growth of culture might be described as learning by the social mind -- for it also is a matter of association or relating of data. Given this analogue, please note that the internet and other PC networks are now coordinating and consolidating public thinking by erasing the barriers of distance. Individual minds often seem like cells in a social brain through unlimited exchange of information. Should this organization continue into a consistent structure, the "virtual" reality of a social mind will materialize into reality. Could part of the currently chaotic state of society be due to just such a social mind undergoing rapid reorganization?

17. Hypotheses of overmind, social mind, and similar concepts should be differentiated from theologically inspired doctrines involving deity, soul, and spirit. Both categories have elaborate and exhaustive histories with adherents too numerous to mention here. In many cases, e.g., Ralph Waldo Emerson's "oversoul," it is difficult to distinguish between them. To clarify a point, therefore, the concept intended here is strictly a scientific interpretation hopefully devoid of any theological overtones.

My personal opinions are akin to those of EINSTEIN, A., *Out of my Later Years.* N.Y.: Philosophical Library, 1950, pp. 59-63. The existence of an outer world is accepted because it is felt that sensation has to be the sensation of some thing, else everything becomes a vagary of the mind. At the same time, it is recog-nized that outer reality can only be known as an analogue representation. This contrasts sharply with SCHRÖDINGER, E., *My View of the World.* Woodbridge, Conn.: Oxbow Press, 1983, who sees no reason whatever to postulate outer reality of any sort. To me, this latter position seems to assume that what is not inside is therefore not outside -- which is not logically justifiable.

Hypotheses of a collective mind deal with something that would be largely *outside*. And whether social, biospheric, or universal, they are fascinating speculations. But it is my (skeptical) conviction that the honest scientist should withhold judgement until more data are forthcoming. This is not the period of the Inquisition, so there is no law saying you have to believe or disbelieve anything. You can hold it in abeyance -- proportionate to the evidence available.

18. For the opinion of KÖHLER, W., see note # 10, above.

19. WALTHAM, C., ed., *Chuang Tzû: Genius of the Absurd* (From The translations of James Legge). N.Y.: Ace Books, 1971. Chuang Tzû was fully aware that communication can never be complete because of the relative isolation of individual minds. For example, ". . . books are only a collection of words. Words have what is valuable: the ideas they convey. But these ideas are a sequence of something else." Bk. XIII, 10.

20. HUXLEY, J., *Knowledge, Morality, and Destiny.* N.Y.: Mentor Books, 1960. This is a very rewarding volume despite Huxley's adherence to orthodox theories of genetics and evolution.

21. Everyone is pretty well aware of what is being referred to when terms like meaning, idea, concept, and belief are used. However, they are almost impossible to define in any acceptable scientific sense. They can only be described in still other equally vague terms because they refer to structures of the inaccessible mental world and exhibit no properties which can be measured by use of the senses.

Nonetheless, certain facts are obvious. What is intended by the expressions we use is not necessarily the same as what others interpret them to mean. Therefore, words are *not* the same as meanings. One man's description of the facts may differ markedly from the facts themselves as well as someone else's understanding of them.

Words can only trigger meanings in the minds of recipients. Though doubtlessly comprised of "flimsy" energy relations in the brain, meanings are nonetheless quite real. Consider a card game, say poker or bridge. Plays can be both complex and intriguing despite the fact that outer reality consists only of printing on pasteboards. Indeed, the game is not a game of cards. It is a game of meanings.

22. WILSON, E. O., *Sociobiology: The New Synthesis.* Cambridge, Mass.: Harvard Univ. Press, 1975, p. 569.

23. TOFFLER, A., *Future Shock.* N.Y.: Bantam Books, 1971. Regardless of our theoretical bias, we better hope that mental evolution *is* occurring! Otherwise the social mind will outpace the individual mind! The information explosion in today's society is so far advanced that we have already topped out in our efforts to assimilate it. In mathematics, for example, we have what is called

"Ulam's dilemma." This refers to research showing that almost 200,000 new theorems are published yearly -- far in excess of what can even be surveyed. To one degree or another, the story is much the same for technical literature in all sciences. It has been estimated that trying to catch up with one year's output of the learned publications would require about fifty years of reading 24 hours a day seven days a week. Even the abstracts present a major problem.

Whether organism or social organization, it should be obvious that nothing can continue to grow indefinitely. The process of compexification must inevitably progress to where it defies integration. Despite computer networks, the sheer volume of information in any discipline then becomes indigestible by the ultimate user, the individual. Human minds at least, have maxima. Thus, medicine, law, engineering, etc., have long since fractured into specialties. Nobody has the overall picture, and the same phenomena get rediscovered over and over again.

Worse yet, even if intelligence *is* evolving, it is not progressing as fast as the culture. The labor market is constantly searching for employees to fill new high-I.Q. positions, while on the other hand the number of low-I.Q. positions disappear quite rapidly. The result is that ever-increasing numbers of the public become basically unemployable. Needless to say, the population explosion contributes to this. Though not pessimistic by nature, I confess that I see no ready solution to the problem.

24. It is somewhat startling to discover that the curve for world population growth has a shape almost identical to that of Figure 11 for cultural growth. One's first thought is that the population increase is what gave rise to the cultural advancement -- an idea suggested by some theorists, e.g., Julian Simon of the Univ. of Maryland. Further study, however, leads one to conclude that the two curves can be only minimally related, if at all. Reason: the rapid acceleration in world popul-ation is mostly contributed by Third World countries. The cultural growth curve, on the other hand, is largely a product of the developed nations whose populations are mostly stabilized or even declining. The similarity of the two curves is therefore misleading. One can't attribute a large orange crop to the sudden increase of apple orchards.

Even within specific nations there are usually reasons why cultural growth cannot be equated with population growth. In western nations at least, there is always an unknown (and often large) part of the citizenry which does not participate meaningfully in the culture. Some may even be alien to it and have their own subculture. Moreover, the lower the the socio-economic level of these groups, the higher the birthrate. So if any population effects exist, they are likely inverse.

References: EHRLICH, P. R., *The Population Bomb, Rev. Ed.,* N.Y.: Ballantine, 1986. Popular articles: EHRLICH, P. R., & EHRLICH, A. H., Population, plenty, and poverty. *National Geographic,* 1988, 174, 6(Dec.), 914-945; BERREBY, D., The numbers game. *Discover,* 1990, 11, 4(Apr.) 42.

25. Students of philosophy will recognize this as a problem dating back to the ancient Greeks. It is a question whether Plato's *ideas* and Aristotle's *forms* (called universals) have any true existence in and of themselves. Some (the Nominalists) said they were only names. Others (the Realists) said they were substantive realities. The problem itself is a classic example of the "either-or" type of thinking which results from assumptions of "thingness." Things have contours determining an inside and outside, and this makes for mutually exclusive this-or-that. (See Note # 24 for Sect. III. Journey into No"thing"ness.)

For the case in point, both answers have to be correct. Certainly the mental concept of trees as a class, represents a set of common identities existing for all trees outside. Were this not so, we would be unable to mentally classify our perceptions, i.e., create concepts representative of items in this outer world. On the other hand, it seems extremely doubtful if any generalized "tree form" exists outside the individual and/or social mind. Poems and melodies are like trees in that their mental surrogates consist of organized complexes of relationships. These do not have to possess mass. They are mind stuff.

26. Besides Huxley (Note # 20. above), one might also cite DAWKINS, R., *The Selfish Gene*. Oxford: Oxford Univ. Press, 1976. It was probably he who popularized the term "meme" -- originally coined by R. Semon in 1921. Like Huxley, he is a proponent of the Neo-Darwinian view and favors Mendelian genetics. Both try to construct a theory of socio-cultural evolution through direct analogy with the existing orthodoxy mentioned. This is now called "evolutionary epistemology" and includes CAMPBELL, D., Evolutionary epistemology. In: *The Philosophy of Karl R. Popper*, P. A. Schilpp, ed. LaSalle, Ill.: Open Court Publ. Co., 1974, 1, 413-453; and KARY, C., Can Darwinian inheritance be extended from biology to epistomology? *P S A 1982*, P. D. Asquith, & T. Nickles, eds., 1982, 356-369.

27. Von DITFURTH, H., *Der Geist fiel nicht vom Himmel: Die Evolution unseres Bewusstseins*. München: Verlag Deutscher Taschenbuch, 1980. (So far as I know, Von Ditfurth is not yet in the English.)

I do not feel comfortable with the logic behind Von Ditfurth's argument. Feet, fins and wings are indeed body parts which developed in response to environmental features, and as he notes, they presuppose the existence of these features. However, the mind is another story entirely. It did not necessarily develop in response to some particular aspect of the environment, nor as a tool to be used with an overmind. Thus, it would appear that he introduces his conclusion surreptitiously as part of his minor premise. For those unfortunates naive enough to consider the brain just another part of the body like the feet, I can see how his argument might be compelling. But for the rest of us, he is adding cabbages and carrots.

28. Needless to say, this position is at odds with Platonists like Kurt Gödel mentioned earlier. They feel that mathematics has objective existence in and of itself, independent of any mathematicians past or present. It is not invented like a language. It is discovered. However, there are numerous reasons for looking upon it as an intellectual tool like language. To cite just one, arithmetic uses a base-10 system because we have ten fingers. The resulting decimal system is awkward. Were arithmetic part of the external world as Platonists contend, one would think we should be using the preferable duodecimal system (base-12). This latter is superior in a variety of ways.

On the other hand, the very fact that mathematics is based on axioms of order (organization) is quite significant for the argument that mind is, indeed, organization. And to this extent, the view presented here coincides with that of the Platonists.

29. ROBERTS, R. M., *Serendipity: Accidental Discoveries in Science.* N.Y.: John Wiley & Sons, 1989.

Thinking is a relating of memories. Nothing from the outside can alter the process without first becoming recorded inside the brain. Within one's head, therefore, the only action possible is rearrangement or reorganization of the data which are already present. It follows that if one's memory banks contain nothing whatever related to something called X, then item X could become known only by chance. Even if it already existed one would be unable to recognize it. It could only be discovered fortuitously. After discovery, of course, It would become related.

When examined analytically, most so-called original inventions are seen to be reassemblies of the known. Their parts and principles have already been in memory. What I am trying to say is that scientific advancement is a *growth* process. It develops from within. It does not accumulate somehow from battles with the environment. It only seems so because thinking is an extension of the mind, and we are usually probing around where the still unstructured may exist.

30. The Malay incident, along with comparable cases, was reported in the semipopular journal *Science Digest*, 1981, 89(9), p. 58, by JANET HOPSON. The best technical sources for such phenomena are the *Jour. of Occup.. Med.,* or the psychiatric journals. However, even the *New Eng. Jour. Med.,* has carried similar reports. This sort of thing has been going on since man first became designated as such. See: MACKAY, C., *Memoirs of Extraordinary Popular Delusions and the Madness of Crowds.* London: 1852.

31. In all fairness it should be mentioned that some are convinced that small human groups do indeed exist and are quite real. References pro and con: WARRINER, C. K. Groups are real: a reaffirmation. *Amer. Sociol. Rev.*, 1956, 549-554; WECHSLER, D., Concept of collective intelligence. *Amer. Psychologist*, 1971, 26, 904-907; JANIS, I. L., Groupthink. *Psychology Today*, 1971, 5(Nov.), 43-46, 74-76; HALL, J., Decisions, decisions, decisions. IBID., p. 51.

For a more recent scientific review of this issue, see: BOWER, B., Return of the group., *Science News,* 1995, 148, 21(Nov. 18), 328-330; and IBID., Ultrasocial Darwinism, pp. 366-367. Bower cites views maintaining that groups can actually possess cognitive powers beyond those of their constituent members, that they are therefore organic entities, and may well be the driving force of evolution!

Considering the recognized inefficiency of committees, it was amusing to note an article in *Business Week* for Apr. 16, 1990. This stated that the reason Congress cannot act, only react, can be attributed to the fact that it is structured into committees. It has 47 such committees and 232 subcommittees each with its own staff and territory. No one person can be held accountable for anything, and by the same token, little gets done.

32. BOWER, B., *Science News*, 1992, 124, 9(Aug. 29), p.132: reported on experimental work done by KAREN WYNN, Univ. of Ariz., Tucson, and published in *Nature*, 27 Aug., 1992.

33. HEISENBERG, W., *Physics and Philosophy.*, N.Y.: Harper Torch Books, 1958, p.107.

34. The popular view has it that pets like dogs and cats have feelings, but that ability to experience pain and emotion somehow disappears as one proceeds "downward" toward more primitive creatures, say insects. About 15 years ago, Cornell biologists THOMAS EISNER and SCOTT CAMAZINE presented evidence that spiders at least, do indeed feel pain. Their reactions to pain-inducing toxins could be interpreted in no other way. See: *Science 83*, 1983, 4, 7(Sept.), p.6.

35. Reported in "Breakthroughs," *Discover*, 1992, 13, 7(Jul.), p. 14.

36. Because many scientists consider the idea of plant behavior ludicrous, data on the subject is found mostly in the popular press. Representative references:
Science and the citizen. *Scientific American*, 1990, 262, 5(May), 32; BOLING, R., Tree ESP, *Omni*, 1982, 5(3), 42; IBID., 1983, 6(3), 52; IBID., 1992, 14, 8, 30; HOROWITZ, K. A., et al., Plant primary perception. *Science*, 1975, 189, 478-480; DELAWAR, G., Do plants feel emotion? *ElectroTechnoloqy*, 1969, April; BACKSTER, C., Evidence of a primary perception in plant life. *Internat. Jour. Parapsychol.*, 1968, 10, 4; TOMPKINS, P., & BIRD, C., Love among the cabbages. *Harpers*, 1972, Nov., p. 90.

Some desert plants, notably Burro Weed, were recently reported to have been studied experimentally by members of the botony dept., Univ. Calif., Santa Barbara. They concluded that these plants not only communicate chemically, but that Burro Weeds "exhibit detection and avoidance behavior as well as self vs. non-self recognition."

Perhaps the most exorbitant claim was discovered in the news media (sic!) dated 12 Feb., 1980. For whatever it is worth, this presumed to report on experiments by Dr. Ken Hashimoto, a director of Fuji Electronics of Tokyo. He was reputed to have developed a machine which translates plant electrical activity into audible sound. Using this device, his wife Yoshi was able to get a plant to answer simple questions in arithmetic. Indeed, it was even possible to teach it some songs in Japanese! Since Hashimoto was into parapsychology, he may have had resources unavailable to the rest of us.

For more serious and recent references on the complex life of plants, refer to: ATTENBOROUGH, D., *The Private Lives of Plants,* Princeton, N. J.: Princeton Univ. Press, 1995; BEHME, R. L., *Incredible Plants,* N. Y.: Sterling Publ. Co.,1993; and TOMPKINS, P. & BIRD, C., *The Secret Life of Plants,* N.Y.:. Harper and Row, 1973.

37. We think of chemical language as something used only in the control of physiological processes. But it also carries messages which determine behavior, and not just in the case of pheromones. Specific cravings provide other interesting examples. It has been demonstrated numerous times that when animals are deprived of some necessary nutritional component, they will search until they "smell it out," thus correcting the imbalance. Consider the weird cravings women sometimes acquire following onset of their first pregnancy. Could this not be due to a scramb ling of the chemical signal system by the sudden deluge of new and unexpected hormones?

38. WILSON, E. O., *The Insect Societies.* Cambridge, Mass.: Harvard Univ. Press, 1971.

39. The mutual cooperation among social insects, enabling them to build complex societies, is attributed to their being 75% related to each other. If we apply this same logic to the cells of our brains, we note that they are virtually 100% related -- being essentially clones of each other. This should tell us something about the ability of brain cells to act cooperatively in problem solution, or even mere building of castles in the air!

40. In the first decade of this century the earliest articles were written proposing that the termitary was an organism in its own right. Quite appropriately, these were by a South African: MARAIS, E. N., *Soul of the White Ant,* trans. by Winifred DeKok. N.Y.: Dodd, Mead & Co., 1937. Some years later, the Nobelist M. Maeterlinck wrote a similarly titled volume and was sued for plagiarism by Marais. For a brief synopsis of the tragic life of Marais, see: ARDREY, R., *African Genesis.* N.Y.: Dell Publ. Co., 1961, Chapter 3.

41. Starting on p. 215 of his monumental volume on social insects (500 double-column 8x10 inch pages!), cited in Note # 38 above, E. O. Wilson does a good job summarizing what is known of the learning capacities of social insects. In his opinion they have achieved most of the basic forms of learning employed by mammals.

42. Whether creatures other than the human can think obviously depends upon how one defines thinking. If it is defined simply as the ability to compensate for environmental change, and to make decisions allowing for continued survival, then virtually all living organisms can think. At the other extreme, if it is defined as the ability to reason abstractly as in understanding advanced mathematics, then only humans (and not all of these) can think.

One definition would be to consider it a type of cognitive simulation of behavior (set). When occurring during sleep, it would be dreaming. Since we rarely dream of abstract matters, this would classify it as *applied* thinking -- as contrasted with the *abstract* variety. Now it is not known whether creatures as simple as fish dream. But the fact that dogs and cats *do* dream should be evidence that some lesser animals can think -- at least by this definition.

The confusion, I would guess, arises from the problem of communication involved. If you try talking with some non-English speaking person, you can point to things and achieve a round-about access to meanings held in common. Thus, the person seems intelligent. However, if you talk to your dog you cannot point to an odor, much less know what that odor means to him. In brief, there is a very meagre body of common meanings between you. Communication would require a double translation as it were. So you consider the pet stupid. That this is unjustified, note how happy he becomes when insight into your behavior enbles him to achieve a common meaning with you.

Despite all this uncertainty and lack of criteria, there is the usual oversupply of opinion. Like the lay public, for example, most philosophers assume that animals cannot think. ADLER, M. J., *Ten Philosophical Mistakes*. N.Y.: Macmillan Publ. Co., 1985, p. 77, bluntly states that animals lack intellects. Nonetheless, quite a few who have spent years studying them are convinced that they *can* think. Notable among the latter is GRIFFIN, D. R., *Animal Thinking*. Cambridge, Mass.: Harvard Univ. Press, 1984. See also: MORGAN, J., Profile of D. R. Griffin., *Scientific American,* 1989, 260, 5(May), 36-38.

Commonly cited examples of animal thinking include: (1) the "waggle dance" language of bees (Von FRISCH, K., *Bees: their Vision, Chemical Senses and Lanquage.* Ithaca, N.Y.: Cornell Univ. Press, 1950; IDEM., Dialects in the language of bees. *Scientific American,* 1962, 207, 78-87; (2) The Boran honeyguide bird which enlists the help of humans to raid trees containing beehives. (*Science,* 1989, Mar. 10, 1343-1346.) (3) The symbiotic behavior of wasps and potato aphids. WEISS, R., Dying aphids obey wasp's commands. *Science News,* 1989, 135, 15 Apr., 231; (4) The "assassin bug" of Puerto Rico which camouflages itself and fishes for termites. (McMAHAN, E., Bugs angle for termites. *Natural History.,* 1983, 92, 5, 40.) And especially (5) the ability of honey bees to predict, in advance, where they will be fed -- best summarized perhaps by THOMAS, L., *Late Night Thoughts on Listening to Mahler's Ninth Symphony.,* N.Y.: Bantam Books, 1984.

43. This particular experiment was reported by TEALE, E. W., *The Strange Lives of Familiar Insects.* N.Y.: Dodd, Mead & Co., 1962.

Consider pigeons! It is reported that these have been taught to identify differences in the artistic styles of painting used by Monet and Picasso -- indicating "higher cognitive abilities similar to humans!" Reported in: Breakthroughs, *Discover,* 1995, 16, 5(May), p. 14.

44. LLOYD, J. A., Aggressive mimicry in *Photurus* fireflies: Signal repertoires by femmes fatales. *Science,* 1975, 187, 452-453.

Use of deceptive comunications, disguises, even planned strategies of this type, are not uncommon throughout the world of "lesser" creatures. The predatory jumping spider, *Portia fimbriata,* has been shown to be a master of such elaborate deceptive ploys --all of which require *thinking* in a brain the size of a pin point! See the excellent text and photos in JACKSON, R. R., Mistress of deception, *National Geographic,* 1996, 190, 5(Nov.), 104-115.

V. BIOSPHERE, GAIA -- AND WHAT ELSE?

1. Language is a relating activity in which sounds and symbols are used to arouse meanings in the minds of others. But it is often overlooked that intelligence is also a relating activity. Spearman originally defined it as the ability to perceive and deduce relationships. Thus, it is logical to assume that these two (language and intelligence) evolved together for much the same reason. Most likely each provided positive feedback for the other. Such positive feedback is suggested by the rapidity of brain growth during the late stages of evolution. The fact that the human has always been a social animal necessarily fueled the process. Community presupposes communication.

It may be that abstract reasoning (vs. that which is immediate and applied), first evolved among the Neanderthals about 100,000 years ago. This conjecture is based on the observation that they appear to have been the first to bury their dead with evidence of rituals. Lesser animals do not bury their dead simply because they have none of the abstract (second-order) concepts pertaining to life, death, after-life, religion, etc. Social insects remove the dead but do so unceremoniously to relieve the clutter, i.e., they are treated only as obstacles.

2. HÖLLDOBLER, B., Communication between ants and their guests. In: *Life at the Edge, Readings from Scientific American.*, J. J. Gould & C. G. Gould, eds. N.Y.: W. H. Freeman & Co., 1989, 111-121.

3. GABEL, N. W., Excitability and the origin of life: a hypothesis. *Life Sciences,* 1965, 4(21), 2085-2096; GOLDACRE, R. J. Surface films, their collapse on compression, the shapes and sizes of cells, and the origin of life. In: *Surface Phenomena in Chemistry and Bioloqy.,* J. F. Danielli, K. G. A. Pankhurst, & A. C. Riddiford, eds. N.Y.: Pergamon Press, 1958.

4. These oldest and simplest of multicellular assemblies are known as the Ediacaran fauna, named for the Australian site where they were discovered. They were soft-shelled marine creatures which, for the most part, looked like tapes, pancakes or films. The amount of internal mass was usually quite meagre. For a small and readable description, see the delightful book of essays by S. J. GOULD entitled *The Flaminqo's Smile.*, N.Y.: W. W. Norton & Co., 1989, 230-244.

It is now thought possible that these early pre-Cambrian structures were not multicellular at all, but rather, simply huge cells which had become compartmentalized, i.e., quilt-like. Discoveries comparable to the Ediacaran fossils have since been made in Mexico and Namibia. Read: MONASTERSKY, R., Living large on the Precambrian planet, *Science News.* 1996, 149, 20 (May 18), p. 308.

Whatever the case, it may be impossible to place any fixed date on the origins of multicellular life because there were no hard (bony or shell) structures to be left in the fossil record. Indeed, there are those who even deny that there was any Cambrian "explosion" -- that it was really a long drawn-out affair. See: ZIMMER, C., An explosion defused? *Discover,* 1996, 17, 12(Dec.), p. 52.

5. MARGULIS, L., *The Origins of Eukaryotic Cells.* New Haven, Conn.: Yale Univ. Press, 1970. For a brief popular synopsis of Margulis' work, see: McDERMOTT, J., A biologist whose heresy redraws earth's tree of life. *Smithsonian,*1989, 20, (Aug.), 72-80.

6. In addition to his professional credentials as a Yale professor of molecular biophysics and biochemistry, HAROLD MOROWITZ is a fascinating writer. See his *Mayonnaise and the Origin of Life.* N.Y.: Berkley Books, 1986, 117-121. Morowitz's question "Do bacteria think?" is not so facetious as might first appear. He notes that one-celled creatures are sensate, behave purposefully, and are constantly discriminating changes in their environments. Were they not unicellular this would be recognized as decision-making -- which involves thinking.

All purposeful behavior presupposes thinking because it requires the memory of a goal. Thinking is the association of memories. Bacteria pass DNA around quite freely, i.e., they are constantly producing new intermolecular memory relationships. Whether or not this is thinking is a matter of definition and viewpoint (theoretical bias). See: LOSICK, R., & KAISER, D., Why and how bacteria communicate, *Scientific American,* 1997, 276, 2 (Feb.), 6873.

7. Actually there is no such thing as a "being." There is only becoming. Whether alive or dead, organisms are a composite of processes. The "I" now writing this is not exactly the same "I" who came into the room awhile back, and even less the "I" of 20 years ago. The change is simply slow, and the person or thing is not noticeably different. Remember, we can perceive only *differences.*

8. SICKLES, W. R., & HARTMANN, G. W., The Theory of Order. *Psychol. Rev.,* 1942, 49(5), 403-421. (Figures 7 through 10, current text, are taken from this earlier publication.) The thesis was further extended by the senior author: IDEM., The psychogeometry of order. *Psychol. Rev.,* 1944, 51(3), 189-199.

9. SICKLES, W. R., Experimental evidence for the electrical character of visual fields derived from a quantitative analysis of the Ponze illusion. *Jour. Exper. Psychol.,* 1942, 30(1), 84-91. Reveals that the contours of a perceived figure create measurable field effects which extend over empty space to influence other items in the visual field. The effect is one of attraction. (See Figure 5 and discussion.)

10. LOVELOCK, J., *Gaia: a New Look at Life on Earth.,* N.Y.: Oxford

Univ. Press, 1979. This is a small book which is enthusiastic, well written, and covers the essential arguments for Gaia. It is highly recommended. IDEM., *The Ages of Gaia.*, N.Y.: W. W. Norton & Co., 1988. A larger and more complete volume, part of which unfortunately has to be devoted to countering numerous irrelevant charges of teleology, holism, religious intent, and similar philosophical vagaries.

Despite the controversy engendered by Lovelock's contention that the earth is a cognizant living organism, the idea is not new and really should not have created such a stir. It dates back at least to the ancient Greek. Part of the more recent history is given in the introduction to his later volume. One notable omission, however, was the name of Gustav T. Fechner (1801-1887) who held much the same views. Ref., EDWARDS, P., Editor in Chief., *The Encyclopedia of Philosophy.* N.Y.: Macmillan Inc., 1967, Vol. III, p. 184.

I have not examined all the books on the Gaia theme which have followed Lovelock. There have been many, and virtually all have supported his views. At last count, these would include SAHTOURIS, E. (Note # 12, below); ALLABY, M., *A Guide to Gaia.*, N.Y.: E. P. Dutton, 1989; JOSEPH, L. E., *Gaia, the Growth of an Idea.*, N.Y.: St. Martin's Press, 1990; and SAGAN, D., *Biospheres, Metamorphosis of Planet Earth.*, N.Y.: McGraw Hill Publ., 1990.

11. Articles and reviews on the Gaia thesis are both pro and con, and are much too numerous to cite here. A typical example of the con variety, charging Lovelock with teleology, holism, and "religious undertones," is HORSFALL, J., The highjack of reason? This originally appeared in *The Guardian* of London and was extracted and reported in *World Press Review*, 1990, 37(8), 20.

12. SAHTOURIS, E., *Gaia: The Human Journey from Chaos to Cosmos.*, N.Y.: Pocket Books, 1989. A delightfully written little volume which is aimed at public consumption and therefore somewhat less rigorous than many. It has one rather amusing feature in that it is noticeably feminist in tenor. This is excusable. After all, one doesn't encounter Greek goddesses too often.

13. Since a goodly portion of the general public, as well as many theologians, equate mind with soul, the idea that the entire universe could be "mind stuff," should have had serious repercussions for them.

It should be mentioned that the idea is not unique to the physicists cited earlier, viz., Jeans, Eddington, and Schrödinger. Many others have come to the same conclusion, including famous names from such diverse fields as biology, astronomy, physics, and philosophy. Indeed, the idea itself comes perilously close, and perhaps coincides with one of the basic tenets of Buddhism. Refer to SUZUKI, D. T., *Zen Buddhism*, ed. by W. Barrett. N.Y.: Doubleday Anchor Bks., 1956.

In my own opinion, it doesn't matter what you call it. Names are mere words. When the entire universe is reduced to one common denominator, or a single substance, there are no longer any distinguishing differences. If the whole world were red, the color red would not exist. So it doesn't matter whether it is labeled mind, matter, or whipped cream. What is the difference between "everything is mind," "everything is matter," or "everything is God"? One may as well say "everything is X." Things exist only by reason of their *differences* -- this is why we can only see differences! This elementary fact seems to have escaped those zealots who would equalize all people, wealth, or whatever. Equal people are dead people.

14. LOVELOCK, J., *The Ages of Gaia..,* N.Y.: W. W. Norton & Co., 1988, Table 1.1, p. 9, & p. 73.

15. IDEM., *Gala: A New Look at Life on Earth.,* N.Y.: Oxford Univ. Press, 1979, p. 92.

16. Numerous writers have described a system as "any arbitrary collection of variables." So far as I know, W. R. ASHBY was the first to take exception to this. In his *Design for a Brain* (N.Y.: John Wiley & Sons, 1952), he noted that such definitions are actually non-definitions. On page 23 he remarked that both science and common sense require that the variables have a "naturalness of association." And on p. 53 he further observed that even the simplest inorganic systems exhibit "goal-seeking behavior," i.e., they are teleological.

17. CANNON, W. B., *The Wisdom of the Body.,* N.Y.: W. W. Norton, 1939. This is the classical work on homeostasis. It should be required reading for everybody in the life sciences.

18. Von BERTALANFFY, L., The theory of open systems in physics and biology., *Science.,* 1950, 111, 23-29.

19. MACH, E., *The Science of Mechanics, 2nd ed.,* trans. by T. J. McCormack. Chicago: Open Court Publ. Co., 1893. Mach observed that systems left to themselves will tend toward orderliness of form and function. But the idea was not elaborated upon, and thus was largely overlooked. The intellectual pièce de résistance of the period was the ill-conceived concept of entropy. As defined by Boltzmann (1844-1906), this led to opposite conclusions. However, Mach is properly considered one of the god-fathers of Gestalt psychology. Köhler picked up where Mach left off. His primary work on the issue still remains untranslated. Ref. KÖHLER, W., *Die physischen Gestalten in Ruhe und im stationären Zustand, Eine naturphilosophische Untersuchung.,* Erlagen: Braunschweig, 1920. Rather extensive excerpts, in English, may be found in: ELLIS, W. D., *A Source Book of Gestalt Psychology.,* London: Routledge & Kegan Paul, 1938, 17-54.

20. LOVELOCK, J. (See Note # 14, above, p.45)

21. IDEM. (See Note # 15, above, p.146)

22. SAHTOURIS, E. (See Note # 12, above.)

23. Over the years there have been numerous experiments establishing that, for lesser animals at least, overcrowding causes a breakdown of normal social behavior. This occurs despite its instinctive basis, and even though all other factors (e.g., nutrition) are held constant. Two classical experiments, one dealing with lab rats, another with baboons, are nicely summarized by SAGAN, C., & DRUYAN, A., *Shadows of Forgotten Ancestors,* N.Y.: Ballantine Bks., 1992, pp. 184 and 324.

As for our own species, I have heard it stated that overpopulation is now at a point where the dead are a minority -- that there are more people currently alive than have ever lived during all history. If true, this is scary because there must be limits to growth -- no matter what is growing.

24. This microbe is named *Methanohalophilus oregonense* (the salt-loving methanogen from Oregon). It was discovered in a toxic waste-dump. Ref., *Internat. Jour. Systematic Bacteriol.,* 1990, 4, 111-116.

An Assoc. Press release, dtd. 1 May '92, reports another instance, this time a bacterium which "eats" chlorofluorocarbons. These pollutants (CFC's) are the principle threat to the ozone layer. The bacterium is currently under study by the U.S. Geolog. Survey. There is even one particularly hardy (explosive?) species which makes a business of converting uranium! Ref., *Science News,* 1992, 142, 7(Aug. 15th), p.107.

25. I confess that this is a highly simplified (and therefore somewhat mis-leading) portrayal of reductionism. It was purposefully exaggerated in order to make the difference between it and the systems approach more readily understandable. In actual practice both procedures are necessary for success. However, to speak of reductionism as a "tinkertoy" outlook is not name-calling. It is simply descriptive. One need only look through any scientific magazine (say *Scientific American*) to find molecular interactions always illustrated as the fitting together of jigsaw puzzle pieces.

In the social sciences, and particularly behaviorism, it is not at all uncommon to find statistical data collected with the hope of later formulating an hypothesis to explain the rationale behind any results which emerge. This carries reductionism to the extreme, with no whole envisioned and emphasis only on particulars! Though theory is necessary to make data meaningful (provide a context), it is often held in low regard. The late B. F. SKINNER even wrote an article asking "Are learning theories necessary?" *Psychol. Rev.*, 1950, 57, 193-216. He insisted that explanation is merely description: IDEM., The concept of the reflex in the description of behavior., *Jour. Gen. Psychol.,* 1931, 5, 445-454. This "conditioned reflex" is the most famous of all the units proposed by those who try to explain the mind as an assemblage of parts. A good runner-up today is the synapse. This is easier to identify.

26. The study referenced was performed at Washington College, Md., by MARY BAENNINGER and DIANA ZARING. They used a series of photos of people's faces previously selected as "look-alikes." Twenty judges rated the faces on overall similarity. Sixteen different facial features (e.g., ears, eyes, nose, etc.) were then rated separately as to their similarity. No relation could be found between the way the features were rated and the ratings for the faces. In other words, the wholes were similar but the parts were not! (Ref: Accustomed to your face, in "Up Front." *Discover*, 1990, 11(8), p.14.)

The basic issue exemplified by this study, as well as the polygons of Figure 12, is the primacy of *form* or pattern perception. That is to say, no perceived form can be meaningfully reduced to parts. This is a Gestalt thesis vehemently denounced by all the prevailing reductionist theories of psychology.

27. Largely through the efforts of STUART SCHREIBER (Harvard) and JERRY CRABTREE (Stanford) there is now little question about the existence of distal molecular resonance effects. The process has been called "dimerizing," or more to the point, "proximity effects." The above researchers have been able to manipulate these, and thus alter communications within and between cells. Though this work does not result in any decoding of the cell's chemical language, it does open up many possibilities for taking corrective action against various medical disorders. Refer to: TAUBES, G., Conversations in a cell, *Discover,*1996, 17, 2(Feb.), 49-54.

28. W. D. Hamilton was probably first to note that altruism among animals is closely correlated with kinship or genetic relatedness. Details of his theory and related studies are nicely synopsized by DAWKINS, R., *The Selfish Gene.*, Oxford: Oxford Univ. Press, 1976. As Dawkins sees it, this means that an animal's genes tend to preserve their own survival. Genes are shared by immediate relatives. So in essence, when an animal is helping relatives, his genes are furthering themselves. This fractionates the organism into the smallest possible units, and perhaps even attributes foresight or intelligence to them. Unfortunately, the gene is not a viable entity -- if, indeed, it can be said to be an entity.

The position taken here is compatible with Hamilton. It states that animals perceive forms, organization, or patterning *directly*. Therefore they also perceive similarity (likeness or approximate match) of such patterning, and especially similarity of smell or stereochemical patterning. This is the major determinant of all social relating among animals. It is a recognition function of the brain/mind and depends upon the similarity (structural "fit") of the sensory input with the respective memory.

Among advanced species, and particularly humans, it extends to other types of similarity well beyond simple appearance or smell. For example, friends almost always share much the same belief systems -- meaning that large portions of their mental structures are similar. For spouses, correlations of resemblance for religion and politics are usually twice as great as those for physical traits. (Smell is seldom measured!) This issue has been reviewed for the popular press by DIAMOND, J., I want a girl just like the girl. . ., *Discover*, 1986, 7(11), 65-68. Reference also: (Note # 28, Sect. II: How it all Began), and accompanying text on identical twins. These have maximal similarity.

I am *not* placing undue emphasis upon things, living or otherwise, being of *like kind.* It is not something superficial which one can be "educated out of." It is part of the way the world acts. Whether it be people, planks or bricks -- they must be of like kind. Otherwise, they cannot fit together harmoniously to form anything greater. Life is a formative process as well as a cooperative socializing process. To say that it can be constructed of dissimilar and discontinuous bric-a-brac is obvious nonsense.

Likeness of patterning (the need for like-kind) underlies all life and culture. For animals the young must smell like the parents. For humans they must resemble their forebears. For the culture behavior must fit the mores -- just as the cheque must fit the debt or the brakes fit the car. This mutual harmony of things and events might be described as synchronization -- another way of saying they must be organized (have *mind,* be rational or sane). Without it music becomes noise, art becomes clutter, and predictability disappears from the environment.

29. Because mental growth is due to relating activity of the mind, and people are the most important objects with which to relate, everyone has a need to belong within some social context however small. It is essential to survival during early years, and later provides a feeling of security and self-worth. This I call belongingness or togetherness (*Zusammengehörigkeitsgefühl*). No species can or does evolve by itself, no child can survive by itself, and no man is an island unto himself. All evince evidence of the fundmental relatedness of life. (see: ALLEN, S., The wish to belong., *Bull. Menninqer Clin.*, 1940, 4, 74-81.

Loneliness is the recognized absence of the above social context. As context is lost, one's individuality also tends to disappear. There is no figure-ground effect. It is not merely a question of the absence or presence of people, but the absence of anyone with whom to *relate.* For a stranger, crowded New York City can be a frighteningly lonely place. Loneliness particularly afflicts the elderly. Perhaps it is part of that slow disconnection from life. Isolation of mice and monkeys at least, produces biochemical changes in addition to those in behavior. TROTTER, R. J., The biological depths of loneliness., *Science News.*, 1973, 103, 3 Mar., 140-142.

Associated with the foregoing is another destructive anti-biological influence which afflicts today's culture and largely goes unrecognized. It might be called "dis-enfranchisement." All creatures (possibly even plants) are territorial. Even the most mild-mannered animal defends its territory. Children prefer to live in areas where they spent their teenage years, and when gathered in gangs they fight for "turf." Almost everyone has a feeling of belongingness for some spot of earth he calls home. Modern society militates against this. Families are often on the move job-wise, and their children feel homeless.

30. Refer to Figure 4 and accompanying discussion for an example how the law of proximity tends to organize and provide form to what is seen.

31. The "growth curve" of evolution may also be the same. All organisms, as well as their social bodies, have growth curves which are sigmoidal, an "S" shape skewed to the right. STEPHEN J. GOULD, perhaps our most ardent and vocal advocate of Darwinism, states his conviction that evolution follows this same curve, and that the area of steep acceleration corresponds to the Cambrian explosion. Though this implies that evolution depicts somethinq growing, it is very doubtful if he would identify it as a biospheric organism, or even a closely knit (mutually self-supportive) social soma. (See essay # 15 in his *Ever Since Darwin*. N.Y.: W. W. Norton, 1973.)

32. For example, RENE DUBOS, On environment. In: *Dictionary of the History of Ideas.*, P. P. Wiener, ed. N.Y.: Charles Scribner's Sons, 1973, Vol. II, p. 121. Also: SAHTOURIS, E., Note # 12, above, p. 91.

33. HO, M. W. & SAUNDERS, P T., eds., *Beyond Neo-Darwinism: An Introduction to the New Evolutionary Paradigm.*, London: Academic Press, 1984; IDEM., A new paradigm for evolution., *New Scientist* 1986, 27 Feb.

Studies indicate there may well be feedback loops from the environment back to the DNA. In my opinion, it seems likely there would have been numerous interlocking feedback loops operating in any ecosystem. Analysis of such issues would now be impossible. In fact, even defining one of our present-day ecosystems is extremely difficult. There are few if any clear-cut boundaries. They interlock and overlap. In a very real sense, the human himself is an ecosystem. As a society of cells he is "international" in character. No matter how neat and clean he may be, there are possibly as many wee beasties residing within and upon him as there are cells. These include viruses, protozoa, bacteria, yeasts and fungae.

34. For a brief popular account of Biosphere II: ANSLEY, D., The new world. *Discover*, 1990, 11, 9(Sept.), 60-69. A brief summary of some of the problems encountered by Biosphere II, as well as the present status of the project, are to be found in *Scientific American,* 1995, 273, 2(Aug.), pp. 24-26; and *Science News,*1996, 150, 20(Nov. 16), 312-313.

35. Like most such publications, the *Kachiron* of MAKIGUCHI has not been translated into English. It was carefully edited after his death by Joei Toda. However, up to the end of the chapter entitled "what is religious value," it is pure Makiguchi. From there on, Toda has interspersed his own fervent belief in Nichiren Sho Buddhism. There is a sect in presentday Japan called Soka Gakkai, or "The Society for Creation of Value." But the degree to which it is Nichiren Sho is unknown to this writer.

VI. THE MECHANISM OF MIND

1. LOEB, J. Reference Note # 16, Sect. II for the works of Loeb.

2. For a brief but excellent coverage of chemical communications among animals, see WILSON, E. O., *Sociobiology: The New Synthesis.* Cambridge, Mass.: Harvard Univ. Press, 1975; IDEM., Pheromones, *Scientific American,* 1963, 208 (5), 100-114. For a review of the role of pheromones in behavior: GLEASON, K. K. & REYNIERSE, J. H., The behavioral significance of pheromones in vertibrates. *Psychol.Bull.,* 1969, 71(1), 58-73.

Recent popular reports on human sexual pheromones include: COMFORT, A., The likelihood of human pheromones., *Nature,* 1971, 230, 432-433; WINTER, R., & McAULIFF, K., Hooked on love., *Omni,* 1984, 6(8), 80; and MONMANEY, T., Are we led by the nose? *Discover,* 1987, 8(9), 48-56. It has even been suggested that sexual compatibility might be detectible from pheromones -- thus leading to lower divorce rates.

It is now thought that the genetic source of the human's sexual pheromones, and possibly the unique identifying body odor detected say, by bloodhounds, derives from the HMC genes (Major histocompatibility complex). These are the most structurally diverse of all genes. See: RICHARDSON, S., Scent of man, *Discover,* 1996, 17, 2(Feb.), 26-27. The olfactory sense which detects pheromones is believed to be the vomeronasal organ (described by WRIGHT, K., The sniff of legend, *Discover,* 1994, 15, 4(Apr.), pp. 60-67.

3. Refer to Note # 59, Sect. II "How it all Began."

4. Literature accumulated on this subject is too massive to cite. Bibliography may be readily obtained from any modern text on ethology or instinctive animal behavior. A selection of the classical writings would include: BAERENDS, G. P., Specialization in organs and movements with a releasing function. In: *Symposia Soc. Exper. Biol., IV: Physiological Mechanisms in Animal Behavior.,* N.Y.: Cambridge Univ. Press, 1950, 337-360; LORENZ, K. Z., The cooperative method in studying innate behavior patterns., IBID.,221-268; BIERENS DE HAAN, J. A., *Die tierischen Instinkte und ihr Umbau durch Erfahrung.,* Leiden: E. J. Brill, 1940; and TINBERGEN, N., *The Study of Instinct.,* London: Oxford Univ. Press, 1951.

5. Again, a prohibitively large literature. See reference Note # 13, Sect. II "How it all Began," and attendant text for learning in protozoa. As for learning in earthworms, planaria, etc., and the role played by RNA, there is now general consensus. JACOBSON, A. L., provided 74 references on this aspect of the subject as of thirty years ago: Learning in flatworms and annelids., *Psychol. Bull.,* 1963, 60, 74-79. Also: GLASSMAN, E., *Molecular Approaches to Psychobiology.,* Belmont, Calif.: Dickenson Publ. Co., 1967. Currently, the issue seems to be on a back burner.

6. .Refer to Notes 12 through 15, Sect. I. "Mind/Body Relation" plus text for discussion of these immunological links. Until quite recently most all such functions were believed completely automated, under control of the autonomic nervous system, and beyond personal influence. Discovery that they were *not* has given rise to the new medical discipline of psychoneuroimmunology.

7. WEISS, P., TAYLOR, A. C., & PILLAI, P. A., The nerve fiber as a system in continuous flow: Microcinematographic and electronmicroscopic demonstrations. (paper presented before the annual meeting of the National Academy of Sciences, Washington, D.C.: 23-25 April, 1962). Abstracted by *Science.*, 1962, 136, 330; WEISS, P., & HISCOE, H. B., Experiments on the mechanism of nerve growth. *Jour. Exper. Zool.*, 1948, 107, 315-395; WEISS, P., *Chemistry and Physiology of Growth.*, Princeton, N.J.: Princeton Univ. Press, 1949; IDEM., Discussion following a paper presented by Ward C. Halstead in: *Cerebral Mechanisms in Behavior*, L. A. Jeffress, ed., N.Y.: John Wiley & Sons, 1951, p. 281; MARKS, N., Some neurochemical correlates of axoplasmic flow., *Diseases of Nerv. Syst.*, 1970, 3(11), *Suppl.* 5-13.

8. FRANCOIS, M., Sur l'influence de la température interne sur notre appréciation du temps., Paris: *C. R. Soc. Biol.*, 1928, 98, 152; IDEM.,Contribution à l'étude du sens du temps. La témperature interne comme facteur de variation de l'appréciation subjectives des durées., *Année Psychol.*, 1928, 28, 186.

9. HOAGLAND, H., The physiological control of judgements of duration: evidence for a chemical clock., *Jour. gen. Psychol.*, 1933, 9, 267-287; IDEM., *Pacemakers in Relation to Aspects of Behavior.*, N.Y.: Macmillan Co., 1935; IDEM., The chemistry of time., *Sci. Mon. N.Y.*, 1943, 56, 56.

10. Chemical theories of brain activity are not new. As early as 1874, T. H. Huxley was playing around with the thought that all living things were carbon structures, and essentially automata. Different states of consciousness were considered most likely to be matters of "molecular changes of the brain substance." HUXLEY, T. H., On the hypothesis that animals are automata, and its history. In: *Collected Essays, Vol. I.*, London: Macmillan, 1901, p. 243.
 Perhaps the latest to support chemical theories of CNS functioning has been neurosurgeon RICHARD BERGLAND, *Fabric of the Mind.*, N.Y.: Viking Press, 1985. His opening statement declares there is little doubt that the brain is a gland. And on p. 109 he goes so far as to point out that the underlying theme of all organic processes is *pattern recognition!* This is said to start at the molecular level and continue to become "the highest form of thought." (Chalk one up for

Bergland!!)

SEMON, R., *The Meme.*, N.Y.: Allen & Unwin, 1921. Defined memories as enduring changes in the "nuclear material of the cell." These were said to be "related to the original much as a reproduction of a picture relates to its original."

MONNÉ, L., Functioning of the cytoplasm, VIII., In: *Advances in Enzymology.*, N.Y.: Interscience Press, 1948, 1-69. Stated his belief that "synthesis of specific proteins is the essential physical phenomenon paralleling memory, fantasy and intuition." Cells were said to be able to synthesize the proteins necessary to represent new percepts and ideas.

Von FÖRSTER, H., *Das Gedächtnis: eine quantenphysikalische Untersuchung.*, Vienna: Franz Deuticke, 1948. IDEM., *Transact. of 6th Conf. on Cybernetics.*, N.Y.: Josiah Macy Jr. Found., 1950. Posited a quantum theory of memory which described memories as large aperiodic molecular structures similar to the DNA. Recognition occurred by resonance and raised the quantum level of memory, thus accounting for the facilitating effects of practice.

KATZ, J. J., & HALSTEAD, W. C., Protein organization and mental function., *Comp. Psychol. Monogr,* 1950, 20, 1-38. Suggested that the shape specificity of protein synthesis could explain sensory input details. Conduction retained this patterning and took place via a traveling wave of denaturation/renaturation (thixotropy) in the axoplasm. Memories were seen to be configured space-lattices of protein most likely located in the cortical neuron's cellular walls. However, the memory pattern was not isotropic with that of the retinal image as in the case of Semon, above. It was "coded."

Starting with a series of publications between 1961 and 1967, by HOLGER HYDÉN, Univ. of Göteborg, there has been a huge variety of experimental work relating RNA to memory. These now number well over fifty.

11. The issue of similarity is immensely important because it is *comparative patterning.* As in the case of form itself, similarity evades all efforts at analysis, measurement, or even definition in reductionistic terms. The absence of such features means that it has been largely ignored by psychologists -- despite the fact that it has been shown to be critical for recognition. Degree of similarity determines how well the sensory input pattern matches (resonates with) the memory pattern. It is the only known means by which memories could be referenced in terms of *content.* Addressing memory by means of location (as in computers) has been demonstrated to be unfeasible because of the jumbled neural architecture.

The influence of similarity on processes of recall is illustrated by what psychologists describe as "retroactive inhibition." Suppose the learning of task "A" is followed by the learning of task "B." Subsequent recall of "A" will depend upon its similarity to "B." If the two tasks are much alike, they become confused. If totally different there is little or no confusion. Such similarity has been shown to be unrelated to the number of "parts" the tasks have in common.

In addition, similarity is responsible for generalization. "Why is that a dog? Because it looks *like* a dog and it sounds *like* a dog!" Probably all animals are capable of mental classifications of this sort. Sensory inputs give rise to conceptual genotypes whose parameters are determined by within-class similarity. In a very real sense, therefore, similarity of patterning constitutes the mechanism underlying mental organization -- the means by which psychological data become classified and related.

The synchronization of many processes might be described as essentially a matching of this wave pattern with that wave pattern on the basis of their congruency. Such matching underlies the structure of musical patterning, the significance of octaves and harmonics, and possibly explains why the auditory sense is able to perform a Fourier analysis on complex sound patterns.

Perhaps the most compelling instances of input matching by similarity occurs with the fusion (resonance) of the disparate images from the two eyes during stereoscopic vision, or the comparable fusion of disparate auditory inputs from the two ears.

For further aspects of similarity in visual processes, see ATTNEAVE, F., Dimensions of similarity. *Amer. Jour. Psychol.*, 1950, 63, 516-556.

12. Visual acuity varies with the method of measurement as well as other conditions. Using alignment of dots, it was found that resolution reached a minimum of 2 seconds of arc, or about 1/10th the diameter of a single retinal cone. (LUDVIGH, E., Direction sense of the eye., *Amer. Jour. Ophthalmol.*, 1953, 36, 139-143.) When using alignment of straight lines, minimum resolution was also found to be 2" of arc, but stated to be 1/30th of a cone cell diameter. This is not inconsistent. Cone cells vary in diameter. (PLATT, J. R., How we see straight lines., *Scientific American*, 1960, 202, 121-129.) It is interesting to note an accompanying comment by Platt to the effect that we don't see objects, but *relationships!* (Chalk one up for Platt!)

Two seconds of arc subtends a retinal distance of about .0001 mm., or 0.1 microns! This places visual resolution well into the size range of large organic molecules. For instance, molecular DNA in solution has been estimated to have volumes 5 times that size, or 0.5 microns! Memory molecules could be even larger. These have been estimated to have possible mean molecular weights of 20 million or more, and average diameters as large as 10 microns! See an early work by DOTY, P., Configurations of biologically important macromolecules in solution. *Reviews of Modern* Physics, 1959, 31, 107-117.

13. For many years it was assumed that intermolecular forces are of very brief range, e.g., about 10^{-5} mm. Acting en masse, of course, these have rather extensive effects as seen in surface tension. However, such limited scope of activity left many phenomena unexplained. Fortunately, it was later discovered that these molecular interactions were much more extensive than originally thought. (LONDON, F., On centers of Van der Waals attraction., *Jour. Phys. Chem.*, 1942, 46, 305-316; ROTHEN, A., Long range enzymatic action on films of antigen. *Jour. Amer. Chem. Soc.*, 1948, 70, 2732-2740; DZYALOSHINSKII, I. E., et al., General theory of Van der Waals forces., *Soviet Physics USPEKHI*, 1961, 4, 153-176. N.Y.: Amer. Inst. of Physics, Inc.)

Highly colored molecules can produce particularly strong London -Van der

Waals effects -- as borne out by the behavior of certain dye stuffs. In consonance with this it is noteworthy that both the retina and olfactory epithelium are pigmented. Both contain light-sensitive vitamin A. A London - Van der Waals theory of how the sense of smell works was proposed thirty years ago by DRAVNIEKS, A., Possible mechanism of olfaction., *Nature*, 1962, 194, 245-247.

With respect to the retina, I strongly suspect that these attractional force fields are even more extensive than suggested by existing theory, possibly reaching a range of 1.2 mm. (1200 microns), the approximate distance subtended by 4° of retinal arc. Reasons for this suggestion: one contour in the visual field will inhibit formation of another within 4°; apparent motion (the phi phenomenon) cannot be obtained beyond 4.5°; binocular fusion becomes affected beyond 4°; spiral after-effects, retinal spatial summation and certain illusions all undergo change at approximately this distance. Such curiosa were noted 40 years ago by OSGOOD, C. E., *Methods and Theory in Experimental Psvcholoqy.* N.Y.: Oxford Univ. Press, 1953.

In brief, 4° of arc seems to be a limiting value which pops up in all manner of visual phenomena. Since mutual attraction would commonly occur between masses of molecules, it may be that this apparently large distance represents some sort of maximal "clumping" or overall limit to molecular (liquid crystalline) aggregation. See note # 14, below, on "swarming effects" observed in liquid crystals.

14. Liquid crystals (aka paracrystals) have largely disappeared from publications in the biological sciences. This does not mean they have been shown not to exist. Rather, interest has been merely eclipsed by current theoretical trends. It has been known for many decades that a variety of such microstructural conditions prevail in the CNS. For example, lipids, cerebrosides, and phosphatides have been so identified. It has even been stated that with cerebron genuine crystals are found which pass over into a paracrystalline phase. See the early publication by RINNE, F., Investigations and considerations concerning paracrystallinity., *Faraday Soc. Sympos. on Liquid Crystals and Anisotropic Melts.*, London: Faraday Society, 1933, 1016-1032.

BONNER, J. T., discusses liquid crystals in his book *Morphogenesis,* Princeton, N.J.: Princeton Univ. Press, 1952, p. 45 ff. But the latest publications I have are: FERGASON, J. I., Liquid crystals., *Scientific American.*, 1964, 211(2), 77-85; and GRAY, G. W., *Molecular Structure and the Properties of Liquid Crystals.*, N.Y.: Academic Press, 1962. This latter is particularly recommended.

Liquid crystals are uniquely adapted to living structures because they represent an intermediate state between solid and liquid. They provide some structural stability without the usual accompanying rigidity. A few of the many properties making them important for biological processes, and listed by Gray (above), are repeated here. (1) Ability to change orientation in an electric field. Particles can turn through 180° rotation, with full reversal of polarity, in as little as 1/300,000th of a second. (2) Swarming and other mass orienting behavior. (3) Marked and rather abrupt changes in viscosity accompanying changes of internal organization. (4) Unique and specific reactions to different energies, e.g., changes in the proton magnetic resonance signal. (5) Sensitivity to temperature differences. (6) The highly polarizeable nature of both the molecules and their swarms.

Clues to their possible involvement in CNS operations are suggested by changes in viscosity (item # 3, above). Both here and in Russia, experiments have shown that axoplasm exhibits marked viscosity changes, swelling, stickiness, and light diffraction alterations under conditions of excitation. Refer to: TOBIAS, J. M., Further studies on the nature of the excitable system in nerves., *Jour. Gen. Physiol.*, 1960, 43, (May Suppl.), 57-71; and LIUDKOVSKAIA, R. G., Some structural and chemical phenomena in the stimulated neuron., *Biofizika*, 1957, 2, 589-601.

The destructive effects of ultrasound on nerves may also be significant. It produces irreversible damage with loss of function. This is said to be selective, specific, and suggests vibration which breaks up molecular structures within certain size ranges. See: FRY, W. J., Action of ultrasound on nerve tissue -- a review., *Jour. Acoust. Soc. Amer.*, 1953, 25, 1-5.

15. It is in the white fatty material of the CNS that a most surprising regularity of paracrystalline microstructure is found. It is intricate, exact, and appears quite similar to that of the retinal rods and cones, the Golgi apparatus, or the mitochondria. This suggests that it may be somehow involved with storage or transfer of energy, possibly possesses some of the properties of semiconductors, or may even act as a condenser. One cannot help wondering why theorists have not given it some meaningful role. Nature is usually quite frugal in her engineering efforts, and if myelin is no more than insulation this is the most remarkable case of over-engineering in all biology!

The sequence of myelinization in the CNS of the developing baby is the same as in the evolution of the CNS itself. (a) More primitive structures such as brain stem and cord acquire myelin prior to more recent areas like the cortex. (b) Neural tissues related to the same *functional* systems myelinate at about the same time. (c) Acquisition of myelin does not occur significantly without sensory stimulation. (d) Sensory neurons and sensory areas of the cortex develop myelin early, and much of it. Whereas, those associated with muscular activity develop myelin late, and less of it. (e) The optic tract starts myelinating rapidly at birth and is virtually complete by the end of the 2nd month. (f) Numerous experiments establish that the process depends upon visual input. Such being the case, it *has* to be related to sensory functioning in some unknown manner.

16. Like liquid crystals and myelin, the structural implications of phosphenes have also been disregarded. They are provocative in that almost everything else about the CNS is highly irregular, twisting, and appears to be branching results of growth. This is particularly true of the brain. Nonetheless, we use these irregular structures to perceive and imagine constructs which are extremely accurate. Such accurate perceptual phenomena have to occur somewhere, somehow, in this jumbled tissue. To say they are "coded" not only dodges the issue, it confuses it to a point where some sort of supernatural entity must be invoked.

Because phosphenes bear no resemblance to any neural structures, appear only when we disrupt the normal status of the eye, and are so geometric, they strongly suggest that their perception may be brought about by liquid crystalline reorientations in the microstructure of protoplasm itself. Representative literature on the phenomenal aspects of phosphenes: WOLFF, J. C., et al., The patterns seen when alternating current is passed through the eye., *Quart. Jour. Exper. Psychol.*, 1968, 20(1), 1-10; KNOLL, M., Anregung geometrischer Figuren und anderer subjektiver Lichtmuster in elektrischen Feldern., *Schweiz. Zeitschr. Psychol. Anwend.*, 1958, 17, 110-126; CLAUSEN, J., *Visual Sensations (Phosphenes) produced by AC Sine Wave Stimulation.*, Copenhagen: Ejnar Munksgaard, 1955. (102 item bibliography); BARLOW, H. B., et al., Visual sensations aroused by magnetic fields., *Amer. Jour. Physiol.*, 1947, 148, 372-375; GOLDSCHMIDT, R. H., Beobachtungen über exemplarische subjektive optische Phänomene., *Zeitschr. f. Psychol.*, 1916, 76, 289-436.

17. SJÖSTRAND, F. S., The molecular structure of membranes., In: *The Future of the Brain Sciences.*, S. Bogoch, ed. N.Y.: Plenum Press, 1969, 117-157. Reports experiments performed on retinal tissue using an electron microscope. Changes in molecular configuration were said to occur with stimulation.

A PR from AT&T Bell Labs, dtd. 5/6/'88, reported extremely rapid molecular rotation in rhodopsin (a light-sensitive retinal component) with excitation. This was said to produce a chain reaction within a few thousandths of a second. (See popular announcement in *Science Digest*, 1988, Dec., 33-34.) I have been unsuccessful in obtaining any follow-up on this.

Since that time, investigation has proliferated rapidly. *Science.* Oct. 18th, 1991, as well as *Proceedings, Nat'l. Acad. Sciences.*, Nov. 1, 1991, carry research reports indicating that a chemical bond in the rhodopsin molecule changes orientation in about 200 femtoseconds when activated by laser light. For other related work see *Discover.*, 1991, Nov., pp. 67-72.

18. Reference is made to Notes # 19 and 20, Sect. II (How it all Began), plus accompanying text. For an interesting popular article, see: ANGIER, N. A., A stupid cell with all the answers., *Discover*, 1986, 7(11), 70-83.

WEISS, P., Interactions between cells., *Reviews of Modern Physics*, 1959, 31, 449-454., was early to point out that cells seem to find their way to their proper destinations even when deprived of their customary routes. Developing nerve cells are particularly able to recognize each other as well as their surrounds.

In the past there have been several reports of exotic long range energies operating in the CNS. Most notable of these, perhaps, was GURWITSCH, A. G., *Mitogenetic Analysis of the Nervous System.*, Amsterdam: N. V. Noord-Hollandsche Uitgeversmaatschappij, 1937. The energy was presumably radiation. Though seemingly far-fetched, this should not be dismissed out-of-hand. Bioluminescent radiation at least, is quite common among lesser creatures.

A more recent suggestion was made by JACQUES BENVENISTE, director of the immunopharmacology unit at INSERM (French Nat'l. Inst. Health and Med. Res., Paris). He noted what appeared to be long range conduction and retention of information at the molecular level. The medium was water, and the energy was said to be electromagnetic. For a popular report on Benveniste's work, see: LAWREN, W., The case of the ghost molecules. *Omni.*, 1992, 14(9), p. 51ff. Benveniste, like Gurwitsch before him, has met with resounding ridicule from the orthodox establishment. But whether justified or not, there are many instances of what appear to be longer range cellular interactions. These suggest some sort of currently unknown (and more extensive) information conduction in the system. Considering our almost total absence of any knowledge about what is occurring, it behooves us not to suppress efforts along these lines, no matter how ridiculous they may seem to us. As it stands, it is almost worth one's professional life to pursue such matters -- shades of the Inquisition!

19. In addition to the chemical gradient hypothesis, it now seems there is also the possibility of a rapid "chemical wave." Cf.: KAAISER, J., Pathfinding made easier by chemical waves, *Science News*, 1995, 147, 6(Feb. 11), 84-85.

20. Refer to Figures 4 and 5 for illustrations of the effects of energy fields inside and outside figural contours respectively. For an explanation of how the same attractional forces bring about depth perception during the fusion of disparate retinal images, see: LINSCHOTEN, J., *Strukturanalyse der binokularen Tiefen-wahrnemung: Eine experimentelle Untersuchung.*, Groningen, Netherlands: J. B. Wolters, 1956.

21. Disparate imges, being slightly different shapes, create molecular-level field effects when superimposed, i.e., when they resonate. It is noteworthy that exactly the same thing happens with molecular differences sensed by the two prongs of the snake's forked tongue! These carry molecular shape signals to theJacobson's organs (vomeronasal bodies) in the roof of the mouth, thence to the brain's olfactory lobes -- though not to the same areas fed by the nose. Here intensity differences between the separate sensory configurations provide the snake with something very comparable to stereo vision, thereby enabling it to track prey, females, and other items of interest. See: SCHWENK, K., The serpent's tongue, *Natural History*, 1995, 104, 4(Apr.), 48-55. *Please note that this is an exact analogue of what is proposed here for vision -- also an ancient pigmented sense.*

22. Both time and growth are unidirectional and irreversible. This suggests that time is our awareness of change. Any other view quickly becomes paradoxical. For example, suppose some "real" time existed in the external world, i.e., some one-way continuum which was objective and independent of both clocks and observers. Since every past is the future of everything preceding it, past and future would have to co-exist. Time would then become everywhere static and eternal. And since all events occur in time and involve motion, change would become impossible.

Though time is said to have only one direction (forward or ahead), it is actually we who look forward to the future or backwards to the past. Both are mentalisms as shown by the fact that they are not the same for everyone. Change has no direction except as you observe it. What is approaching one may be receding from another. Because all judgment is egocentric, each of us is a sort of hyphen floating on a surface which shifts from past to future. The direction taken is that of least resistance (2nd law of thermo -- Tao!) There is no overall direction. Only you have a past and future -- and then only with reference to you. History is the memory of an overmind.

23. In relativity theory, time may be measured as a fourth dimension of space. However, it is conceded that this fourth coordinate (t) must be given the imaginary magnitude of the square root of -1 multiplied by the speed of light. Thus, the time taken by any event becomes an imaginary measure relative to the speed of light. Though such treatment greatly facilitates calculation, the fact that it is imaginary (and violates basic mathematical logic), puts it in the realm of *noumena* -- however physical it might also be. Time does not move forward. It is we who move internally, and our awareness of the rate of motion is what we call time.

Thus, the reason we cannot directly experience time is simple enough. It doesn't exist. What we experience is change, or the effect of process. And even this is only in terms of a difference between NOW and memory of a then. From these differences we infer the passage of something we call time. Time is a continuum because change is a continuumm. To measure either we must cut time into pieces of like kind, else we have no yardstick. Such pieces are arbitrary, superficial, and do not characterize the outer world. The earth does not stop in its spinning that we may reckon year, hour, or nanosecond. Again, we make "things" out of no-things by fractionating event-continua into objects and pieces.

24. In a series of very important articles between 1928 and 1931, J. F. BROWN presented results from several ingenious experiments. These conclusively proved that visually perceived events, involving motion, space, and time, followed the classical relationship in the equation $V=S/T$. In other words, they duplicated events in the outer world. (BROWN, J. F., The visual perception of velocity., *Psychol. Forsch.*, 1931, 14, 199-268.) Since that time, there have been numerous other publications, all confirmatory, and dealing with different aspects of the same issue. Including those done in Japan, these would be prohibitive to list.

25. WATTS, A., *Cloud-hidden, Whereabouts Unknown.*, N.Y.: Random House, 1973, p. 65. Related comments made earlier by Gustav Fechner (1801-1887) include the statement that when a man dies one eye of the universe closes.

26. BEARDSLEY,T., Smart genes., *Scient. Amer.*, 1991, 256(2), 87-95.

27. IBID., p. 95.

28. KAUFFMAN, S. A., Antichaos and adaptation. IBID., 78-84.

29. Computer simulations conducted by LESTER F. HARRIS, now indicate that interactions between DNA and the many regulatory proteins, are indeed three-dimensional (stereochemical) affairs. Cf. Issue 2, 1994, of the *Jour. Biomolec. Struct. & Dynam.*. For a brief summary: *Science News.* 1995, 147, 13(Apr. 1), 200.

30. GABLIK, S., *Maqritte.*, N.Y.: Thames and Hudson, 1985, p. 87. I can find no evidence that Magritte was a Zen enthusiast. Suzi Gablik knew the family personally and makes no mention of Zen. However, she does note that he used painting instead of words to portray meanings, and that he tried to shock the observer out of his complacency, forcing him back into the HERE and NOW. This was done by such stunts as picturing huge boulders suspended in mid-air. Zen does much the same thing with its use of "koans." These are meaningless problems which often sound as though they should be meaningful -- e.g., "what is the sound of one hand clapping?" When finding it impossible to visualize or answer, the thinker realizes he is bogged down in the morass of memory. Hopefully, enlightenment (satori) follows and he is reoriented in the HERE and NOW.

31. According to the Zen view, infinity presents itself in every passing instant. Only the HERE and NOW exists, and this is all that has ever existed. Both past and future are mentalisms and have no external reality. Every instant is said to have a personality of its own -- a unique character which has never occurred before and will never occur again. Therefore, it should be this to which we attend. To the degree to which we do not live in the HERE and NOW, to that degree we are encased in our own minds, engaged with dead material, and do not really live.

ADDENDUM: A Penny for Your Thoughts

(An hypothetical example illustrating how chemical energies could create what we experience as perceptual phenomena.)

Assume that the chemical factors we have been discussing are feasible. The next question is whether it is possible to use such concepts to describe what happens when we see something. I believe it is. But one must recognize that with our present state of knowledge, it would have to be labeled pure hypothesis, unsupported by empirical evidence. To make it understandable, it will first be necessary to describe the receptor area. The retina has several layers and is far from simple. Diagrams from any text on the eye might be helpful.

(1) The first retinal layer consists of the pigmented rod and cone cells. The exact method by which they achieve their effects is not known. The over-all result obviously has to be that of a transducer. However, since they possess an intricately laminated microstructure, it has also been suggested they might have other properties such as those of condensers. In the present hypothesis, their role will be described as we proceed.

(2) Immediately adjacent to the rods and cones there is a middle layer into which these receptors feed. Structurally, this layer is rather like a flattened web, and further down it contains the bipolar cells which relate the output of the receptors to the ganglion cells. There is no discernable regularity to this intermediate area.

(3) Finally, there are the ganglion cells themselves, the long axons of which go to make up the optic tract. It is noteworthy that there are about 130 million rods and cones, but little more than a million optic tract fibers. This ratio of 100 to 1 suggests that impulse data cannot be carrying the retinal image. Serious size reduction and/or consolidation of the retinal imagery *must* be taking place in the preceding middle layer. This is an important point to which we will soon return.

Pribram (1971) states that cutting the optic nerve close to the eye does not disturb the electroretinogram. Therefore, the ERG must be recording activity occurring within the middle layer. Data is cited to the effect that this middle layer of cells exhibits hyperpolarization. As will be apparent later, such intense polarization would be predicted by the theory being formulated. Almost as interesting is the comment that no impulses have been known to take place *peripherally to the ganglion* layer. This prompts one to ask a question. To wit: if the impulse does not carry information within the receptor itself, by what logic can we ascribe such transmission to the remainder of the system?

It is perhaps best to sidestep such conundrums of neural architecture and move on to what is thought to happen in the above structures when we perceive some small object. Let us suppose it to be a penny held at arm's length, about the distance necessary to produce a retinal image of 0.25 mm. diameter (250 microns). The steps of the process are then predicted to be as follows.

(1) Ambient light reflected from the penny would carry with it a distribution of luminous intensity differences (brightnesses) corresponding to the contours and essential highlighted features of the penny. These intensity differences would disequilibrate the existing energy distribution within the cone receptors. Being pigmented, these receptors are most likely capable of generating exceptionally strong London - Van der Waals energies. (Pigments are known to possess such capability.)

(2) Molecular structures within the stimulated cones would then undergo spatial reorientation (also known to occur). Energy released from this molecular change would be transmitted to the horizontal middle layer immediately adjacent. The intensity distribution of the transmitted energy would be proportionate to the luminous energy by which the cones were stimulated. That is to say, it would *not* be a matter of fixed all-or-none values as in the case of neural impulses. Rather, it would be more like the reaction in a photographic film.

Seen as a whole, this should result in high fidelity transduction of the penny's image, retaining all its various features. Offhand, it might be thought that any such image would have to be a mosaic like those assumed to result from the compound eyes of insects. However, we don't know anything about the vision of insects, and our own visual acuity has been shown to be as fine textured as 1/20th of the diameter of a single cone! So receptor size is not a limiting factor. They do not act individually.

Now, let us consider the microstructure of the second retinal layer -- the one into which receptor energies fire. Somehow, it has to consolidate and miniaturize the receptor input. Such activity requires a radical departure from existing theory. Thus, it is suggested that this intermediate layer consists to a major degree of highly sensitive, long polarized molecules, i.e., *liquid crystals!* These would have some freedom of movement. Paracrystallinity is suggested by the fact that (a) it exhibits hyperpolarization, (b) the "swarming" activity of liquid crystals would permit the required image size reduction, and (c) their semi-fluid nature would explain why the retina becomes "detached" so easily . Even a minor blow can result in blindness.

(3) It would be expected that receptor energies impinging upon such a matrix of quasi-mobile polarized molecules would cause them to reassemble or "swarm" about the newly energized loci of the projected image. Action would occur via the London-Van der Waals attraction, and would result in a rearrangement of their prior energy distributions. The entire operation would be extremely rapid. It has been estimated that such particles can turn through 180° for a full reversal of polarity in something like 1/300,000th of a second.

Returning to the hypothetical figure of a penny, it is now believed to be meticulously imaged in a molecular distribution which is paracrystalline. A rather crude simulation of what happens may be obtained by floating magnetized needles fastened through corks placed on the calm surface of water. The slightest disturbance and they will shift rapidly into a variety of complex arrangements not unlike what is experienced with phosphenes. Given that there were billions of them, very tiny, and one were able to impose a meaningful energy pattern upon them from above, they would immediately replicate the pattern with emphasis upon contours and highlighted details. The resulting arrangement might look very like a sand-painting done with extreme care and sand so fine it was not discernable as such.

For psychologists interested in perception it should be noted that certain immediate effects could be predicted from the attractional nature of the energies. For example, contours which were closer to each other would give rise to more intense intermediate fields, and would therefore tend to attract each other to a proportionate degree. This should result in the total visual field being broken up into figure and ground. The contours would "belong" to the figural portion of the display because of the stronger forces binding them together. It has been shown that this figure-ground differentiation has to occur at subcortical levels because only the figure references memory -- not the ground.

Sudden reversals of figure-ground (as in classical illusions like the Necker cube or Rubin vase-and-face drawings) are readily explainable upon the basis of the equally balanced intensities of alternative fields. This would permit sudden changes of liquid crystalline polarity and/or orientation. By the same token, the Gestalt law of proximity would become explainable. The much-investigated phenomenon of "lateral inhibition" would be due to the non-figural (ground) portion of the display becoming inoperative and therefore not contributing to the visual organization. Indeed, after years of looking over the broad panoply of such perceptual field effects, none could be found which were not amenable to solution in these terms!

(4) Back to our replica of the penny waiting patiently in the second layer of the retina. Inasmuch as the next step in its processing is somewhat difficult to understand, let us digress for a moment to reexamine what happens in the olfactory sense. Here there are no elaborate transducers such as in the retina. Apparently the pigmentation suffices. Nonetheless, molecular patterning is picked up and transported directly to the forebrain with high fidelity. There are no synapses or "relay stations" in the thalamic area like those which intervene for other senses.

Question: if neural structures themselves can detect and conduct stereo-chemical patterning *without* transduction (and this certainly appears to be the case for olfaction), then what is the *raison d'etre* behind all the elaborations present in other senses, e.g., the retina? To answer this we must recognize that olfaction is the only sense whose input already possesses molecular dimensions. And we know that it references memory because we recognize smells! From prior studies we know that memories have to be molecular. Input from senses other than olfaction, by contrast, are many orders of magnitude larger than any molecules. Besides transduction, therefore, the next most important role of structures like the retina must be to reduce the *size* of the input, and to do so with extreme speed and accuracy of form. Otherwise, no visual data could reference memory and be recognized.

Bearing these facts in mind, let us now return to our image of the penny. Fortunately it is made up of mobile molecular entities whose patterning is held together by mutual attraction. Thus, along with the figure-ground differentiation, and for exactly the same reason, *the figural portion of the display should begin to shrink in size!* There would be simultaneous and mutual attraction between all parts of the pattern, and these attractions would be proportional to the intensities of the original luminous input. Therefore, the shape of the pattern should remain unchanged. (See Note # 5, Sect. III, "Journey into no'thing'ness").

In earlier psychological literature there exists a sizeable body of experimental evidence suggesting that we may be able to experience this diminution of the stimulus directly. These experiments have to do with what was then called the *Zeitfehler*, or "time-error." Suppose light A (of given intensity and duration) is presented to a subject. It is then immediately followed by an identical light B. When asked to compare these, the subject will report light A to have been significantly less bright than the more recent light B -- and the difference in apparent brightness will be proportional to the time interval between them. It should be noted that in the absence of contextual cues, judgments of stimulus brightness will co-vary with stimulus size. "Less bright" could therefore indicate "lesser size."

Back to our image of the penny again -- now undergoing size reduction in the semi-fluid paracrystalline matrix of the second layer of the retina. In all cases, the diminishing figure should retain the same form which was presented to the receptors. However, it should lose size while gaining internal field intensity proportionately. This exchange of size for intensity (with shape constant), should continue until the total was quite small -- though over-all dimensions could still be many thousands of Ångström units. In the world we perceive, and where sensory patterns may be compared directly, there is a similar exchange of size (distance) and intensity. But in this case the relationship is inverse. Bright, large or loud stimuli seem close. Whereas small, dim, or barely audible ones appear further away.

The intermolecular London -Van der Waals energies are believed to be the agents responsible for this contraction of the retinal image. Their operation would necessarily pull the structures together into a delicately patterned bit of space lattice. Such a mechanism assumes the energies to be relatively long range. However, a somewhat different possibility would be a successive shift of the heightened energy level of the configuration, from molecule to molecule, toward the center of the figure. This latter would presuppose short-range forces which propagate themselves much like a wave of polarization change. I have been told that this is possible, and that such waves of changing polarization have been observed in liquid crystals. However, I have had no personal experience with them.

Whatever the process details, forces of mutual attraction could not help but bring about size reduction of the image while maintaining shape constancy. And since this miniaturization could not continue indefinitely, an equilibrium state would be finally reached. It is assumed that reduction would proceed until the constituent molecules were so close together that a counterbalancing force of repulsion would arise from approach of atomic nuclei of like sign. When this repulsion equaled the attraction, equilibrium would be achieved and shrinkage would cease.

The end product of this process I have chosen to call the "input residuum." It is visualized as a faithfully miniaturized copy of the figural portion of the original retinal image -- not unlike what one would get with extreme photographic reduction. In brief, we could still see the date on the penny! The final limits of this visible detail is felt to be approximately two seconds of arc, subtending an original retinal distance of 0.1 microns -- or 1000 Ångströms. This is the proved limit of visual resolution.

Though the final input residuum might be called a configured piece of space lattice, or even a macromolecule in its own right, I find it simpler to understand as a minute pattern in energy. When compared to the familiar DNA molecule, its size might be similar, but its design would be much more intricate, less rigorously configured, and obviously of greater diameter. Functionally, it would provide sensory experience, immediate memory, and would serve as a "template" with which to reference (resonate with) previously stored permanent memory structures during recognition. If "fixated," it could become permanent itself. Over-all dimensions would be well within the neighborhood of those proposed earlier for memory molecules, namely, 10 microns or thereabouts.

Vision was very early on the evolutionary scene. It was already highly developed in primitive multicellular creatures of the Cambrian period. So the origins of the process had to have been something very basic and simple. It should be remembered that there are various other molecular structures which organisms create for internal communication. This suggests that the mechanism which produces the input residuum was most likely some early evolutionary development which extended existing processes. It is easy to see how pheromones could arise as simply further use of hormones. And it is also readily recognized that such techniques would be inadequate for detection of new and varied sensory input from a distance. Auditory and visual signals required the evolution of transducer/reducer sense organs which, in effect, amplified details of the environment. In óther words, the environment had to be viewed through the focal end of a microscope!

Evolution of the eye from light-sensitive spots on the skin, followed by invagination to form an eye-cup, seems straight-forward. But the step from there to use of liquid crystals is not so clear. The evolution of vision either coincided with (or closely followed) that of the nerves themselves, so it could be they are simply an unrecognized component of neural axoplasm. In any case, it should be obvious that sensory development could not have progressed significantly beyond olfaction without seriously reducing the dimensions of the sensory input. It had to be made compatible with the dimensions of memories -- which are molecular. Otherwise, there would be no way in which memories could be acquired by learning or referenced in processes of recognition and recall.

But let us return to our final product, the input residuum. Existence of a terminal equilibrium state could explain why memories seem to have their own intensity values. Learned data which are reactivated during recognition or recall lack the full emotional tonus (intensity) which was present with the initial stimuli. Once learned, recognition acts primarily to trigger memory. This same "standardizing" of emotional tonus also characterizes many of the inherent behavior patterns of lesser creatures, particularly reptilia. Their behavior appears emotionless and stereotyped..

(5) Because of the extreme rapidity of liquid crystalline activity, it is felt that terminal size reduction would have occurred well before any image reached the ganglion layer of the retina itself. With every saccadic movement of the eyes a new image would necessarily be brought into existence. In other words, there would be a rapid staccato of different (though often closely related) molecular patterns picked up by the ganglion cells and conducted via the optic tract to the thalamus. This does not mean they would travel a piece here and a piece there, down the tract as a volley of separate events like neural impulses. Rather, everything would hang together by mutual attraction. The image would retain its identity as a penny.

Even more startling perhaps, is the suggested possibility that when necessary, conduction could occur transneurally, or across cell walls. The myelin sheathing which characterizes sensory nerves and their midbrain projections, and which has a microstructure like that of the rods and cones themselves, could well play some unknown role in these cases. That transmission does occur transneurally there can be little doubt. Numerous experiments have demonstrated that except for major tracts, information conduction routes may have little relationship to where the neurons go. It is almost as if the input goes where *it* needs to go, and not necessarily where the nerves go. It is recognized that this statement will be very disturbing to some. But many instances exist where such conclusions are unavoidable. Visual and auditory fusion of separate and disparate images is only one such case.

A template-reproduction system has often been suggested as a means of pattern conduction. But as currently visualized, it would be much too slow for either perception or immediate memory. Instead, it is thought that patterned information transport may take place via rapid polarization changes in the liquid crystalline protein structures -- either that or some equivalent transmission of the respective charges. If paracrystalline changes of this sort are what create the input residuum, there seems little reason to assume some different process to account for its transmission. As mentioned earlier with reference to olfaction, it appears virtually certain that stereochemical configurations are being transported in neural axoplasm. No matter how this is accomplished, the energy itself could only be an energy of attraction. This would be necessary for the molecular-structured image to hold together during transit. It is an important distinction. Were it somehow made up of impulses, the self-repellent nature of the ions would make such coherence impossible.

The residuum, now mobile, would continue down the optic tract unrestricted as to fiber walls or tract areas. It would follow what I choose to call a path of chemical affinity. I admit that calling it "affinity" doesn't explain anything. But some sort of chemically-determined path is being used. This is shown by the fact that it is possible to sever 98% of the cat's optic tract without interfering with its ability to discriminate differences of shape. (Galambos, R., et al., 1967). This and numerous other surgical findings (particularly those of K. S. Lashley) become totally inexplicable without assuming the image to be extremely small and its routes variable.

At the midbrain fusion would occur via resonance between the separate but similarly configured residua from the two eyes. If one were to credit orthodox neural impulse theories, such binocular fusion would require the reassembly somehow of four half-patterns. And again, there would be no way of explaining such processes. This is why most such theories ignore questions of binocular or binaural fusion.

As explained here, binocular and binaural fusion are due to resonance between large molecular structures having closely similar stereochemical shapes. Structures of this sort are known to produce a strong mutual attraction which is proportional to their configural similarity. Only optical images which are nearly identical are able to fuse. Those which are dissimilar produce what is called "retinal rivalry." The images hold together separately but appear alternately.

The same concept of molecular resonance is proposed to explain an equivalent fusion which occurs when the sensory pattern references the memory pattern during recognition. This also depends upon similarity of patterning. It is a commonplace that almost all mistaken identifications occur between objects which are similar. It even seems possible that the same phenomenon might assist in synchronizing the flow of slightly different patterns arriving at the midbrain with shifts of attention. For example, as I walk around a building, the building appears unchanging. But the retinal input of the building undergoes continuous deformation.

Because most sensory tracts channel into a small area of the thalamus, inputs from the different senses could influence each other in direct proportion to their spatio-temporal compatibility. This would create intersensory effects. None of these intersensory phenomena (e.g., synaesthesia) have any other feasible explanation. For the most part, interactions between the senses are considered mere curosa unless something pathological happens. Nonetheless, *it is the nature of our senses to coordinate with one another,* to stay "in register" as it were. We hear things where we see them and vice versa. To keep our perceptual world in order, our eyes compensate for head movements. And if our senses disagree, we are alerted immediately.

The final equilibrium state of the residuum further adds to this constancy which characterizes our perceptual world. It is determined only by the shape or patterning of the original input. This means that any other inputs having the same shape will reduce to the same state regardless of retinal size. It is a highly significant point because it accounts for the otherwise bewildering fact that form recognition takes place independently of size, color, brightness, area of retina used, whether in silhouette, or even when presented by a different sense modality. Again, there would seem no other way of explaining such capabilities.

Psychologists call the phenomenon "transposition," but they make no effort to explain it.

Phylogenetically, the midbrain is an older part of the CNS than the cortex. It is therefore thought to be a more likely center for perceptual processes like the foregoing. Creatures possessed senses long before the cortex evolved. Thus, the midbrain is best pictured as a highly active kind of "display and operations" center. Whereas, the cortex is more of a reference and research facility.

1

Given this task, it is interesting to note that the midbrain is closely tied in with the emotional components of behavior. Emotions have important glandular aspects, and the pituitary or "master" gland is essentially part of the midbrain. The point I am trying to make here is that creatures also possessed emotions long before they had any cortex of significance. Having controls for emotion closely situated with those for sensory display would have been helpful. Survival may well have depended upon emotional responses being rapidly triggered by certain specific sensory patterns, particularly those of predators, potential mates, or possibly food.

In contrast to the midbrain, our more recently acquired cortex is thought to be largely a storage area for acquired memories and their interrelations. It is a place where the residuum gets classified and filed, but not conducted any appreciable distance. The primary functions of the cortex, therefore, are learning (memory acquisition), recognition and recall (memory referencing), and thinking (memory interrelating). This not only explains why the cortex is so large in humans, but also why damage to cortical areas is usually far less life-threatening than equivalent damage to older parts of the brain. Thus, it has been observed that when parts of the rat's cortex are removed, the location of the excised tissue has less effect on its behavior than the sheer amount of tissue removed (Lashley, K. S., 1929).

As for the specific locations of permanent memories, it is thought likely they would be printed (induced by template action) into the most readily available cortical site commensurate with their stereochemistry. Access routing by means of chemical "affinity" would prescribe the general area and thus determine much of the over-all classification of memory content. In other words, it is believed that memory is well organized, as indicated by the ease with which it is usually accessed, but that the organization is in terms of stereochemical similarities of structure.

The acquisition of a specific memory (learning) would be described as the recording of macromolecular stimulus patterning and its contextual relating to adjacent structures. Memories could be located anywhere, but are probably in the walls of cortical neurons. They would be automatically associated with other memories having approximately the same stereochemical properties. For example, isomers of a substance may differ only in symmetrical orientation -- one a mirror image of the other. Because of this near-identity of configuration, the memories of their odors would be alike. This would result in their being located adjacent to each other, therefore causing them to become confused during recognition.

Whatever the details of the system, it is doubtlessly quite simple (primitive) by reason of being phylogenetically very ancient.

The "printing" process which sets up these permanent memories could easily be the same basic mechanism invoked long ago by Alexander (1950) to explain the formation of shape-specific antibodies. As adapted here, this would mean that the molecular energy pattern of the stimulus (residuum) would act as a template from which an oppositely charged but geometrically congruent image would be induced in the membrane. That is to say, it would create a mirror-image isomer of opposite sign. Along these lines it is interesting to note that the organism *does* have fixed preferences for certain isomers -- so it obviously distinguishes between them.

Also pertinent here is the observation that physiological processes of antibody formation are thought to require a time lapse, or "incubation" period. If permanent memories were induced by some analogous process, one might expect a similar time requirement. Experiments suggest that this is indeed the case. Interference with cortical functions at different time intervals following learning establishes that permanent memories evolve from immediate memories only after an appreciable lapse of time.

Depicting the cortex as primarily a warehouse of memory structures does not mean that it is inactive. Quite the contrary. There is present an ever shifting free energy of attraction which we know phenomenally as attention. One area after another becomes temporarily lighted up so to speak, as we pay attention to this or that, or when we engage in recognition, recall, thinking, dreaming, and so forth.

It is very much as if one had a huge room whose ceiling and walls were closely packed with small light bulbs, all of which were wired together in a net. If plugged into a wall switch, none of these would glow because the electricity would disperse to equilibrate over the total net. And exactly the same thing would happen if the energy were made up of ions such as constitute neural impulses. With forces of mutual attraction on the other hand, the energy would hold together and flit from one bulb-cluster to another. Similar "random" activity has been observed during the swarming of liquid crystals.

The physical process which brings about these shifts of attention, thereby energizing particular memory structures, is proposed to be that originally suggested by Von Förster (1948). He attributed it to the heightening of the molecular energy levels (a rise in quantum value) of the structures in question. This should result, for example, from resonance with input patterning regardless of source. It is also possible that much of the activity is spontaneous, as in dreaming. The reason dreaming is necessary is that it allows the system to equilibrate the tensions which accumulate from the day's mental activities. These involve simulations (sets).

The problem of how the memory trace gets accessed has troubled numerous investigators. And because neural distributions offer very few clues, most of them have concluded that some sort of resonance process was necessary to account for recognition. In these cases, resonance simply implied that there had to be some unknown physical and/or chemical means by which the properties of the input pattern could locate the corresponding memory pattern without having to travel a predetermined neural route. I call it "affinity." It was a need also recognized by the mathematician, Norbert Wiener (1954). He spoke of the operation as one in which an unaddressed message spreads throughout the system in all directions until a "receiver" is found which can be stimulated by it, and by it alone. He further remarked that were he to construct a learning machine, he would employ these "to whom it may concern" techniques. This, he felt, should be relatively easy to accomplish electrically.

Though I have no insight as to how Wiener would have gone about this electrically, it is thought that the hypothesis suggested here satisfies his essential requirements. Given that every cortical neuron has a slightly different chemical signature (as now believed), a message for neuron "X" would be answered only by "X" and not by "Z." Of course, if the memory patterns of the two were quite similar, "Z" might also answer, then hang up -- wrong number! Something quite similar happens during recall. Resonance processes are known to exist and would explain why a given memory trace can identify with some "to whom it may concern" input pattern. Moreover, both confusion and travel time would be minimized by routing via chemical affinity -- whatever that may turn out to be. In brief, the message would follow the zip code to the location where memory "X" was stored.

AFTER NOTE: Admittedly, the foregoing is pure hypothesis -- but unlike neural network theory, it *is* capable of being tested. All aspects hinge on the assumption that sensory and cortical information is conducted chemically as molecular pattern changes. Evidence already exists suggesting such transient changes in neural axoplasm when stimulated. (See Note #14, Sect. VI, on the mechanism of mind.) Moreover, Janos Hajdu, of Oxford, has developed a technique which, if I understand it properly, would be ideally suited to their detection. His article appeared in *Nature*, Sept. 10, 1987.

REFERENCES

ALEXANDER, J., (1950) *Colloidal Chemistry, Vol. VII.*, N.Y.: Reinhold Pub.

FÖRSTER, H.Von (1948). *DasGedächtnis: eine quantenphysiklische Untersuchung*. Vienna: Deuticke.

GALAMBOS, R., NORTON, T. T. & FROMMER,C. P.,(1967). *Exper. Neurol.*,18.

LASHLEY,K.S.,(1929). *Brain Mechanisms and Intelligence.* Chicago:Univ.Chicago Press.

PRIBRAM, K. H., (1971).*Languages of the Brain*. Englewood Cliffs: Prentice-Hall.

WIENER, N., (1954)., *The Human use of Human Beings, 2nd ed.*, N.Y.:Doubleday.

INDEX

(Includes only the names of those authors cited in the body of the text.)

The significance of sex, 139-140
Of ecological systems, 211, 312
As a growth phenomenon, 123, 134, 279, 311-312
As biospheric embryology, 181
Seen as *mental* evolution, 54, 68, 79-80, 123-124, 148
Neo-Darwinism, 68, 74, 76, 80
Lamarckian explanation, 79
Is too rapid for chance, 71, 78-79
Is more a matter of cooperation than competition, 74-76
The crucial problem of metamorphosis, 84-85
The Cambrian "explosion," 53, 74, 76, 305-306
Is evolution still in progress? 81, 148-149, 280
Cultural evolution, 149-150

FEELINGS AND EMOTION
As related to molecular memory, 24, 90
In lesser creatures, 302
Are *not* transmissible, 162-163
Close involvement with the senses, 329

FIELD EFFECTS
Perceived proportionality (transposition), 97-99, 167
Intro-figural (See *figures 4 & 6*), 93,98, 206
Extro-figural (See *figure 5*), 96
Proposed mechanism, 325
Limits of, 317
In the outer world, 134

FIGURE-GROUND EFFECT (Required for identification)
Perceptual (as background), 35, 88, 168
Conceptual (as context), 146-147, 191, 209, 211
Due to energies of attraction (See *figure 4*), 93, 325

FORESIGHT (See *Set*)

FORGETTING (Inability to reference memory), 20

FORM (Patterning)
Has historic origins, 108, 283
As the external aspects of organization (See *figure 10*), 121-122
Perceived directly, 92, 98
Exists independently of matter, 99, 287
As the carrier of *all* information, 94
Molecular form has unique information capability, 225, 230
Innate recognition of form, 222

Does not permit recall of odors, only recognition, 90-91
Atrophied in the human, 168-169, 176

SOCIAL INSECTS (General)
Complexity of their societies, 82-83, 171
Possible social memory, 171
Exhibit social homeostasis, 173

SOCIAL MIND
What is it? 151-153
Multiplicity of terms, 145
J. Huxley's viewpoint, 147-148
The underlying logic for, 187-188, 207
Must be more than the sum of its participants, 161-162, 172-173
Summary of the evidence for, 156-166
Growth of, 136, 149-150, 160, 297, 298-299
Now exceeds human adaptability? 149, 298
As an information network, 153
Differentiated from theological concepts, 297
Among social insects, 82-85, 171-172

SOCIAL SOMA
Description and criteria for, 142-143
Analogy with the human, 137-140, 143-145
Implied by a social mind? 154
Size limits? 209
Possible diagnostic value? 137
Role of sex in, 139-140
In social insects, 171, 303
Social genetics? 300
Dependence upon like-kind, 310-311

SOCIOBIOLOGY, 60, 139, 147, 208, 274, 298, 310

SPEARMAN, C. E., 121, 290

SPECIES, a necessary but highly questionable concept, 140, 291, 296

SPENCER, H., 185-186

SPENGLER, O., 143, 296

SPINOZA, B., 113, 289